*Physiology of exercise*

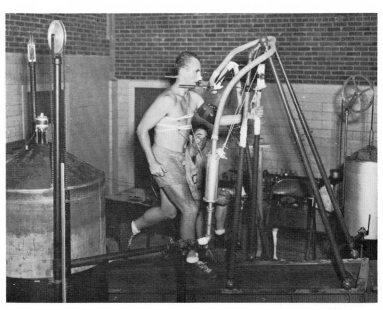

An athlete performing an exercise experiment on a motor-driven treadmill. The subject is breathing oxygen from the small gasometer at the right, and his expired air is being collected in the large gasometer at the left. Chest electrodes lead to a cardiotachometer, which records the heart rate. The cuff on the left arm is for periodic measurement of blood pressure. Chemical changes in the blood are followed by analyzing finger-prick blood samples using microchemical methods.

Fifth edition

# Physiology of exercise

Laurence E. Morehouse, Ph.D., F.A.C.S.M.

*Professor of Physical Education, University of California at Los Angeles, Los Angeles, Calif.*

Augustus T. Miller, Jr., Ph.D., M.D.

*Professor of Physiology, University of North Carolina Medical School, Chapel Hill, N. C.*

*With 48 illustrations*

The C. V. Mosby Company

*Saint Louis   1967*

# *Preface*

The central theme that runs through much of modern physiologic research and thinking is that of *regulation,* and an important aspect of regulation is *adjustment,* or the responses that the body makes to those things which threaten to disturb regulation. Perhaps nowhere are these principles illustrated more clearly than in the study of the physiology of exercise, since strenuous exercise is the most common of the situations in which regulation is threatened and adjustments are made.

The importance of the scientific study of the physiology of exercise does not rest solely (perhaps not even primarily) on its applications to physical education and athletics. It has increasingly important applications to medicine, to military operations, and to man's conquest of his environment. It is our hope that the student of exercise physiology will always be aware of these broader horizons.

We recognize the great diversity of scientific backgrounds of students of exercise physiology and have attempted to provide the basic physiologic information necessary for an understanding of the applied aspects of the subject. We beg the indulgence of readers for whom this is not necessary.

Exercise physiology is a rapidly advancing science, and it is impossible to review all the current literature in a small book. The references cited include a sufficient number of recent papers to indicate important trends and to suggest the sources of information that will enable the student to continue his education.

*Laurence E. Morehouse*
*Augustus T. Miller, Jr.*

# Contents

*Part four*

# Fatigue and training

*Part five*

# Fitness and health

# Glossary

# Weights and measures

# Part one

# The nature of neuromuscular activity

# 1

# *Structure of skeletal muscle*

Muscle is a machine that converts chemical energy into mechanical work or tension. The shortening of the muscle against a load or resistance results in the performance of work, while tension without shortening may serve to prevent movement, as in the maintenance of a posture. The contraction of muscle involves three distinct though interrelated events: (1) stimulation of the muscle by impulses from the central nervous system, (2) chemical changes that furnish the energy for contraction, and (3) the rearrangement of some of the structural elements of the muscle fibers into a shorter form. Studies[1-4] with the electron microscope have provided a reasonably clear picture of the fine structure of muscle fibers and of the structural changes that take place during contraction and relaxation. Our knowledge of the chemical reactions that furnish the energy for contraction[3, 4] and of the transmission of the excitatory stimulus from the nervous system to the muscle[3-5] is also satisfactory, at least in broad outlines. The largest gaps in our knowledge concern the way in which nervous excitation induces the chemical changes and how these in turn bring about the structural rearrangement resulting in shortening of the muscle.

In Chapter 1 the structure of skeletal muscle will be described, and in subsequent chapters the details of muscle stimulation and contraction will be discussed.

## Muscle fibers

A skeletal muscle is composed of thousands of fibers bound together with connective tissue. Each fiber is an elongated cell varying in length from 1 to 40 mm. The thickness of the fibers varies from 10 to 100 or more microns (1 micron = 0.001 mm.); apparently the thickness depends not on the length of the fiber but on the type of animal and the particular muscle.

3

**Fig. 1.** Two striated human muscle fibers in a teased preparation with stained nuclei. The upper fiber is crushed in the middle, and here the sarcolemma is seen. Between the fibers are several spindle-shaped connective tissue cells. (×250.) (From Bloom, W., and Fawcett, D. W.: A textbook of histology, ed. 8, Philadelphia, 1962, W. B. Saunders Co.)

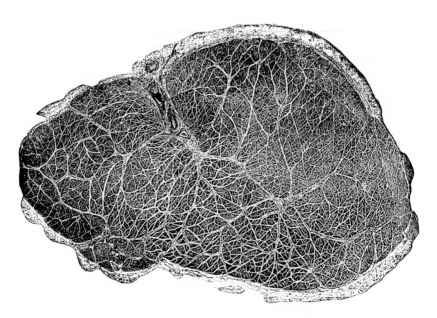

**Fig. 2.** Cross section through a human sartorius muscle showing the subdivision into bundles of various sizes by connective tissue. (×4.) (Photograph by Müller; from Heidenhain in Bloom, W., and Fawcett, D. W.: A textbook of histology, ed. 8, Philadelphia, 1962, W. B. Saunders Co.)

In general the more primitive muscles, such as those of the eye, have thinner fibers. Fibers of varying diameter may be found in the same muscle, perhaps indicating different amounts of usage since the thickness of fibers is known to increase under the influence of strenuous muscular activity.

Each muscle fiber consists of a mass of protoplasm called the *sarcoplasm* in which are embedded long filaments known as *myofibrils*, the contractile elements. The fiber is covered by a thin membrane, the *sarcolemma*, and each fiber contains a number of *nuclei* located at intervals just beneath the sarcolemma. Some fibers contain large amounts of red pigment, *myoglobin*, which is chemically related to the hemoglobin of the blood and probably is important as a reserve store of oxygen within the fiber[4] or in the intracellular transport of oxygen.[6] Muscles in which this type of fiber predominates are called *red muscles*; they are capable of slow, powerful contractions and are not easily fatigued. The diaphragm and the extensor muscles that maintain posture are red muscles. Other fibers contain much less myoglobin. Muscles in which these fibers predominate are called *white muscles*; they are specialized for speed rather than strength and fatigue more easily. They include most of the flexor muscles. If the tendon of a red muscle is cut and then sewed to the tendon stump of a white muscle so that the red muscle is forced to take over the function of the white muscle, its myoglobin content and resistance to fatigue gradually diminish.[7] This indicates that the appearance and endurance of a muscle are largely the results of the type of work it must perform.

## Organization of muscle fibers in muscle

Groups of 100 to 150 muscle fibers are bound together with connective tissue to form a *fasciculus*; the functional significance of this unit is discussed in Chapter 3. Groups of fasciculi are bound together into still larger units, and in turn are bound together to form the muscle itself, which is also invested with a connective tissue sheath. At each end of the muscle these various connective tissue sheaths merge with the tendon bundles that attach to the bone.

## Nerve and blood supply of muscle

The sarcolemma of each muscle fiber insulates it from adjacent fibers so that excitation of one fiber does not directly affect neighboring fibers. Hence each muscle fiber must be supplied with a separate motor nerve twig. A motor nerve supplying a muscle is composed of many nerve fibers, each originating from a separate nerve cell in the spinal cord. In the substance of the muscle each nerve fiber breaks up into numerous branches, and each branch penetrates the sarcolemma of a single muscle fiber to terminate in a specialized mass of protoplasm known as a *motor end-plate*. When a single motor nerve cell in the spinal cord discharges impulses to a muscle, all the muscle fibers supplied by the branches of the corresponding nerve fiber are stimulated and contract together. This group of muscle fibers, which forms the smallest functional unit under normal conditions, corresponds roughly to the fasciculus previously mentioned. A single motor nerve cell in the spinal cord, together with its nerve fiber and the group of muscle fibers supplied by its branches, form the basic neuromuscular unit commonly referred to as the *motor unit.*

In addition to the motor nerve supply, skeletal muscles are also supplied with sensory nerve endings, some of which lie between the groups of muscle fibers while others are associated with muscle tendons. These sensory nerve endings are stimulated by changes in tension in the muscle (contraction, relaxation, stretching) and send impulses to the central nervous system. These impulses play an important role in maintaining muscle tone and in adjusting the rate and extent of muscle movements. (See Chapter 3 for details.)

Each muscle receives blood through one or more arteries. These arteries break up into profuse capillary networks in the connective tissue surrounding the individual muscle fibers. Under resting conditions most of these capillaries are closed, but they open when the muscle becomes active. In this way the blood supply to a muscle is adjusted in accordance with the degree of muscular activity. (See also Chapter 13.)

## Structure of the myofibril

Skeletal muscle is sometimes referred to as striated muscle because of the characteristic cross striations (alternate light and dark bands) of the sepa-

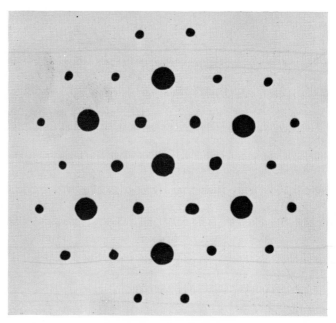

**Fig. 3.** Cross section through a myofibril (schematic). The large dots represent myosin filaments and the small dots represent actin filaments. (From Huxley, H. E.: The ultrastructure of striated muscle, Brit. M. Bull. **12:**171, 1956.)

**Fig. 4.** Low-power electron micrograph of section of rabbit psoas muscle. The pattern of A, I, Z, and H bands may be seen much more clearly than in light microscope photographs, and the longitudinal filaments that make up the contractile material are also visible. (×24,350.) (From Huxley, H. E.: Muscle cells. In Brachet, J., and Mirsky, A. E., editors: The cell, New York, 1960, Academic Press, Inc., vol. 4.)

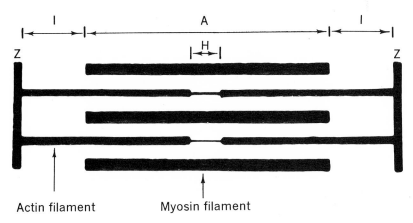

**Fig. 5.** Schematic diagram of the arrangement of the filaments in a longitudinal section of a single segment of a myofibril. (From Huxley, H. E.: The ultrastructure of striated muscle, Brit. M. Bull. **12:**171, 1956.)

rate fibers. (Striations also occur in heart muscle but not in smooth muscle.) If a skeletal muscle fiber is carefully dissected under the microscope, it can be seen that each myofibril is also striated. The striated appearance of the fiber is thus the result of the matching of the light and dark bands of the individual myofibrils that lie side by side.

Changes in the relative thickness of the light and dark bands associated with contraction of the muscle have been observed for many years, but only recently has the significance of these changes and, in fact, the significance of the bands themselves been established. The story is complex and only the bare outlines can be given here.

Chemical studies have indicated the importance of two of the muscle proteins, actin and myosin, in the shortening of muscle during contraction. Electron microscope and x-ray diffraction studies suggest that the actin and myosin molecules exist as long fibrous strands that are intermingled in a definite pattern, as shown in Fig. 3. The modern concept of the basis of the alternate light and dark bands is illustrated in Figs. 4 and 5. Each myofibril is divided into segments by transverse disks (the Z lines). The dark A band is made up of alternating filaments of actin and myosin, whereas the lighter I bands are composed of actin filaments alone. The central zone of the A band is lighter than the remainder of the band because of failure of the actin filaments to bridge the gap. The light central zone is the H band. It is now believed that when muscle shortens the two types of protein filaments slide past one another and that actual shortening or folding of the protein filaments occurs only in extreme degrees of shortening. This is discussed at greater length in Chapter 2.

## Advanced study topics

1. How are the structure and composition of muscle related to the type of work it must perform?
2. Review the recent literature on the structure of skeletal muscle in current issues of *Physiological Review*.
3. Describe an electron microscope and its capabilities.
4. Observe various cuts of meat and describe structure and composition in terms of the animals' activities.
5. How should swimmers train in order to increase the myoglobin content of their skeletal muscles?

## References

1. Perry, S. V.: Relation between chemical and contractile function and structure of the skeletal muscle cell, Physiol. Rev. 36:1, 1956.

2. Huxley, H. E.: The ultrastructure of striated muscle, Brit. M. Bull. 12:171, 1956.
3. Huxley, H. E.: Muscle cells. In Brachet, J., and Mirsky, A. E., editors: The cell, New York, 1960, Academic Press, Inc., vol. 4.
4. Rodahl, K., and Horvath, S. M., editors: Muscle as a tissue, New York, 1962, Mc-Graw-Hill Book Company.
5. Katz, B.: The role of the cell membrane in muscular activity, Brit. M. Bull. 12: 210, 1956.
6. Wyman, J.: Facilitated diffusion and the possible role of myoglobin as a transport mechanism, J. Biol. Chem. 241:115, 1966.
7. Bach, L. M. N.: Conversion of red muscle to pale muscle, Proc. Soc. Exper. Biol. & Med. 67:268, 1948.

# 2

# Contraction of muscle

Skeletal muscles in the body normally contract only when they are stimulated by nerve impulses coming from the brain or spinal cord. This stimulus-response mechanism is highly complex and is more easily understood after a consideration of the simpler response of an isolated muscle to direct electrical stimulation.

### Muscle twitch

If the gastrocnemius muscle of a frog* is removed, one end secured in a rigid clamp, and the other end attached to a muscle lever, the response of the muscle to stimulation may be recorded on a moving strip of paper. Electrical shocks are used for stimulation because the strength, duration, and frequency of the stimulus are easily adjusted and because electrical shocks of moderate intensity do not injure the muscle.

If a single shock is applied to the muscle, the response is a single contraction and relaxation, known as a muscle *twitch* (Fig. 6). Although some simple reflexes such as the knee jerk may be single twitches, most muscular activity involves a more prolonged type of contraction known as a *tetanus*, which is described later.

The total duration of a single twitch varies greatly in different types of muscle. Thus the extraocular muscles that move the eyeball are extremely rapid (twitch duration = 7.5 milliseconds = 0.0075 second), while at the other extreme, the soleus, a red muscle, has a very long twitch duration (94 to 120 milliseconds).

### Summation of contractions—tetanus

When a muscle is stimulated twice in such rapid succession that the second stimulus falls during the response to the first, the tension devel-

---

*The muscles of cold-blooded vertebrates are usually employed in laboratory experiments because their low rate of metabolism renders them less susceptible to damage when their blood supply is removed.

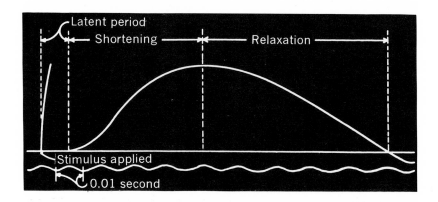

**Fig. 6.** A single twitch of a muscle of a frog recorded on a rapidly moving smoked drum. (From Carlson, A. J., and Johnson, V. E.: The machinery of the body, ed. 2, Chicago, 1941, University of Chicago Press.)

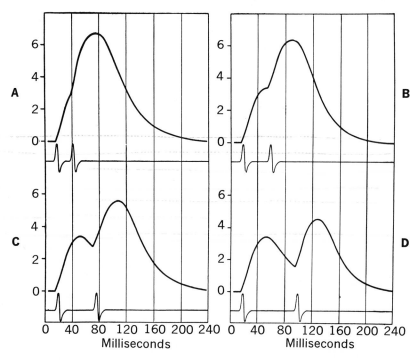

**Fig. 7.** Diagrams illustrating the summation of contractions in a muscle stimulated twice in rapid succession. In each diagram the upper curve is a record of the tension developed and the lower line indicates the spacing of the stimuli. (From Amberson, W. R., and Smith, D. C.: Outline of physiology, Baltimore, 1939, The Williams & Wilkins Co.)

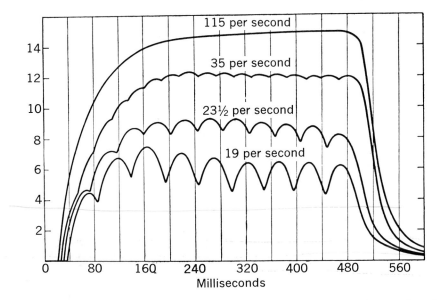

**Fig. 8.** The development of tetanus by increasing rates of stimulation. Complete tetanus, represented by the top curve, was obtained with a stimulation rate of 115 per second; the tension developed was more than 3 times that of a single twitch. (From Amberson, W. R., and Smith, D. C.: Outline of physiology, Baltimore, 1939, The Williams & Wilkins Co.)

oped in the second twitch is greater than that in the first twitch (Fig. 7). This may be explained as follows: A certain minimal amount of time is required for the muscle to undergo maximal shortening because of the structural rearrangements that must take place in each fiber. A single twitch is of such short duration that these changes cannot be completed during the period of excitation of the muscle, and hence maximal shortening cannot occur. If, however, two or more contractions occur in rapid succession, these structural changes may go to completion and greater tension is developed. If the muscle is stimulated with a rapidly repeated series of shocks, there is not sufficient time for relaxation between successive contractions, and the result is a steady, prolonged contraction known as a *tetanus*. Most muscle contractions in the body are of this type. The tension developed during tetanus may be 3 or 4 times that of a single twitch. If the rate of stimulation is not rapid enough to produce complete tetanus, there may be partial relaxation between contractions. The result is a jerky type of contraction known as incomplete tetanus (Fig. 8).

*Isotonic and isometric contractions.* If a light weight is suspended from a muscle, the weight will be lifted when the muscle shortens. This type of contraction is called *isotonic*. If, however, a weight too heavy for the muscle to lift is attached, stimulation of the muscle will result in the development of tension without shortening. This is an *isometric* contraction. Muscular effort that does not result in movement is isometric; muscular effort that results in movement is isotonic. Isotonic contractions involve the application of a force through a distance and result in the performance of work (work = force × distance). No work is done in isometric contractions (distance = zero), and all the energy of the contraction is eventually converted into heat.

## Factors influencing muscle contraction

Numerous factors influence the force that an isolated muscle can exert in response to electrical stimulation. The same factors influence muscles contracting normally in the body, but they are more easily studied in isolated muscles.

It was mentioned previously that a muscle can exert greater tension during a tetanus than during a single twitch because of the summation of contractions; thus the frequency of stimulation is one factor that determines the force of contraction. Within limits, increasing the intensity of the stimulus also increases the force of contraction. Since experiments on single muscle fibers have shown that a fiber contracts maximally in response to any stimulus that is strong enough to excite (all-or-none law), the increasing force of contraction of a whole muscle in response to increasing stimulus strength must result from the progressive stimulation of more fibers. When the stimulus strength is adequate to excite all the fibers in a muscle, no further increase in tension follows increased intensity of the stimulus. Under special experimental conditions it can be shown[1] that the all-or-none law applies not to the contractile elements in the muscle fiber (they contract more forcefully in response to stronger stimuli) but rather to the intensity of the excitation transmitted along the fiber membrane in response to the usual type of stimulation. Since muscle fibers in the intact body are always stimulated by an excitation wave conducted along the fiber membrane, they obey the all-or-none law. The nature of the excitation wave will be discussed later.

The force exerted by a contracting muscle is influenced in a complex manner by the *resistance* against which the muscle shortens and by the *velocity* of the shortening. In an isolated muscle the velocity of shortening is greatest when there is no resistance, and it diminishes progressively with increasing load or resistance. The interrelations of load, velocity of shortening, and efficiency of work in the intact body are discussed in Chapter 20.

*Warming up.* Performance is improved if the muscles have been slightly warmed up just before the activity. Most baseball pitchers, for example, work better on warm days. Failure to warm up before vigorous activity may lead to an actual tearing loose of muscle fibers from their tendinous attachments.

Observations on the contraction of isolated muscles provide a clue to the nature of the warming-up process. If the muscle is warmed, the speed with which it contracts and relaxes and the force of contraction are increased. If a previously inactive muscle is stimulated repeatedly, the first few contractions are often small and irregular, and relaxation is incomplete. After this the contractions become stronger and relaxation is complete. It is probable that warming up is due in part to these changes in the muscle itself, involving a local rise in temperature and the accumulation of metabolic products. It is possible that the viscosity of the muscle is thereby decreased, allowing contraction and relaxation to occur with greater promptness. In the body these same factors also increase the local blood flow through the muscle by dilating the small blood vessels. This improves the functional condition of the muscle by increasing its oxygen supply.

The muscles most frequently torn during strenuous activity that has not been preceded by a warming-up period are the antagonists to the strong contracting muscles. These "cold" antagonistic muscles relax slowly and incompletely when the agonists contract and thus retard free movement and accurate coordination. At the same time the force of contraction of the agonists and the momentum of the moving part exert a terrific strain on the unyielding antagonists, with consequent tearing of the muscle fibers or their tendinous attachments.

*Fatigue.* When an excised muscle is stimulated repeatedly at a frequency of about once per second, the height of each contraction eventually begins to decrease (Fig. 9). Not only is the amount of shortening diminished but also the relaxation becomes slower and incomplete (contracture). Finally the muscle fails to respond even to the strongest stimulation; that is, its irritability is completely lost. This diminished capacity for response that results from previous activity is called *fatigue*.

If a fatigued excised muscle is cut across and the cut surface tested with litmus paper, it is found that the interior of the muscle is acid. Since the normal muscle gives an alkaline reaction with litmus, it is apparent that fatigue is associated with an accumulation of acid. Chemical analysis reveals that the amount of glycogen (energy-yielding carbohydrate) is less in the fatigued muscle than in the normal muscle. These experiments suggest that fatigue may be caused by the accumulation of acid waste products that decrease the irritability of the muscle or by exhaustion of stored fuel supplies. The accumulation of acid waste products (largely lactic acid) in the excised muscle is due in large part to the absence of a normal circulation of blood. As a result the amount of oxygen supplied to the muscle is not sufficient to oxidize the lactic acid, nor can it be removed from the muscle by diffusion into the circulating blood. Conditions are, of course, different in the case of muscles in the body. The fuel is constantly being replenished by way of the blood, the oxygen supply is adequate to oxidize most, if not all, of the lactic acid produced, and much of the lactic acid that is not oxidized or reconverted to glycogen diffuses into the blood and is carried away from the muscle. As a result muscles in the body can perform large amounts of work before their capacity for response is abolished by fatigue.

*Site of fatigue.* When muscles tire during exercise (for example, weight lifting), the defect might be in the muscles themselves or in the nervous

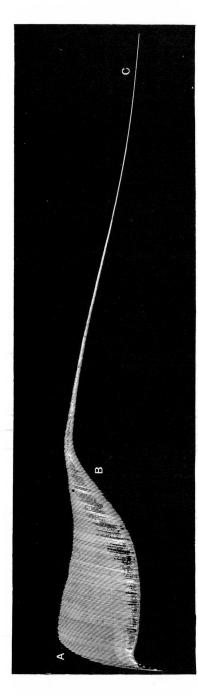

**Fig. 9.** Development of fatigue in an excised muscle of a frog stimulated repetitively. **A,** Staircase or treppe; **B,** contracture (incomplete relaxation); **C,** complete fatigue. (From Francis, C. C., and Knowlton, G. C.: Textbook of anatomy and physiology, St. Louis, 1950, The C. V. Mosby Co.)

system. The classical view has placed the principal blame on the nervous system because of experiments of the following type:

1. If a frog muscle is stimulated repeatedly via its motor nerve until it fails to contract and the stimulus is then applied directly to the muscle, a contraction results.
2. If voluntary muscle contractions are carried to the point of fatigue and the motor nerve is then stimulated by electrodes placed on the skin just over the site of entrance of the nerve into the muscle, contractions of the muscle may be obtained.

Carefully conducted experiments[2] have cast doubt on the validity of these earlier experiments and have produced evidence favoring the view that the site of fatigue is in the muscle itself, not in the nervous system or in the transmission of the stimulus from the nerve to the muscle. It is best to reserve judgment concerning the site of fatigue; probably both the muscle and the nervous system are involved.

## Muscular pain, soreness, and stiffness

During and following strenuous muscular exercise, particularly in untrained subjects, there may be muscular pain, soreness, and stiffness.

Muscular pain commonly occurs during exercise, whereas soreness and stiffness usually appear some hours later. It is well known that when muscles are forced to work without adequate blood supply (for example, rapid flexion and extension of the fingers with the circulation occluded by a blood pressure cuff) severe pain results. The inadequate blood flow results in failure of complete removal of the products of muscle metabolism, and it is probable that the pain of strenuous exercise is the result of an accumulation of acid metabolites that irritate the receptor organs of pain located in the muscles.

Fluid collects in muscles during activity, and a number of hours may be required for its reabsorption into the bloodstream. The resulting swelling of the muscle causes it to become shorter and thicker and more resistant to stretching. This gives rise to a sensation of stiffness when the muscle is stretched during the contraction of antagonistic muscles.

The cause of muscle soreness is not completely understood. Two types of muscle soreness have been postulated: (1) general soreness resulting from the presence of diffusible metabolic waste products that usually disappears within 3 or 4 hours after the cessation of exercise and (2) localized soreness or *lameness* that appears 8 to 24 hours after exercise and may persist for several days. The second type of soreness is probably caused by the rupture of muscle fibers or of the sarcolemma, which transmits the contraction to the tendon. The less frequently used fibers and the sarcolemma covering them are probably more susceptible to strain than are the fibers more frequently used in ordinary contractions. The generalized type of soreness is alleviated by light work that hastens the circulatory removal of the metabolic waste products, while the localized lameness, which is caused by actual injury, needs rest with heat and only enough exercise to prevent adhesions between the injured muscle fibers.

## Heat production of muscle

The energy for muscle contraction is derived from a complex series of chemical reactions. Unfortunately these chemical changes are so small and so fleeting that they can be measured accurately only after the muscle has performed a number of contractions, so that it is difficult to determine the sequence of the changes or even whether they occur during contraction or during relaxation. However, the chemical changes result in the production of heat, and methods are available for measuring very small and very rapid temperature changes in a muscle with great accuracy. Since the amount of heat that is liberated by each of the known chemical reactions in muscle can be determined by studying these reactions in the test tube, a knowledge of the time course of the heat liberation during contraction and recovery of a muscle provides valuable clues concerning the chemical reactions.[3] When a muscle performs a single twitch, heat is liberated in two fairly distinct bursts. The first, which is called the *initial heat*, is associated with the shortening of the muscle, and the second, or *delayed heat*, is associated with the recovery of the muscle after the twitch has been completed. No heat is liberated during the relaxation phase of the twitch, which supports the modern idea that relaxation is a purely passive process.

The initial heat is of the same magnitude whether the muscle contracts in an atmosphere of oxygen or of nitrogen. This indicates that the chemical changes that provide the energy for shortening are nonoxidative (anaerobic). The delayed or recovery heat, on the other hand, is greatly diminished in the absence of oxygen so that oxidation plays a major role in the recovery of muscle from the effects of contraction. Apparently the energy for the contraction of muscle is liberated by the explosive breakdown of compounds with high potential energy, and oxygen is not necessary for this breakdown. During recovery these compounds must be rebuilt in order that energy may be available for subsequent contractions. This process of rebuilding requires energy that is obtained, at least in part, from oxidations.

Although these heat changes do not identify any specific chemical reactions, they do suggest the types of reaction that should be looked for and the sequence of these reaction types during contraction and recovery.

## Source of energy for muscle contraction

The energy for muscle contraction is obtained from a complex series of chemical reactions that are reversed during the recovery period. The immediate source of energy for all cellular activities is the breakdown of certain high-energy compounds, notably adenosine triphosphate (ATP), and the ultimate source of energy is the oxidation of foodstuffs for the resynthesis of ATP. In muscle there is an intermediate reaction involving a second high-energy compound, creatine phosphate (CP). The most recent evidence indicates that CP cannot act as an immediate source of energy since its breakdown has no effect on the contractile proteins of muscle but that it provides the energy for the resynthesis of ATP. Energy for the resynthesis of CP is derived from oxidations. These reactions may be summarized as follows:

(1) ATP → ADP (adenosine diphosphate) + P + Energy for contraction
(2) CP + ADP → C + ATP
(3) C + P + Energy from oxidations → CP

It will be noted that the liberation of the energy, which actually results in the contraction of muscle, does not require the presence of oxygen (that is, it is an *anaerobic* reaction). This partially explains the ability of a muscle to contract for a while under conditions of inadequate oxygen supply, as in the initial stage of any exercise and throughout periods of very strenuous exercise. Eventually, of course, restoration of an adequate supply of oxygen is essential for recovery of the muscle. Actually, the situation is more complex than this. When working maximally, mammalian muscle uses about $10^{-3}$ moles of ATP per gram of muscle per minute. Since the amount of ATP in resting muscle is only about $5 \times 10^{-6}$ moles per gram, there is only enough to meet the demand for about 0.3 second of intense activity. Muscle must, therefore, possess an anaerobic mechanism for the rapid regeneration of ATP, and we have seen that this is provided by the breakdown of CP. However, the supply of CP is also limited, and its complete breakdown would regenerate only enough ATP to support a few seconds of intense activity. It is thus apparent that still another anaerobic mechanism must operate to restore the CP, which in turn restores the ATP during severe muscular activity. This demand is met by the conversion of glycogen to lactic acid. This process can continue under anaerobic conditions for considerable periods of time until activity is terminated by exhaustion of the glycogen supply or increased acidity caused by lactic acid accumulation. This is a very wasteful procedure since the conversion of glycogen to lactic acid liberates far less energy than does its oxidation to carbon dioxide and water, but it permits muscle to contract for a while despite the absence of an adequate supply of oxygen.

According to the scheme just presented, it should be possible to demonstrate a decrease in the amount of ATP and an increase in the amount of ADP in the muscle as the result of a single twitch. This has been accomplished by experiments in which the resynthesis of ATP (by the breakdown of creatine phosphate and from other sources) was prevented by chemical inhibitors.[4]

The exact manner in which the energy liberated by the breakdown of ATP (or some other high-energy compound) causes the shortening of the contractile elements of muscle is the subject of intensive investigation at the present time. Some of the current hypotheses will be mentioned in the following discussion.

## Mechanism of muscle contraction

By combining what is known about the structural and the chemical changes that occur in muscle during the processes of contraction and relaxation, it is possible to propose a tentative model that explains most of the facts. It was thought at one time that shortening of a muscle was the result of folding of the contractile proteins (actin and/or myosin). This theory was suggested by the fact that chemical extraction of muscle yields threads of actomyosin (a combination of actin and myosin) that can be made to shorten by the addition of ATP. Recent experiments indicate that actomyosin probably does not exist as such in the intact muscle and that folding of either actin or myosin is unlikely to be the factor responsible for muscle shortening.

The theory that is most widely accepted today (the "sliding filament" theory) was suggested independently by A. F. Huxley and Niedergerke[5] and by H. E. Huxley and Hanson.[6] It is analyzed in detail in a recent review by H. E. Huxley.[7] It will be recalled that electron microscope and x-ray diffraction studies indicate the presence in the myofibril of two types of filaments with quite different diameters. The larger type occurs exclusively in the A zone. The smaller type begins at the Z line (or disk) and extends through the I and most of the A zone; it is absent from the H band. These relations are illustrated in Fig. 5, where it is shown that the large- and small-diameter filaments interdigitate with each other. It has been possible to subject muscle fibers to chemical procedures that extract either actin or myosin alone and then to determine microscopically which filaments remain. In this way it has been clearly established that the large-diameter filaments are composed of myosin and the smaller ones of actin. In addition it has been known for many years that when a muscle fiber shortens, the I band decreases in width, whereas the A band remains unchanged. As a result of the decrease in width of the I bands, the Z lines of the sarcomeres are closer together in a contracting fiber; that is, they are pulled toward the A band. Since the two disks are attached to the sarcolemma, this results in a shortening of the entire fiber. According to the sliding filament theory (Fig. 10) the actin filaments slide farther into the A band between the larger myosin filaments that remain stationary, and this pulls the Z disks, to which the actin filaments are attached, closer together.

If the sliding filament theory is correct, there must be some force that produces the sliding. There is a large body of evidence that suggests that cross bridges exist between the adjacent actin and myosin filaments, and they can actually be seen in very highly magnified electron micrographs (Fig. 11). If these bridges initially run somewhat obliquely between actin and myosin filaments and then undergo shortening, they will pull the actin filaments a short distance along the stationary myosin filaments. The bridges then detach and re-form in the oblique direction, and the cycle is repeated many times in the course of a single contraction, each cycle requiring energy derived from the breakdown of ATP. It is not entirely clear which phase of the cycle requires the energy; it has been suggested that the attachments of the cross bridges form spontaneously and that energy is required to break the attachments. The details of the interaction between ATP and the proteins of the filaments are beyond the scope of this book; they are reviewed at length by H. E. Huxley and A. F. Huxley.[7, 8]

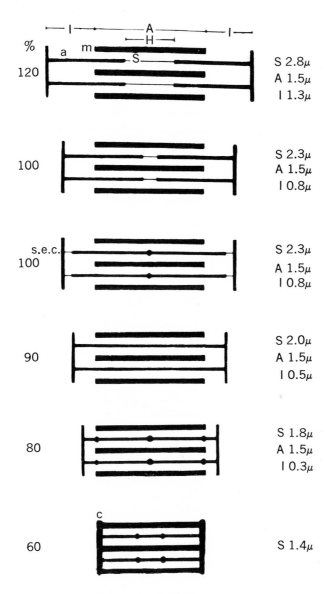

**Fig. 10.** Schematic representation of the changes in a single myofibril during stretching (top diagram) and shortening (lower four diagrams). The second diagram is a control. The figures on the left represent percent of resting length, and those on the right represent the absolute dimensions of the components of the myofibril. (From Hanson, J., and Huxley, H. E.: The structural basis of contraction in striated muscle, in fibrous proteins and their biological significance, Soc. Exper. Biol. Symp. **9:**228, 1955.)

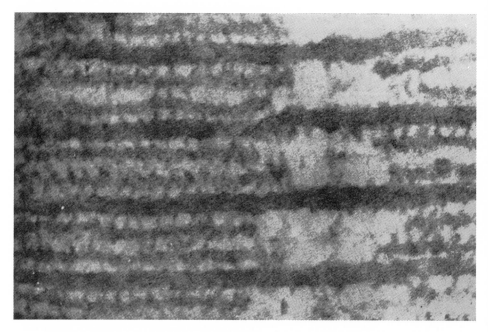

**Fig. 11.** Highly magnified electron micrograph through A band of myofibril from rabbit psoas muscle showing the system of cross connections between the large and small filaments. (×444,000.) (From Huxley, H. E.: Muscle cells. In Brachet, J., and Mirsky, A. E., editors: The cell, New York, 1960, Academic Press, Inc., vol. 4.)

The coupling of excitation and contraction, that is, the manner in which the nerve impulse is transmitted to the muscle fiber and brings about the events just described, is discussed in Chapter 3.

When a muscle fiber contracts, the tension developed by the contractile filaments in the myofibrils must ultimately be transmitted to the tendons by which muscle inserts into bone. Recent studies[9] suggest that the tension is transmitted to the sarcolemma, which in turn transmits it to the tendon. The means by which tension is transmitted from the myofibrils to the sarcolemma is not clear, since the only anatomical continuity is by way of the delicate sarcoplasmic reticulum.

It should be emphasized that the description of contraction given here is limited to skeletal muscle. Electron microscopy usually shows no such organization of filaments in smooth muscle, but both actin and myosin are present. It has been suggested[10] that the interdigitating arrangement of actin and myosin filaments makes possible the more rapid shortening that is one of the characteristics of skeletal muscle.

### Advanced study topics

1. How is the contractile power of a muscle controlled?
2. Review the recent literature on the contraction of muscle in the current issues of *Nature*.
3. Describe an electrical muscle stimulator and its uses.

4. Work a muscle to exhaustion and describe its changes in function during fatigue and recovery.
5. Devise a warming-up routine that prepares muscles for action without fatiguing them.

## References

1. Sichel, F. J. M., and Prosser, C. L.: Summation and the absence of a refractory period in isolated skeletal muscle fibers, Am. J. Physiol. **128**:203, 1940.
2. Merton, P. A.: Problems of muscular fatigue, Brit. M. Bull. **12**:219, 1956.
3. Hill, A. V.: The thermodynamics of muscle, Brit. M. Bull. **12**:174, 1956.
4. Davies, R. E.: Adenosine triphosphate breakdown during single muscle contractions, Proc. Roy. Soc. (Biol.) **160**:480, 1964.
5. Huxley, A. F., and Niedergerke, R.: Interference microscopy of living muscle fibers, Nature, London **173**:971, 1954.
6. Huxley, H. E., and Hanson, J.: Changes in the cross-striations of muscle during contraction and stretch and their structural interpretation, Nature, London **173**:923, 1954.
7. Huxley, H. E.: Muscle cells. In Brachet, J., and Mirsky, A. E., editors: The cell, New York, 1960, Academic Press, Inc., vol. 4.
8. Huxley, A. F., and Huxley, H. E.: A discussion of the physical and chemical basis of muscular contraction, Proc. Roy. Soc. (Biol.) **160**:433, 1964.
9. Street, S. F., and Ramsey, R. W.: Sarcolemma: transmitter of active tension in frog skeletal muscle, Science **149**:1379, 1965.
10. Zierler, K. L.: Mechanism of muscle contraction and its energetics. In Bard, P., editor: Medical physiology, ed. 11, St. Louis, 1961, The C. V. Mosby Co.

# 3

# *Nervous control of muscular activity*

One of the distinguishing features of a good athlete is the skill with which he executes complex muscular movements. This is largely a matter of the central nervous system; in a very literal sense the muscles are the servants of the brain. The development of motor skills of various types, one of the major objectives of physical education, consists primarily of improvement in the speed and accuracy with which the nervous system coordinates activity. These skills can, of course, be acquired without any knowledge of the workings of the nervous system, but an intelligent understanding of the physiology of exercise requires at least a passing acquaintance with these matters.

## *Excitation of muscle*

The nerve impulse, which originates in a motor nerve cell in the spinal cord, travels along a motor nerve fiber to its termination in a muscle fiber. The nerve impulse is transmitted along the membrane of the nerve fiber as a traveling wave of electrochemical change; as it travels along the nerve fiber it excites the next region of the fiber, while the region of the fiber just traversed reverts to the resting state. When the impulse reaches the junction between the nerve fiber and the muscle fiber, it causes the release of a chemical substance, *acetylcholine*, which transmits the excitation to the membrane of the muscle fiber and is then rapidly destroyed by the enzyme cholinesterase. The muscle membrane distributes the excitation over the entire length of the muscle fiber, but the manner in which the excitation is transmitted to the contractile myofibrils in the interior of the muscle fiber has only recently been explained.[1]

When the surface of a single muscle fiber was stimulated with a microelectrode, it was observed that contraction of the fiber occurred only when the electrode was placed on a definite site, while stimulation of most regions of the surface membrane was ineffective. The effective sites were at the Z line in some fibers and at the junction of the A and I bands in other fibers. Furthermore, electron microscope studies showed that the sites at which stimulation of the surface of the fiber produced contraction of the fiber corresponded to places where the sarcolemma made contact with the sarcoplasmic reticulum (a network of longitudinally arranged tubules that surrounds each myofibril). This arrangement appears to function as an intracellular conduction system for the rapid spread of the excitation from the sarcolemma to the contractile elements in the myofibrils. Calcium ions are directly involved in the activation of the contractile mechanism in the muscle fiber[2, 3] and it has been suggested that they are released from the sarcoplasmic reticulum in response to the excitation transmitted inward from the sarcolemma. This arrangement would reduce the time required for stimulation of the myofibrils by the action potential conducted along the sarcolemma by causing the release of the $Ca^{++}$ very near the actual contractile elements.

## Grading of the strength of muscle contractions

It is a matter of common experience that the strength of a muscle contraction is adjusted in accordance with the force required to perform the muscular act. The lifting of a heavy weight requires a more powerful muscle contraction than does the lifting of a light weight. If muscle contractions were always of maximal strength, they would be very wasteful of energy in most of the activities of daily life. The manner in which the nervous system determines the strength of contraction that is adequate will be discussed later. At this time we are concerned rather with the manner in which this adjustment is carried out in the muscle. Two basic mechanisms are involved: (1) variation in the number of muscle fibers that contract and (2) variation in the frequency with which the muscle fibers contract. These two mechanisms will be considered.

Each motor nerve cell in the spinal cord sends a single nerve fiber to its muscle. Within the muscle the nerve fiber breaks up into branches, each of which supplies a single muscle fiber. In this way a single nerve cell controls the contraction of about 100 to 150 muscle fibers or perhaps as many as 1,000 fibers in man according to one study.[4] The nerve cell, its nerve fiber, and the group of muscle fibers supplied by the terminal branches of the nerve fiber constitute a *motor unit.* When the nerve cell discharges an impulse, all the muscle fibers in that motor unit contract. The average skeletal muscle may have about 300 motor units, which means that a group of 300 nerve cells in the spinal cord controls the contraction of the muscle. This group of nerve cells is called the *motor pool* of the muscle. Theoretically a contraction of the muscle could involve any number of motor units between 1 and 300. On this basis a contraction involving 200 motor units would be twice as strong as a contraction involving only 100 motor units. This is the first and probably the more important mechanism for grading the strength of a muscle contraction.

The second basic mechanism that determines the strength of a muscle contraction is the frequency of stimulation of the muscle. It was pointed out in Chapter 2 that a muscle develops greater tension when the rate of stimulation is great enough to produce complete tetanus. At lower frequencies of stimulation there is partial relaxation between contractions, and the tension developed is less. On the average, the tension developed in tetanus is about 4 times that of a single twitch. Incomplete tetanus has the advantage of requiring less energy expenditure than does complete tetanus so that the requirements of a weak contraction may be met by incomplete tetanus in a fraction of the total number of motor units. The jerky type of contraction obtained with incomplete tetanus in the laboratory does not normally occur in the intact organism because the different motor units are not all active at the same time. At any one time some units are active, while others are not, so that the average tension does not fluctuate.

The operation of these two basic mechanisms may be illustrated by the following example. In lifting a 100-pound weight all 300 motor units might be active, each exerting 4 units of tension in complete tetanus and requiring 100 nerve impulses per second along each motor nerve fiber. The total tension would be $300 \times 4 = 1,200$ units. In lifting a 25-pound weight perhaps only 150 motor units are active, each unit exerting 2 units of tension because of lower frequency of stimulation, say 50 nerve impulses per second. The total tension in this case would be $150 \times 2 = 300$ units.

## Basic types of muscular activity

Muscle contractions normally accomplish one of two things—they maintain a posture or they cause movement. *Posture,* in the physiological sense, means a certain orientation of the body in space (for example, standing) or of parts of the body in relation to other parts (for example, arms outstretched). Frequently the posture opposes the force of gravity (as in standing) and involves the mechanisms for maintaining balance and for restoring balance if it has been disturbed. *Movements,* on the other hand, either change the position of the body in space or of parts of the body in relation to other parts. Movements may be either reflex or volitional. A *reflex* is an invariable response to a definite stimulus affecting a sensory receptor. Many acts that are often referred to as reflexes because they do not require attention (for example, walking) are actually very complex acts involving many of the higher brain centers. Reflexes do not have to be learned; they are inborn. The acquired or conditioned reflexes described by Pavlov are in a sense an exception to this statement. They consist essentially in retraining a reflex so that it is elicited by a different stimulus, but once established it resembles the usual type of reflex in being an automatic and predictable response to a specific stimulus.

## *Posture and balance*

One of the basic elements in posture is the *stretch reflex;* when a muscle is stretched, sensory receptors in the muscle and around the tendon are stimulated, and nerve impulses are transmitted to the spinal cord, bringing about a reflex contraction of the same muscle. At one time it was thought that the firmness of muscle, called muscle tone or tonus, is caused by the stretch reflex, evoked by the slight degree to which a resting muscle is stretched to bridge the gap between its origin and insertion. This concept has been questioned[5] because of the failure to detect any electrical signs of contraction in resting muscles. Nevertheless the stretch reflex is of undoubted importance in the maintenance of posture and balance and is best developed in the extensor muscles, which are ordinarily involved in maintaining a posture against the force of gravity. (For this reason they are often called the antigravity muscles.) For example, in order for the body to be held erect, the tendency for the weight of the body to cause flexion at the hip and knee must be counteracted. If the knees begin to buckle under the influence of gravity, the extensor muscles acting across the knee joint are stretched, and their sensory receptors (proprioceptors) are stimulated. The resulting reflex contraction of the extensor muscles then straightens the knee joint and preserves the upright posture.

Although the basic element in posture is, thus, reflex in nature, the participation of higher centers in the brain is necessary, as indicated by the fact that loss of consciousness abolishes the ability to stand erect.

Another group of postural reactions that is of paramount importance in sports is concerned with the maintenance of equilibrium or balance. In complex motor skill activities it is essential that the body be in the correct posture for the performance of the necessary movements. A boxer who is staggered by a blow or a football player who stumbles while running "automatically" makes compensatory movements that tend to restore the normal erect posture. These movements are not "thought out"; they can occur in the absence of the cerebral cortex so that they must be considered to be complex reflex patterns.

There are three major sources of sensory impulses that initiate these reflex movements: (1) visual stimulation, (2) proprioceptors in the inner ear (the semicircular canals and the otolith organs), and (3) stretch receptors in the neck muscles. The example of the football player who stumbles and begins to fall may clarify the operation of the mechanisms of balance. The abnormal *position* of the head in space results in altered stimulation of nerve endings in the retina of the eye and in the otolith organs of the inner ear. There follows a reflex contraction of the neck muscles that restores the head to its normal position in space. Some of the neck muscles are stretched by this movement of the head, and the resulting stretch reflex causes reflex movements of the arms, trunk, and legs that serve to restore the rest of the body to its normal position. The abnormal *movement* of the head during falling and also during the performance of gymnastic maneuvers such as turning somersaults or cartwheels causes stimulation of receptors in the semicircular canals of the inner ear which produce the same types of corrective movements as those just described. The maintenance of posture and the corrective movements that restore balance involve the activities of a large portion of the skeletal musculature and many parts of the central nervous system. Every movement starts from a posture and ends in a posture, but during the execution of the movement the postural contractions are altered or abolished. This implies an accurate coordination between postural contractions and phasic contractions (those that produce movements).

## Reflex and volitional (voluntary) movements

Spinal reflex activity is primitive and unlearned in spite of its seeming purposiveness. The character of the reflex response to stimulation of any particular area of the body surface is determined largely by the type of receptor stimulated. Thus, painful stimulation of the sole of the foot causes flexion of the leg that withdraws the foot from contact with the injurious agent. On the other hand, gentle pressure applied to the same point elicits extension of the leg because of stimulation of pressure receptors just under the skin. This "extensor thrust" reflex is an integral part of the whole reflex mechanism of walking and is normally operative on contact of the sole of the foot with the ground.

All reflexes are not of this simple spinal type. Some involve higher brain centers (for example, the instantaneous turning of the head toward the source of a sudden, loud noise). Despite their greater complexity of nervous pathways, however, the general principles are the same as for the simpler types; a reflex is an invariable, predictable response to stimulation of a particular type of receptor, and the response always accomplishes a useful purpose that is related to the nature of the stimulus.

*Volitional movements* are initiated by impulses that are discharged from certain areas of the cerebral cortex. Cortical (volitional) activity differs from reflex activity in several respects, one of the most important of which is that, unlike spinal activity, it is unpredictable. This results from the fact that it is determined not only by the nature of the immediate stimulus (if any) but also by the stored memories of past experiences.

The nerve impulses that bring about volitional movements originate in nerve cells located in certain areas of the cerebral cortex. The impulses pass down in the corticospinal tract, most of the fibers crossing to the opposite side in the medulla so that the left cerebral cortex controls the movements of muscles on the right side of the body and vice versa. The muscles of the face, however, receive fibers from both sides of the cerebral cortex. The location of the cortical areas that control muscular movements has been investigated by several methods. The cortex may be stimulated systematically by applying electrodes to various regions and by observing the muscular movements that result. Much information has also been obtained by a study of the impairment of movements that follows destruction of various areas of the cortex. Both methods have been used to study cortical representation of motor activity in experimental animals and in man. The results have sometimes been conflicting and are often difficult to interpret. It is difficult to duplicate the natural processes of cortical activity by artificial methods of stimulation, and the results of localized destruction of cortical areas are often surprisingly slight because of the multiple representation of a single function in various areas of the cortex and in subcortical structures. For these reasons it is dangerous to be dogmatic about the details of the cortical control of muscular activity, and much of the presentation that follows must be considered to be a tentative summary of current opinions.

If the surface of the cerebral cortex is explored by stimulating electrodes, muscular movements are evoked by the stimulation of many areas— in fact from a large portion of the cortex. However, finely coordinated movements are obtained most readily by the stimulation of a strip of frontal lobe cortex lying just anterior to the central fissure, and this region has been designated the *motor area*. As shown in Fig. 12, the muscles for each portion of the body have separate representations in the motor area. The size of the cortical area that controls the activity of a given group of muscles is determined not by the size of the muscle group but rather by the complexity of its activity. For example, the cortical area that controls the movements of the fingers is much larger than the cortical area for the entire musculature of the trunk. This suggests that one of the prerequisites for finely coordinated movements is their control by a large number of cortical neurons.

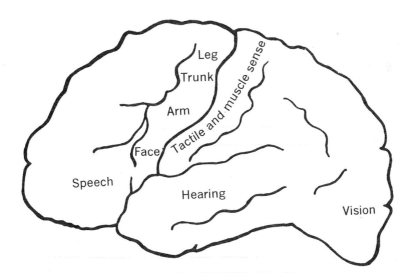

**Fig. 12.** Diagram of the locations of cortical areas. Areas labeled leg, trunk, arm, and face are the areas controlling contractions of the muscles of those parts of the body. (From Hamilton, W. F.: Textbook of human physiology, Philadelphia, 1949, F. A. Davis Co.)

Electrical stimulation of the motor cortex characteristically evokes movements, not contractions of single muscles, and this fact has led to the concept that the "cortex thinks in terms of movements, not of muscles." On the other hand, there is good evidence[6] that the neurons that ultimately control the contraction of a given muscle are grouped closely together in the cortex, although the zones for closely related muscles may overlap to some extent. It appears that while the cortex thinks in terms of movements this is not due to the arrangement of neurons in the motor area in discrete loci representing movements but rather to the multiple interconnections between neurons in the "motor area" and those in other cortical areas. At least two other adjacent areas (the second motor area and the supplementary motor area) have been shown to be involved in the control of muscle movements. The sensory areas of the cortex also play a role in the control of motor activity by interconnections with the motor areas so that movements are adjusted in accord with sensory information from the muscles and joints. Many subcortical brain structures likewise play important roles in the regulation of motor activity; of these, the cerebellum is perhaps the most important, and its contribution will be discussed later.

For many years a simple and attractive hypothesis on the cortical basis of the acquisition of motor skills was generally accepted. This was based on the belief that while the direct control of the contractions of individual muscles was exercised by the "motor area" (area 4) of the cortex, the integration of individual muscle contractions into meaningful patterns of movement was the result of activity in the "premotor area" (area 6). It was thought that the "memory" of combinations and sequences of muscle contractions necessary for skilled motor acts was "stored" in the premotor area and that the acquisition of motor skills involved essentially the gradual transfer of control from the motor area to the premotor area. Unfortunately this concept has proved to be untenable in the light of more recent work, and the modern trend is away from such precise assignment of functions to particular cortical areas. It must be confessed that we are unable to describe the basis of motor skill learning in simple, neurophysiological terms. Improvement in motor skill may be largely a matter of the more accurate adjustment of cortical activity to the modulating influence of information transmitted to the cortex from other parts of the brain and from a variety of types of sensory receptors (visual, proprioceptive, etc.).

Although the motor area of the cerebral cortex thus initiates the muscle contractions that make up skilled activities and ensures that they are performed in proper sequence, other portions of the nervous system are required to adjust the strength, duration, and range of movements of muscles. The *cerebellum*, through its connections with the motor areas of the cortex on the one hand and with the proprioceptors of the muscles and joints on the other, is the key structure in this coordination. As a muscle begins to contract, its muscle spindles and tendon organs are stimulated, and some of the impulses are transmitted up the spinal cord to the cerebellum. In this way the cerebellum is kept constantly informed of the strength of muscle contractions and of the range of movement at the joints. Through its connections with the motor areas of the cortex, it is then able to increase or decrease cortical motor activity and thus to adjust the strength, duration, and range of movements of muscles to the requirements of the act.

Adjustment of the range or extent of movement necessary to accomplish a given act is largely a matter of experience. We learn to correlate our visual impressions of the necessary range of movement with the corresponding proprioceptive impulses from the muscle spindles so that eventually we are able to make this adjustment in the absence of visual stimulation. For example, in learning to type we must guide the movement of our fingers to the appropriate keys by sight. With practice, proprioceptive impulses are sufficient to guide our movements. If the cerebellum is injured, proprioceptive information is faulty, and our tendency is to overreach or underreach the keys; constant visual guidance becomes necessary.

There is evidence that the sensory receptors in the muscles and joints may suffer fatigue during exhausting exercise. This may partially account for the faulty neuromuscular coordination that is often associated with extreme fatigue.

## Advanced study topics

1. How is motor skill improved?
2. Review the recent literature on the nervous control of muscular activity in the current issues of the *American Journal of Physical Medicine.*
3. Describe an electroencephalograph and its uses.
4. Demonstrate a spinal reflex by stimulating the receptor and observing the response.
5. Construct a principle concerning head position during skilled movement and apply the principle in the form of an instruction to a beginner.

## References

1. Huxley, A. F., and Taylor, R. E.: Local activation of striated muscle fibers, J. Physiol. 144:426, 1958.

2. Gergely, J.: The relaxing factor of muscle. Introductory remarks, Fed. Proc. 23: 885, 1964.
3. Frank, G. B.: Evidence for an essential role for calcium in excitation-contraction coupling in skeletal muscle, Proc. Roy. Soc. (Biol.) 160:480, 1964.
4. Feinstein, B., Lindegaard, B., Nyman, E., and Wohlfart, G.: Morphologic studies of motor units in normal human muscles, Acta Anat. 23:127, 1955.
5. Ralston, H. J., and Libet, B.: The question of tonus in skeletal muscle, Am. J. Phys. Med. 32:85, 1953.
6. Ruch, T. C.: The cerebral cortex: its structure and motor functions. In Ruch, T. C., and Patton, H. D., editors: Physiology and biophysics, ed. 19, Philadelphia, 1965, W. B. Saunders Co., pp. 262-270.

# 4

# *Origin of human movement*

Man's musculoskeletal and nervous systems are estimated[1] to be the products of perhaps 350,000,000 years of evolution. They may be traced in an unbroken series from the elementary vertebrates and amphibians through the fossil forms to *Homo sapiens*. Their structure and function have become increasingly varied and better coordinated, but basically the nervous pattern of man is only an elaboration of the ten pairs of cranial nerves found in the fish. The spinal cord and its sensory-motor arrangement have altered relatively little, other than to become increasing complex as the need for coordinated functions increased.

## *Upright posture*

The vertebrate structure arose in the horizontal position of the fish; it is only comparatively recently that the vertical position was acquired. Man was permanently altered structurally and neurologically when his remote quadruped ancestors became arboreal dwellers whose weight was *suspended*. Brachiation permitted gravity to pull the body into a vertical position, with the lower limbs extended in line with the body. Hanging and swinging strengthened the upper limbs and increased their ability to supinate and pronate. Structure and nervous system were again altered when man's less remote ancestors abandoned the trees and became terrestrial dwellers whose weight was *supported*.

Support allowed gravity to work on the lower limbs. The necessity for the feet and legs to bear the stress of the body weight resulted in the enlargement and strengthening of these members.[2] Less happily, the pelvis adapted itself to the upright posture but in a way that is apparently unsatisfactory and probably incomplete.[3] Man's hindquarters remained like those of his quadruped ancestors, but his torso was acutely angulated at the lumbosacral joint. This imposes an extreme mechanical disadvantage, and it has been remarked that the phrase, "Oh, my aching back," has an evolutionary significance.[4]

Nevertheless the attainment of completely erect bipedalism is a characteristic that distinguishes man from all other animals. In the upright posture the forelimbs are no longer needed to support and carry the body and are freed for manipulative tasks. The hand, thus liberated, has developed into a tool of varied and delicate uses. Since the hands rather than the jaws are used for catching and carrying, the muzzle of the animal is recast into the human face. This reshaping is one of the factors necessary for speech. Changing the shape and use of organs requires an appropriate change in the central nervous system. Thus the adaptation of the human body to the upright posture determined to a large extent the nature of human performance and behavior.

Man's upright posture governs the way in which he experiences the world. The vertical and horizontal axes of perceived space are established only with reference to gravity. Visual clues assist the postural ones, but when the direction of the pull of gravity is altered by centrifugal force, a deviation of the perceived vertical occurs even though vision is intact,[5] demonstrating that the postural clues are the more important. Since the very framework of perceived space is dependent upon the necessity of maintaining postural equilibrium against the pull of gravity, the way man sees the world depends upon his upright posture.

## Patterns of movement

Certain reflex actions, originally patterns of movement necessary for survival and now outmoded, still linger at the lower level of nervous system response. The tonic neck reflex is one example of a pattern of movement with an evolutionary background. The tonic neck reflex consists of turning the head and eyes in a given direction, thereby activating and influencing certain responses of the upper and lower extremities. If the person is face down as the oral cavity is turned to one side, there is a lateral movement of the eyes and extensor movement of both extremities on the same side. This is the *homolateral* movement seen typically in the crawling salamander and other amphibians and is often observed in convulsive seizures in man.[1]

Another type of evolutionary movement is the *homologous* pattern in which both upper extremities and both lower extremities are used simultaneously. This produces the hop of the frog, the jump of the rabbit, and the gallop of the horse. It is noted in man when he leaps at a foe or jumps with fright. Both the homolateral and the homologous patterns are observable in a young baby placed prone in shallow water.

Babinski's reflex consists of dorsiflexion of the big toe upon stimulation of the sole of the foot. It occurs in lesions of the pyramidal tract and is one of the signs that distinguishes between organic and hysteric hemiplegia. This has been related[1] to the amphibian stage in which the toes are spread to give the frog more surface for the take off on his jump.

A higher type of movement is that found in the turtle in which the lower extremity advances in coordination with the opposite upper extremity. This is known as the *crossed extensor* pattern and is present in walking as one arm swings in time with the opposite leg.

## Righting reflexes

Posture, both static and dynamic, is the result of the coordination of a great number of reflexes, many of which have a tonic character. Magnus[6] found that in an animal the righting function is carried out by five groups of different reflexes: labyrinthine-righting reflexes, body-righting reflexes acting upon the head, neck-righting reflexes, body-righting reflexes acting on the body, and optical-righting reflexes. Little is known about the way these reflexes react to produce erect posture in man, but it has been shown[7] that whiplash injuries are likely to affect these reflexes and thus injure a person's coordination and balance.

*Labyrinthine-righting reflexes.* Labyrinthine-righting reflexes originate in the labyrinths and disappear after removal of the labyrinth or after detachment of the otoliths. Labyrinthine-righting reflexes are controlled by gravity and act primarily on the neck muscles to provide for orientation of the head in space. One of the problems of manned space flight lies in the fact that the postural-righting reflex seems to cease to function after a few seconds of weightlessness.[8]

*Body-righting reflexes acting upon the head.* Asymmetrical stimulation of pressure sense organs in the surface of the trunk evokes righting stimuli. The head becomes oriented in relation to the surface with which the body is in contact.

*Neck-righting reflexes.* When the head is turned, the neck is twisted. This evokes a reflex by which the thorax is moved and brought into symmetry with the head. In skilled athletic events such as springboard diving and gymnastic tumbling the effect of a slight turn of the head in altering body movements is well known.

*Body-righting reflexes acting on the body.* Sensory nerve endings of the body surface that are stimulated asymmetrically by pressure cause the body to move to secure symmetrical stimulation.

*Optical-righting reflexes.* Visual impressions contribute to the orientation of the head. In the off-balance position there is a minute dilation of the pupil, which returns to the normal size when balance is recovered.[7]

## Mass movement patterns

Stimulation of the motor cortex in man and other primates results in combinations of motion termed mass movement patterns. These are all diagonal movements, suggesting that straight movements such as flexion, extension, abduction, and adduction are derived from the synergistic action of contracting diagonal movements. A mass movement pattern will give a greater response against maximum resistance than will a straight pattern.[9] Mass movements of this type result from natural pathways in the central nervous system and are not learned. They appear in normal activities, such as throwing and striking. To a large extent the way in which a person moves to accomplish a task is instinctive. Automatic movements are carried out with a rather high degree of efficiency; others must be learned, and the time taken to acquire efficiency in their use may be prolonged.

## Principle of least resistance

The nervous system functions on the principle of utilizing the path of least resistance. Thus, if a person attempts to make a given motion that requires him to use weak muscles, he will soon learn to substitute stronger ones to accomplish the act. If the hip flexors are very weak, for example, he may substitute the quadratus lumborum and develop a pattern of pelvic elevation when walking. As this abnormal pattern becomes habitual the weakened hip flexors are atrophied because of disuse and finally may become completely paralyzed. Even if innervation of the flexors should be recovered, the abnormal pattern of movement may be so embedded that the flexors continue to be excluded from the pattern of movement. Abnormal patterns of this kind may result in muscle imbalance, and the deformity may become progressively worse.

## Significance of human movement

Although certain reflex actions of a person may be simply an incongruous survival of once useful but now outmoded patterns of movement, most forms of movement present in contemporary man are significant to human existence. According to Van Den Berg[10] movement receives its significance from three sources:

1. The way in which the individual regards his world necessitates his responding to it with certain movements. Thus among the early Greeks a nod comprised a particularly binding and sacred form of promise. The *psyche* was assumed to dwell in the head, and a man's physical strength was regarded as its executive power. To nod the head was to involve the psyche and one's strength in a promise.[11]

2. A person's inner self has a functional reciprocity to the world. Posture, for instance, is largely a matter of habit. If good, it contributes to the appearance and efficiency of the body; if bad, it spoils the appearance and makes the body inefficient. Good or bad, if a given posture is assumed often enough, a neuromuscular response is established that becomes typical of a person.[12] A person's posture at rest and in motion often indicates the image that he has of himself and expresses the attitude with which he faces life.

   The pompous stride of the weighty man signifies to the world that he carries a heavy burden but sustains it well. The stiff, upright posture of the military man expresses his identification with austerity, decisiveness, domination, and mercilessness. By his inflexible posture the dictator seeks to impress his inflexible will upon the consciousness of his people. Straus[13] has suggested that the differences in the way in which boys and girls throw balls are not physiological or anatomical but rather psychological and actually expressive or the difference with which the two sexes tend to face the world and space. It is for this reason that modern textbooks on corrective physical education[14] emphasize the social and psychological effects of posture as much as they do the physiological and mechanical.

3. The attitude toward others modifies human movement and behavior. It is a common experience that a skilled pattern of movement that is accomplished easily in private may become impossible when it is performed in public. A speaker or an actor may be seized with "stage fright," a hunter may get "buck fever," or an athlete may "tie up." The common factor in each case is the interpretation of the audience's reactions, and the underlying mechanism of a person's response is the same.

## Gesture analysis

Each person has his own characteristic gestures. These are consistent in appearance and originate in internal conflicts, of which they become symbolic. Gestures are generally modified in accordance with culturally accepted patterns of behavior. Unaccepted motions are thus blocked. If the resolving of the conflict were not blocked, the effector system might provide outlets for it. Since it is blocked, the impulses escape as gestures of which the individual is not cognizant and which provoke no action from others in his cultural setting.[15]

## Relation of posture and movement to human aspiration

The erect position is psychologically the highest form of motor expression. A person who is unable to assume it becomes dependent upon others for his survival. Recognition of this humiliating circumstance is implicit in such common terms as "down and out" or "flat on his back." To be knocked down is to be forced into a posture of indignity, one not worthy of man. In formal judo exhibitions a contestant who has been thrown must await permission of the victor before arising, thus publicly conceding that he survives by the latter's mercy. Cripples or others who must assume a primitive horizontal state of progression are psychologically abhorrent to many people.

To maintain erect posture requires that man be engaged in a continual war against gravity. Aging has been described[16] as a matter of diffusion of energy, representing a gradual and continued irreversible process that results in structural and functional alterations. Much of this expenditure of energy is necessitated by the processes supporting erect posture, and it is largely because of the accompanying release from the exacting demands of standing that a person so greatly enjoys the movements of relaxing, lying down, or sinking back.

The constant pull of gravity tends to draw a man together, to cause his body to huddle into a compact mass. To surrender to this pull, to give way to this constant urge to assume constrictive movements symbolizes fatigue, withdrawal, defeat, and resignation. In its most extreme form surrender of this type is seen in a catatonic patient who resumes the fetal position. Opposed to this are the expansive, outward, upward movements such as in the ballet dancer who seeks to attain the freedom of movement of a bird. These symbolize man's aspiration to advance, to rise yet farther above the earth from which he has already freed his forelimbs.

### Advanced study topics

1. What are man's responses to the force of gravity?
2. Review the recent literature on the origin of human movement in the current issues of the *American Journal of Psychiatry*.
3. Describe an electromyograph and its uses.
4. Observe changes in posture relating to changed attitudes and emotional states.
5. How can instinctive reflexes be employed in teaching a beginner a new skill?

### References

1. Fay T.: The origin of human movement, Am. J. Psychiat. 111:644, 1955.
2. Morton, D. J., and Fuller, D. D.: Human locomotion and body form, Baltimore, 1952, The Williams & Wilkins Co.
3. Thieme, F. P.: Lumbar breakdown caused by erect posture in man, Ann Arbor, 1950, University of Michigan Press.
4. Krogman, W. M.: The scars of human evolution, Scient. Am. 185:54, 1951.
5. Gibson, J. J., and Mowrer, O. H.: Determinants of the perceived vertical and horizontal, Psychol. Rev. 45:300, 1938.
6. Magnus, R.: Some results of studies in the physiology of posture, Lancet 211: 531, 585, 1926.
7. Morehouse, L. E.: Body functions and controls in whiplash injuries, Internat. Rec. Med. & General Practice Clin. 169:11, 1956.
8. Gerathewohl, S. J., and Stallings, H. D.: The labyrinthine posture reflex (righting reflex) in the cat during weightlessness, J. Aviation Med. 28: 345, 1957.
9. Kabat, H.: Studies on neuromuscular dysfunction. XIII. New concepts and techniques of neuromuscular reeducation for paralysis, J. A. Phys. & Ment. Rehab. 4:3, 8, 1951.
10. Van Den Berg, J. H.: The human body and the significance of human movement, Philosophy & Phenomenological Res. 13:159, 1952.
11. Orians, R. B.: The origins of European thought, ed. 2, New York, 1954, Cambridge University Press.
12. Metheny, E.: Body dynamics, New York, 1952, McGraw-Hill Book Company.
13. Straus, E.: The origin of human movement, Am. J. Psychiat. 111:644, 1955.
14. Rathbone, J. L.: Corrective physical education, ed. 5, Philadelphia, 1954, W. B. Saunders Co.
15. Krout, M. H.: Autistic gestures, Psychol. Monog. 66:1, 1935.
16. Bortz, E. L.: Stress and aging, Geriatrics 10:93, 1956.

# 5

## Physiological mechanisms in movement behavior

### Levels of function

There are constant shifts between the organism and its environment, and regulatory processes are continually in action. The organism utilizes many mechanisms to restore itself to an optimal condition (homeostasis) after stress. Those simple stimulus-response mechanisms that occur invariably to correct a given environmental change are termed *reflex behaviors*. In most circumstances, however, homeostatic displacements resulting from shifts in the relationships between the organism and its environment call for a set of many responses. The selection among responses in the organism's repertoire is called *adaptive behavior*.

Physical movement is one of the response mechanisms by which a person attempts to interact with his environment. Movement is not always the most important level of function; the human being is organized in great depth, and in some situations action may be essentially at the chemical level. A movement response may occur merely to raise the temperature of the body during exposure to cold or to restore circulation after prolonged sedentary postures.

### Forms of movement

The level of performance of movement in each form of animal life is characteristic of its mode of living. The ant, snail, bird, cat, and human being—each has its own set of equipment for motility and its own patterns of movement. Although the present-day morphological and physiological equipment of any species provides the basis for an intricately interrelated web of responses that are all nicely adjusted to the service of survival and expansion of the species, this by no means implies that each species is constructed in the best possible way for leading its own kind of life in its own kind of niche or even that there is any one best way for doing so.[1] Also, as far as movement is concerned, no form of life can be said to be "higher" than another. In an all-animal athletic contest man would be well behind the pack in track, gymnastic, and aquatic events but would find no competition in field and team sports.

## Thought process in human movement

Man does have a unique method of adapting himself to his environment. Between the receptor system and effector system that are found in all species of animals, man alone possesses a third link in the circle of function which has been designated the *symbolic system*.[2] This unique system of adaptation to his environment has given man a new dimension of reality. Man does not confront reality immediately, responding directly to an outward stimulus. His answers are delayed by slow and complicated processes of thought. With these thought processes impinging on his every response, man lives not merely in a physical universe but also in a symbolic universe. Man does not live in a world of hard facts or according to his immediate needs and desires. In his symbolic universe he is enveloped in linguistic forms, in artistic images, and in mythical symbols or religious rites. These are the basis of human culture and permeate man's forms of movement behavior in sport and dance.

The intrusion of the symbolic system prevents man from confronting reality immediately, and in a sense man is constantly conversing with himself. Answers to outward stimuli are interrupted and retarded by the slow and complicated process of thought. Occasionally the stimulus is misinterpreted entirely and the response is wholly inappropriate.

In the execution of a skilled movement, thoughts about it during the action are intolerable. Concentration is gathered on the wholeness of the act, not upon the parts nor upon the consequence of the outcome. An athlete whose performance has been destroyed by the suggestions of others regarding his style of movement is said to be suffering from "paralysis by analysis."[3]

Military combat teams are drilled to respond "by the numbers" in order to prevent delays in time and errors in judgment that are the inevitable consequences of intermixtures of thought and action. In industry, production is higher and waste is reduced when the workers do not have the responsibility of planning and laying out the work and the foremen who do the planning do not perform the work. Thought and action are kept separate.

The shift in attention from the elements of a task to the signal that is the stimulus for the action to take place is the essence of motor learning. During the training process the action becomes automatic, and the performer ultimately can block out the function of the symbolic system. In this way he gains the quickness and positiveness of a nonhuman animal. From the point of view of maximum performance and efficiency, the symbolic system is an element to be opposed.

## Movement kinesthesia

Ellfeldt and Metheny[4] have approached the study of the movement of human beings from the point of view that a person should be encouraged to develop his distinctively human ability to think about and evaluate his own sensorisomatic experiences. Looking at the movement of human beings in ways other than the effectiveness and efficiency of the performance of a fixed task, they conceive of movement experiences in three interrelated forms which they term:

1. *Kinestructs*—dynamic somatic forms constructed by body masses in motion
2. *Kinescepts*—sensory forms created by kinesthetic perceptions of kinestructs
3. *Kinesymbols*—conceptual forms that are abstractions of the significance or import of kinestructs and their kinescepts within the sociopsychosomatic context of the situations in which they occur

## Individual movement characteristics

When movement takes place, whether in walking, playing games, or performing work tasks, it occurs in a manner that is characteristic of a person. The way a person moves has its basis in the primitive reflexes discussed in Chapter 4 and also is the result of his lifetime experiences, as just discussed.

The nature and genesis of individual differences in movement are the subjects of study in many fields, such as physical education, child development, industrial psychology, psychodiagnosis, and social psychology. The voluminous and widely scattered literature on his subject has been surveyed by Grenzeback.[5]

## Development of movement characteristics

Patterns of movement that characterize a person are established for the most part in the first 3 years of his life. The newborn infant starts life with a basic capacity for movement and a set of movement characteristics that is distinguishable to some degree soon after birth. Patterns of movement that are developed in the human infant during the first 3 years after birth are organized specifically with reference to gravitational forces acting on the body and in relation to the spaces, objects and surfaces in his environment.[6]

Throughout a person's lifetime some changes take place in his movement characteristics. Such changes may be evident in the whole spectrum of a person's movement or only in isolated movements. Change may be temporary, as in alterations of performance caused by fatigue, heat, altitude, light, etc., or it may be prolonged or permanent as the result of training or anatomical alterations by injury or surgery. Grenzeback[5] has summarized changes in movement characteristics that may occur in the following manner:

1. Broadening or narrowing of the movement vocabulary

2. Change in the quality of movement, described as tense, inhibited, exuberant, slow, or forceful
3. Gain or loss of specific skills calculated by comparing accuracy, proficiency, or form with previous records
4. Change in dimensions of movement such as time (tempo or speed of whole body or parts), space (postural alignment, size of movement, floor pattern traced by moving body, direction, or relation to area in which movement occurs), and force (weak or strong)

### Response to new movement experiences

A person interacting with his environment modifies his patterns of movement to meet the demands of new situations. Such modification, however, is much more than the simple process of adding or subtracting motor skills. Each new experience requires some reorganization of the person's whole pattern of movement—termed *movement gestalt* by Grenzeback.

Thus the success with which a person moves to meet the demands of a new situation depends upon how well the required movement fits in with established patterns. In some situations in which the movement requirement is not clearly indicated and the movement vocabulary is narrow in this area of experience, a person may make no response whatsoever at the level of function of movement.

In learning new skills it is necessary for a person to assimilate new motor experiences into his movement gestalt. Failure to learn may reflect his inability to assimilate conflicting motor habits.

### Factors affecting movement characteristics

A person's movement characteristics may be altered by several factors, each operating in interaction with others, some more dominant than others in different individuals and varying further in duration. Major factors include the following:

1. *Age*—The growth and maturation of the nervous system itself, starting in the fetal stage and progressing until a child achieves the upright position, determine when motor learning can take place. Gross motor development is not completed in girls until 14 years of age and in boys until 17 years of age.
2. *Sex*—Skills that require great muscular strength can be performed better by boys than girls at all ages.
3. *Other*—The relationship to movement characteristics of body build, personality, racial and social groups, sensory perceptual ability, attitudes toward the body and movement, and emotional states have been studied extensively. However, Grenzeback in her review[5] finds that the evidence is too conflicting to permit general conclusions.

### Persistence of movement habits

Habits of movement can be either rigidly or less firmly established. Rigid patterns of movement may facilitate the rapid learning of some skills.

but may interfere with the acquisition of others. If rigidly established habits of movement persist for a long period of time, they may alter the physical structure and thus effect a permanent change in the movement characteristics of a person.

Weak patterns of movement can be altered at will and exist only so long as conditions favoring them are in operation. A person whose movement gestalt is characterized by a high degree of variability may also have difficulty in acquiring and perfecting new skills.

## Analysis of individual movement characteristics

The various components comprising the movement of human beings just discussed can be studied using a notation list devised by Valerie Hunt and her students at the University of California, Los Angeles: (1) the whole body in motion is observed, (2) the finer details of movement are examined

*Table 1.* Movement notation*

| Category | Characteristic | Predominant trait or feature and notation symbol (underscored) |
|---|---|---|
| Whole | Body alignment | Erect 1; flexed 7; hyperextended /; forward or backward lean )( |
| | Basic reflexes | Crossed X; flexed 7; extension I |
| | Speed | Slow 1 – 1; fast 1 —— 1; sustained or controlled 1-1-1-1 |
| | Quality | Strong ——; weak ----; flowing S; jerky Z |
| | Size | Small o; large O |
| Parts | Direction (project out or in from center of body) | Out (–) in –I– |
| | Extent or amount of superfluous movement (body English) | Hands w–w; arms Y; legs W; head 9; torso 6 |
| | Accuracy and body control | Stop . ; start –̣– ; turn c; change direction z |
| | Space used and direction | Small c; large C; forward c–; backward –c; sideward ¢ |
| | Frequent use of body parts | Hands w–w; arms Y; legs W; head 9; torso 6 |
| | Rhythm | Even ////; uneven //./; jerky ../ .; smooth .... |
| Impression | Predominance | Consistent patterns of above |
| | Persistence | Degree of variability |
| | Will to move | Degree of incitement or restraint |

*Devised by Valerie Hunt and associates, University of California, Los Angeles.

as parts, and (3) general impressions of a person's movement characteristics are noted. The form used for movement notation is shown in Table 1.

## Analysis of motor performance

An objective approach to the study of motor performance has been devised by Smith.[6] It is based on the premise that motor performance is comprised of three discrete components—posture, travel, and manipulation. An electronic timing device records the duration of each component during a fixed task such as walking, handwriting, and assembly operations.[7, 8] Using this device Smith and associates have found that general stress, such as systemic fatigue or dietary restriction, affects travel movement more than it does manipulative movement. Local fatigue such as that encountered in several minutes of continuous work increases the duration of manipulative movements but not travel movements.[9] Motion tempo and perceptual factors in motion have also been studied using this technique.[10]

## Advanced study topics

1. Why does human movement differ from the movements of other animals?
2. Review the recent literature on the physiological mechanisms in movement behavior in the current issues of *Perceptual and Motor Skills*.
3. Describe a system of movement notation.
4. Describe the differences in movement characteristics of two individuals performing the same activity.
5. Enumerate the conditions under which motor learning can and cannot take place.

## References

1. Muller, H. J.: Human values in relation to evolution, Science **127**:625, 1958.
2. Cassirer, E.: An essay on man: an introduction to a philosophy of human culture, New York, 1953, Doubleday & Company, Inc.
3. Morehouse, L. E., and Rasch, P. J.: Sports medicine for trainers, Philadelphia, 1963, W. B. Saunders Co.
4. Ellfeldt, L., and Metheny, E.: Movement and meaning. The development of a general theory, Res. Quart. **29**:264, 1958.
5. Grenzeback, J.: Unpublished doctoral dissertation, University of California, Los Angeles, 1958.
6. Smith, K. U.: Application of scientific motion analysis techniques to the experimental study of behavior (paper presented to the Seminar on Perceptual-Motor Performance), Midwestern Psychological Association, 1958 (mimeographed).
7. Hecker, D., Green D., and Smith, K. U.: Dimensional analysis of motion. X. Experimental evaluation of a time study problem, J. Appl. Psychol. **40**:220, 1956.
8. Smith, K. U., and Bloom, R.: The electronic handwriting analyzer and motion study of writing, J. Appl. Psychol. **40**: 302, 1956.
9. Smith, P. A., and Smith, K. U.: Effects of sustained performance on human motion, Perceptual & Motor Skills **5**:23, 1955.
10. Smith, W. M., Smith, K. U., Stanley, R., and Harley, W.: Analysis of performance in televised visual fields: preliminary report, Perceptual & Motor Skills **6**:195, 1956.

# 6

# *Skill*

Skill is that element of performance which enables the performer to accomplish a large amount of work with a relatively small amount of effort. Skill is acquired mainly through a refinement of the coordination of different muscle groups. The apparent ease of muscular work characterizes a skillful movement. Lack of skill is characterized by awkwardness of movement and the appearance of great effort in accomplishing the work.

In a skillful body movement the motor impulses from the central nervous system arrive at the muscles in such numbers and with such timing as to bring about the correct sequence of integrated events. The graceful exercises of the skilled gymnast and the skilled diver are composed of highly integrated events.

An analysis of swimming action demonstrates the preservation of energy in skillful movements. The application of the driving force in the arms and legs against the water is steady and efficiently applied. Each stroke is smooth and apparently effortless, and yet the distance traversed with each arm cycle is often more than double that traveled by the unskilled swimmer who fights his way through the water with wild, clumsy strokes. The unskilled swimmer may require 5 times as much energy as the skilled swimmer even though they are both swimming at the same speed.

## Negative feedback theory of skill improvement

Human response to new tasks tends to be characterized by oversensitivity and overactivity. With practice there appears to be developed an active inhibitory force that serves to control the movements, making them more direct and efficient. The mechanism of this improvement may be an alteration of the whole system of receptor and effector interaction.

Receptor and effector processes in the nervous system are mixed in such a way that information fed back to the receptors during performance acts to determine effector function. When a new movement is performed, the feedback tends to be predominantly positive in that the taking of the action encourages its own continuation. The behavior resulting from positive feedback is erratic and clumsy.

After practice the feedback becomes predominantly negative; the taking of action tends to reduce the continuation of the action, and the system becomes self-regulatory. With the onset of negative feedback dominance, the performance takes on two beneficial characteristics.[1]

1. The action is related more to the requirements of the situation than to momentary variations in the individual.
2. The performance tends to remain constant in the face of disturbing elements in the environment so that the achievement is only slightly affected by outside influences.

## Quality of champions

A common quality of champions in all sports is that grace of movement which gives the spectator the impression that the athlete is not forcing himself and that the event is easy. The skilled pole-vaulter easily clears 14-foot heights, whereas the unskilled person seems to strain every muscle in order to clear the bar at 10 feet. The skilled runner glides rapidly over the track with easy ground-covering strides and with no perceptible up-and-down movements of the head and trunk. The skillful striking movements of the medalist golfer, the champion tennis player, and the big league baseball batter do not reveal the power exerted by the muscles of the wrist, arm, and shoulder as the impact is made with the ball. The movement is so direct and unstrained that the blow appears to be light, but the ball seems to be given wings.

Trained runners differ from untrained runners in that the thigh is brought forward with greater speed and the stride is about 7 to 8 inches longer. Greater leg speed in trained runners is attained through improved coordination of antagonistic and synergic muscles and more intense muscular contractions. Longer stride is achieved through reduced resistance of antagonistic muscles, a reduction in the muscular adjustments required to resist the tendency of the femurs to move in a rotatory motion about the hip joint during the fore and aft movements of the legs, and a reduction in the side-to-side movement of the hips as a result of the lessening of the lateral oscillation of the trunk.[2]

The movements of skilled workmen in industry are often as graceful as those of the athlete. The easy, graceful movements of the woodcutter conceal the force applied to the ax.

An error common to the beginner in attempting most physical activities is that of using strength as a substitute for skill. He even calls for muscles to push, forgetting that muscles only pull. He actually ties himself up with his own muscles until he learns that the movement is more skillful when fewer muscle groups are involved.

## Factors that limit skill

The maximum skill that can be achieved may be limited by the following factors: (1) body weight, (2) body height, (3) timing, (4) accuracy of movement, which includes eye-muscle coordination, kinesthesis, balance, reaction time, speed of movement, precision, and visual aim, and (5) muscular tension.

**Body weight.** The heavier the weight of a person in relation to his musculature, the greater the limitation of his physical skill. Added weight in the form of fat increases the effort needed to perform a movement. The fatty tissue may also be considered to have a hobbling effect on movement. A reduction of this inactive tissue will aid in improving performance of a skill exercise.

**Body height.** A tall person displaces his center of gravity through a greater distance than does a short person when the same movement is performed by each. The taller person's center of gravity is always farther from his base of support. When the exercise requires displacement of the center of gravity in any direction except along a horizontal plane, the taller person having the greater displacement requires more muscle activity to achieve the positions and maintain posture during the exercise. The shorter athlete has the advantage in many skill exercises. Errors in diving form are magnified in the tall diver and are less noticeable in the short diver. The same is true in gymnastics. The taller basketball player or baseball pitcher, however, may have better control by being able to guide the ball through a larger range of movement. Tall tennis players have an advantage in covering the court and placing the serve and the return.

**Timing.** A skill exercise requires a fine coordination in the timing of the muscular contractions. As the movements of an exercise proceed, each muscle involved must contract or relax at the proper instant or the movement will be interfered with or misdirected entirely. As learning of a skill exercise progresses, there is an improvement in the timing of the muscular contractions and relaxations that control the various movements. The limiting factor in developing the highest degree of muscle timing is the capacity of the central nervous system. A person with an inferior central nervous system cannot, even by improved muscular development, attain a high degree of skill in any exercise that requires precise neuromuscular coordination.

**Eye-muscle coordination.** Accuracy of movement is essential in all skill exercises. Accuracy involves coordination of eye and muscle, proprioceptive sensibility, and integration of the touch receptors, the inner ear, and other organs of balance and positioning. *Eye-muscle coordination* establishes the relationship of the target object to the body so as to guide the movements directly to the target. Eye-muscle coordination is the dominant feature in learning a skill exercise. During the learning period the background of distance relationships is combined with movement-in-space experiences under the guidance of visual observation. As skill is improved the eye-muscle factor becomes less dominant. When the skill is perfected, it can be performed with the eyes closed (Chapter 3).

*Kinesthesis.* The proprioceptor nerve receptors are located in the muscles, tendons, and joints. These nerve endings are stimulated by stretching. The response to the proprioceptor stimulus is a *kinesthetic impression, or* awareness of a change in the position of the body or of some part of the body. This mechanism enables the tennis player to watch the ball and the court position of this opponents without also having constantly to check the position of his stroking arm and racket in order to contact the ball at the proper time and at the proper place on the racket. The golfer is able, through kinesthetic impressions, to gauge the extent of his backswing and the position of his wrists and hands without looking away from the ball during the backswing. The gross movements of the stroke that involve a coordination of the movements of the legs, hips, waist, shoulders, arms, and wrists become so accurate in practice that the face of the club strikes the ball with force and accuracy, and the ball is sent to a small target 200 yards away. With further practice the timing, accuracy, and force of the stroke are improved and as a result the ball travels farther and lands closer to the target with no greater expenditure of energy.

*Balance.* Many types of skilled exercise require an accurate *sense of balance* and a rapid restoration of the body to its normal position when balance has been disturbed. This ability depends on nerve impulses originating in the labyrinth of the inner ear (the otolith organs and the semicircular canals).

There are two main groups of labyrinthine reactions: (1) the acceleratory reflexes and (2) the positional reflexes. Acceleratory reflexes are evoked by movements of the head, and the effective stimulus is acceleration (a change in velocity). The response to linear acceleration is useful to the jumper in effecting a landing on the feet. Upon angular acceleration the responses are evoked in the muscles of the eyes, neck, limbs and trunk. Rotary acceleration produces eye movements known as nystagmus, which is a quick swing of the eyes in the direction of the rotation, alternating with a slow deviation in the opposite direction. If the rotation continues at a constant rate, the nystagmus gradually dies away, an example of the fact that this type of reaction depends upon acceleration, not velocity. Cessation of the rotation may cause turning of the head, body, and arms in the direction of the previously experienced movement, with the result that the individual tends to fall to that side. An example of the positional reflex is the righting reaction that acts upon the neck muscles to keep the head in a normal position regardless of the position of the body. Another example of a positional reflex is the compensatory deviations of the eyes that are evoked by changes in the position of the head. When the body is placed in an abnormal position, there is an immediate effort to restore it to its normal position. A normal, blindfolded person standing on a platform readily adjusts the position of his body when the platform is gradually tilted, but deaf-mutes (in whom the inner ear is defective) immediately fall. Impressions from the labyrinth together with the visual and proprioceptive impressions from the muscles control the process by which physical equilibrium is gained or maintained. Impressions from the labyrinth are especially concerned with maintaining the normal position of the head.

Overstimulation of the labyrinthine receptors, as in whirling or rapid tumbling, may produce dizziness and even nausea. Seasickness results from a certain type of overstimulation of these receptors. Dizziness reduces skill and accuracy of movement. A common practice of dancers and figure skaters, whose routines include rapid spins, is to fix the eyes on a distant point and to watch that point until the head has turned as far as is compatible with comfort. The head is then shifted quickly in the direction of the spin until another point is sighted. The eyes rest on this object until the limit of the turn of the head is reached and the shift is repeated. This momentary pause in the rotation of the head provides a brief resting period that reduces the dizziness of overstimulation. The susceptibility to dizziness upon continued turning is diminished during training so that skill and accuracy during spinning or tumbling movements is increased.

*Reaction time.* The time required to react to a stimulus is greatly affected by the nature of the stimulus. Response to a sound or a touch is quicker than to a light signal. The reaction time to all types of stimuli will be lengthened if the stimuli are complicated. Sound signals that continually vary in pitch and loudness are very difficult to react to. Intermittent distracting noises slow up reaction, but a continuous noise does not seem to affect reaction time.

Reaction is usually faster to easily perceived stimuli. If the sound signal is very faint or the light signal is short, small, dim, or hazy, the reaction is slowed. There is probably a maximum limit of strength of stimuli beyond which increases in loudness, size, and brightness will not speed up reaction and may even slow it down.

Men react faster than women and shortest reaction times in both sexes are during the age period between 21 and 30 years. There are great differences in reaction time among persons. Practice considerably shortens reaction time but does not erase differences in persons. Champion athletes have better than average response times, and sprinters react faster than distance runners.

*Speed of movement.* Work is accomplished at a faster rate if component movements are in a continuous curved motion than if movements involve abrupt changes in direction. Maximum velocity of movement is inversely related to weight handled. Also the time required to attain maximum velocity is correlated with weight. Horizontal motions are more rapid than similar motions in a vertical plane.

Urging a person to move more rapidly will increase his speed of movement, but his accuracy will be decreased. Reaction time is unaffected.

*Precision.* Manual tasks in which movement is away from the body are performed with less error than those in which movement is toward the body. Movement in a downward plane is inaccurate because of a tendency to overshoot. Under stress of speed muscle tension is increased, which in turn decreases motor coordination and results in more errors. Some workers tend to preserve stability of performance under stress and thereby maintain efficiency.

Movements are made most quickly and accurately with the right hand if performed in a counterclockwise direction and more quickly with the left hand if in a clockwise direction. Accuracy and speed of manipulation are best when both hands are used. One hand, either right or left, is 90% as effective as when both are used together.

Positions demanding muscular distortion, such as reaching backward or above shoulder level, are made with difficulty. Motions directly forward or to right or left are made more quickly and accurately. Estimations of displacements of limbs and parts of the body depend somewhat on the physical effort involved during the judgment; more effort leads to greater accuracy.

*Visual aim.* The accuracy of aim in directing an object toward a distant target is enhanced if a closer object is used as a reference point. The spot system in bowling utilizes this principle. Instead of taking aim on the pins, aim is taken on or near a spot on the alley about 16 feet ahead of the foul line. Because of the defects in the optical system of the eye, visual acuity is greatest when the pupil is fairly constricted. In the act of accommodation the pupil is constricted for near vision and dilated for far vision. For objects near at hand the visual acuity is remarkable. Most persons can see the width of the finest hair at arm's length. The width of the retinal image of the hair is 0.0049 mm., and this is practically the diameter of a single cone in the fovea. The lens is flattened when viewing objects at least 20 feet away and must bulge for clear vision of objects closer than 20 feet (in the normal eye). Associated with the accommodation reflex when an object is viewed at close range is the convergence reflex by which the two eyes are turned in toward the nose through contraction of the internal recti and simultaneous relaxation of the external recti of each eye. The kinesthetic impressions from the converging eye muscles provide an estimate of the distance, the convergence becoming greater as the distance is shortened. Near objects (within 20 feet) viewed with the eyes naturally converged are seen with stereoscopic vision, which allows an estimate of the length, width, and thickness of the object. This spatial discrimination is diminished when the object is viewed from afar. When near objects are viewed with only one eye, spatial discrimination is also lost. The appreciation of the size and shape in three dimensions improves the accuracy of aim and the judgment of distance.

*Muscular tension.* The degree of muscular tension during the performance of an activity affects the energy requirement of the task, the rate of movement of body parts, and the onset of fatigue. Muscular tension during manual work can be measured by recording grip pressure of the idle hand and of the used hand, by recording the pressure of the point of the pencil in writing, by recording muscular action potentials, and by observations of increases of blood lactic acid.

The level of muscular tension habitually exhibited by a person during muscular activity characterizes him as a tense or relaxed person. Too much tension makes movement jerky, awkward, and often painful. Too little tension makes movement weak and unsteady.

The level of muscular tension is determined by the intensity of the activity of the central nervous system, particularly the cortical and subcortical centers. Impulses from the sensory nervous system received by these centers elicit a discharge of motor impulses that stimulate skeletal muscles, causing a general increase in tension. Mental and emotional experiences affect tension. States of sadness and depression diminish tension and result in slouched posture and "halfhearted" movements. States of happiness and confidence elevate tension and result in more erect posture, alertness, and movements that are more direct and less fatiguing. Fear and intense excitement can increase tension to the point of incapacitating contracture ("scared stiff") and resultant muscular fatigue. Such spasticity during excitement interferes with coordination and often results in fumbles and inaccurate performances during an athletic event. Thinking about muscular performance has been shown to produce an increase in the tension of the muscles that would participate in actual performance. This phenomenon suggests that learning and perfection of skills can proceed through reading and thinking about the technique of the event. Thus a golfer during the winter season may improve his swing by studying texts written on the subject. Divers commonly repeat in their imagination the movements of a new dive before attempting to perform it off the springboard or platform.

Just as thinking about muscular performance increases muscular tension, increased muscular tension during activity also increases the activity of the central nervous system. Clenching the fists exaggerates the knee jerk reflex response. Muscular relaxation reduces the amplitude of the knee jerk response. In one experiment the rate of learning various tasks was improved by induced tension achieved by gripping a hand dynamometer.[3] Restlessness and incidental activity such as clenching a fist while writing an examination may conceivably contribute sufficiently to the stimulation of cortical activity to improve the student's score.

## Body-sense area of the brain

The proprioceptive impressions from the muscles, tendons, and joints and the senses of touch and pressure are represented in the contralateral postcentral convolution of the cerebral cortex. This area is known as the body-sense or somesthetic area. Impulses arriving at the body-sense area result in an awareness of the following:

1. The position of the parts of the body that are being moved
2. The location and extent of the body area that is being touched
3. The weight of an object
4. The size and shape of the object in three dimensions

Combining these sensations we are able to perceive the size, shape, weight, and texture of the stimulating object and also to recognize the position of the parts of the body that are moving to handle the object.

## *Learning*

Learning of skills involves a familiarity with the objects to be used and a coordination of the body movements that are required in handling the object. Skills that are unnatural and highly complex are learned more easily if the various elements in the movements can be separated and learned singly. The simplest skill elements are taken up first, and as these are learned there is a progression to the more complex elements. The elements may then be combined and the various skill elements added gradually until the whole skill is performed. Natural activities in simple forms can be learned by practicing the whole skill with attention given to improving the form.

## *Specificity*

There is specificity in learning skills just as there is specificity in muscular training. Although two activities may be similar in that like movements are involved, a difference in the objects employed may impede a transfer of the skills learned in the one activity to those used in the other. Badminton practice does not necessarily improve tennis skill. Baseball batting does not necessarily improve golf skill. Also the practice of one skill using an object does not necessarily improve another skill using the same object. For example, passing a football will not necessarily improve the ability to kick a football. Thus during practice those objects and movements that will be employed in the final performance should be used.

The method of training to perform a skill event should be related to the dominant feature of the event. If speed is the dominant feature, as in fencing or tennis, the skills should be practiced at a rapid rate. Practice of such events at a slow speed will produce high initial accuracy, but as speed is increased, further increases in accuracy will be very slight. Race horses are ridden in early training by lightweight jockeys to accustom the horses to the greatest possible speed under the small weight. After this the horses will tend to retain the same speed even while carrying heavier jockeys. When accuracy is the dominant feature, such as in the operation of a telephone switchboard, the new operator should first strive for accuracy at a slow rate and then gradually increase speed.

### Advanced study topics

1. How is central nervous system function modified to improve the skill of movement?
2. Review the recent literature on the subject of skill in the current issues of the *Quarterly Journal of Experimental Psychology*.
3. Describe a hand grip dynamometer and its uses.
4. Analyze a new game or action toy in terms of the most rapid way to master the skill involved.
5. Evaluate control devices on an automobile in terms of motion characteristics.

### References

1. Welford, A. T.: Aging and human skill, London, 1958, Oxford University Press, pp. 30-31.
2. Morehouse, L. E., and Cooper, J. M.: Kinesiology, St. Louis, 1950, The C. V. Mosby Co.
3. Jacobson, E.: Electrical measurements of neuromuscular states during mental activities. II. Imagination and recollection of various muscular acts, Am. J. Physiol. 94:22, 1930.

# 7

# Strength

Strength may be defined as the ability to exert tension against resistance. This ability depends essentially on the contractile power of muscular tissue. However, as was suggested in the first three chapters of this textbook, there are many factors that affect muscle contraction. Of even greater influence are the factors other than muscle itself that affect the strength of voluntary effort. It must be remembered that the bulky muscle tissue masses are but obedient slaves patiently awaiting the bidding of their tiny masters, the impulses that dart from nerve pathways to prick them into action.

## Factors determining the strength of muscle

If all other factors were equal, the absolute strength of muscle would be roughly proportional to its *circumference.* Absolute values vary from muscle to muscle, and calculations of the strength of muscle tissue per square centimeter of cross section range from 3.6 to 10 kilograms.[1, 2] Fluctuations within these values among persons are unrelated to age from 13 to 48 years.

Two muscles having the same circumference may differ in strength simply because of the difference in the amounts of *fat tissue* that they contain. Fat not only lacks contractile power but it also acts as a friction brake, limiting the rate and extent of shortening of the muscle fibers.

*Arrangement of muscle fibers.* The arrangement of muscle fibers determines the force of the shortening action. Muscles whose fibers run parallel to the long axis of the muscle are not as powerful as those whose fibers are placed at an oblique angle (Chapter 9).

*Fatigue.* Fatigue reduces the excitability, power, and extent of contraction of muscle. Unless the stimulus is great, fatigue reduces the number of fibers that respond in repeated muscular contractions. Such reduction in the number of contractile elements reduces the power of contractions. The range of each contraction is also diminished by fatigue because of the reduction in the number of fibers stimulated and because of the reduction in the amount of shortening of each fiber.[3]

*Temperature.* Muscular contraction is most rapid and most powerful when the temperature of the muscle fibers is slightly higher than the normal body temperature. In this slightly warmed condition the muscle viscosity is lowered, the chemical reactions of contraction and recovery are more rapid, and circulation is improved. The heat of muscular contractions thus tends to improve the condition of the muscles for further work. Elevations of 8° to 10° F. in skin temperature have been observed in the vicinity of exercised muscle.[4] Excessively high temperatures overcome the capacity of the body for circulatory adjustments and may also destroy the tissue proteins. Temperatures below the normal body temperature elevate the irritability threshold[5] and increase the viscosity, making the muscles sluggish and stiff and therefore weak.

*Stores of energy foodstuffs.* If stores of energy foodstuffs, muscle glycogen, and phosphocreatine are diminished by starvation or prolonged work without adequate feeding, the elements essential for contraction are consumed in the metabolic processes and contractile tissue atrophies. The decline in strength during weight loss is negligible until starvation is well advanced. Rats may lose as much as 38% of their body weight before marked decrements occur in muscle strength. Shortly after this point, however, when the body weight loss is over 40%, death occurs.[6]

*State of training.* The state of training plays a potent role in the contractile power of muscular tissue. In a muscle weakened by disuse, gains in strength due to an exercise regimen commonly exceed 50% within the first 2 weeks. Where these gains come from is discussed later in this chapter.

*Ability to recover from work.* An additional factor affecting the strength of muscle is its ability to recover from a bout of work. This is dependent upon the supply of oxygen to the muscle tissue, the rate of removal of carbon dioxide and other wastes, the provision of energy foodstuffs, and the replacement of minerals and other elements expended in muscular work. The circulation must be adequate to carry these materials to and from the working muscles. The greater the flow of blood through a muscle during contraction and relaxation, the more rapid is the recovery. Short, frequent rest pauses result in greater efficiency in muscular work than do prolonged, infrequent rests[7] and are equally important in preventing loss of efficiency in skilled performance.[8] Following exhaustive exercise of the muscles that flex the elbow, there was found[9] to be a pronounced loss in strength (31%) still evident after 30 seconds of rest. After a rest pause of 2.5 minutes the loss in strength was 18%; at the end of 7.5 minutes the decline was 13%, which decreased very gradually thereafter to 5% at the end of 42.5 minutes.

## Factors determining the strength of voluntary effort

In general the strength of contraction of a muscle may be adjusted in two ways: (1) *by increasing or decreasing the number of motor units in action* and (2) *by increasing or decreasing the frequency of discharge in each individual unit.* It appears that the frequency of discharge responds quite evenly to needed changes of tension, whereas each addition or sub-traction of motor units represents a separate step.[10]

A fast, powerful contraction is the result of a short burst of impulses from a large number of motor neurons. A slower and less powerful con-traction results from a more prolonged discharge at a slower frequency and from fewer motor neurons. The terrific rate of impulse discharge re-quired for a fast, powerful contraction cannot be maintained for more than a brief period. The heaviest weights lifted overhead by weight-lifting champions are raised by rapid movements known as the "clean and jerk," and the lifters can support these heavy weights for only a very few seconds once they are lifted. Lighter loads can be lifted slowly, and the lifts can be repeated a larger number of times. When a light load is moved by a mus-cle, fewer fibers need to be brought into play. The remaining fibers are at rest and stand ready to act if they are needed in succeeding contractions. As the working fibers become fatigued during light work, the threshold of irritability is raised, and these fatigued fibers fail to respond to the stimuli. The stimuli pass into fresh fibers whose threshold of irritability is low, and the burden of the work is thus shifted from the fatigued to the fresh fibers in the muscle.

*Emotional states.* Emotional states influence the strength of the stimulus by reinforcing or depressing the discharge of the ventral horn cells. Clinch-ing the fists or contracting muscles in parts of the body not involved in the movement may increase the nervous discharge to the muscles involved in the movement by *irradiation* of nerve impulses in the central nervous sys-tem. Excitement and the cheering of spectators may intensify the nervous discharge of the muscles and may also liberate *adrenaline*, which increases the strength of the muscles and allays fatigue (Fig. 13).

*Inhibition.* Commencing with the thesis that the expression of human strength is generally limited by psychologically induced inhibitions, Ikai

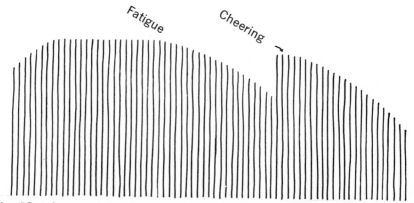

**Fig. 13.** Influence of cheering on performance of work as indicated by an ergogram of the movements of an arm. Vertical lines represent maximum lifts at the rate of 1 per second.

and Steinhaus[10] examined means of increasing performance by reducing inhibitions. Using pavlovian procedures they demonstrated that maximum pull of the forearm flexors could be increased (or decreased in some instances) in a predictable fashion by a pistol shot, by a shout from the subject, by hypnosis, and by alcohol, adrenaline, or amphetamine.

## Mobilization and synchronization

When strength is taxed during prolonged effort, a mobilization of the higher nervous system that results in improved synchronization of motor units has been observed.[11] The phenomenon occurs in the following manner: After 5 minutes of work consisting of supporting a 22-pound weight at the end of the forearm, the subject's motor units were activated in a disorganized manner (as shown in electromyograms); muscles trembled, the character of the breathing changed, the skin became red, perspiration became visible, there was a tensing of other muscles, the position of the body was disturbed, and the subject cried out, "My arm is breaking!"

With a great effort of the will the task was continued. Then came some changes in the nervous control of the work. Gradually the activity of the motor units became rhythmic and muscle potentials became larger, indicating that mobilization of a larger number of motor units had occurred and that they were operating with a greater degree of synchronization. Now the work could be continued at a high level for a considerable time. This phenomenon is termed the "phase of overcoming fatigue."[12]

Training is observed to bring the mobilization and synchronization sooner during this phase of overcoming fatigue.

Eventually, of course, despite maximum voluntary effort the work declines and becomes impossible. This is the "phase of complete exhaustion." The two phases are considered as quite separate, the first as a means of extending performance and the second as a limit of maximum work.

## Mechanical factors

Two factors influence the amount of power that a muscle can supply to its lever: (1) variation in the strength of the pull resulting from different degrees of *stretch* of the working muscles and (2) the *mechanical advantage* of the lever. The position of a muscle at contraction affects the strength of the pull of the muscle. The position of greatest pull is one in which the muscle is slightly stretched. The strength of the pull is decreased when there is no stretch on the muscle, and of course, there is no further pull in the muscle when it is completely contracted. The biceps is in the position for strongest pull when the elbow is fully extended and the biceps is stretched. The triceps is in position for the strongest contraction when the elbow is fully flexed and the triceps is stretched. When the elbow is fully extended, the biceps pulls the radius and ulna against the humerus, and only a small force is directed toward flexion of the joint. With the elbow at one half flexion (the lower arm at right angles to the upper arm) the force of the biceps is entirely employed in the flexion, and the lever is in the position of maximal mechanical efficiency. With the elbow three-fourths flexed the pull is again against the humerus, and the efficiency of the pull is very low; also the biceps in this position is nearly fully contracted and possesses very little additional strength for movement of the lever (Fig. 14). If a heavy book is placed on the palm of the hand when the arm is extended along the top of a table, it may be observed that it is difficult to lift the book from this position. If the upper arm is raised to one-fourth flexion at the start of the lift, the lift is easier. The lift is easiest with the elbow flexed so that the upper arm is at a right angle to the lower arm. With the elbow fully flexed it is obviously impossible to lift the load farther. The combination during movement of these two factors, the advantage of muscle stretch and the mechanical advantage of the pull from a right angle, allows a great percentage of the entire force to be exerted over a wide range of movement.

As a further mechanical factor, the degree of pronation or supination

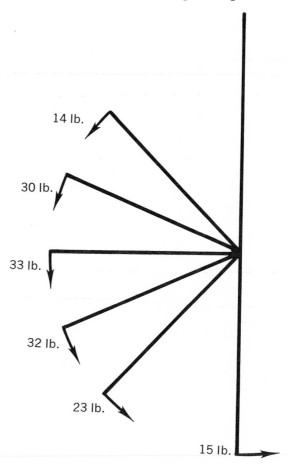

**Fig. 14.** Maximum steady pull of forearm against a spring scale showing the effect of the angle of pull.

in rotatory joints affects the strength of the movement. In the elbow the strength of elbow flexion is greatest when the forearm is in midposition, less when it is supinated, and least of all when it is pronated.[13] This is probably due primarily to changes in the mechanical advantage of the pronator teres as the forearm is rotated.[14]

Studies of weight-lifting champions show that in general the lighter man is stronger in proportion to his *body weight* than is the heavier man.[15] A small man cannot be expected to have as much strength as a larger one, but at the same time he needs less strength to move his smaller body. Hence the concept of strength per pound of body weight is more meaningful than is that of total strength.

Strength is related to *age* and *sex.* Strength scores of males increase rapidly from 12 to 19 years of age and at a rate proportional to weight increases. They then increase more slowly up to 30 years of age, after which they decline at an increasing rate up to 60 years of age. The strength scores of females increase regularly from 9 to 19 years of age, more slowly to 30 years of age, and then decrease.[16] (See also Chapter 27.)

Adult men are on the average stronger than women, even when allowance is made for differences in body height. The male superiority in strength is greater in the trunk, arms, and shoulders than in the legs.[17]

## Measurement of strength of voluntary effort

The absolute strength of body musculature cannot be measured. However, the torque exerted about a joint may be conveniently measured by the use of various types of dynamometers, tensiometers, ergographs, and other instruments.[18, 19] The sum of the scores of the right and left handgrips, the back lift, and the leg lift is generally considered proportional to the total strength of the body.

The ability to sustain a muscular force is termed *strength endurance.* This ability is significantly correlated with the strength of a brief maximum effort.[20]

## Effects of strength training

The classical studies on the response of muscle to exercise are those of Morpurgo and of Siebert.[21] Morpurgo removed the sartorius muscle from one leg of each of two dogs and then exercised the animals on a treadmill for 2 months. He found that the corresponding intact sartorius muscles increased in size, with no increase in the number of muscle fibers or their length. He concluded that hypertrophy was caused by an increase in the amount of sarcoplasm. Siebert found that hypertrophy resulted from an increase in the intensity of the work done and that the total amount of work was without significance. Only when a muscle is overloaded does it respond by undergoing hypertrophy.

Recently some of Morpurgo's findings have been challenged. Careful measurements[22] have shown that in hypertrophy the bulk of each fiber is slightly enlarged and the total number of myofibrils is increased.

The average diameter of fibers in most muscles is said to be 40 to 50 microns, and as a rule of thumb, fibers wider than 80 microns are often considered to be hypertrophied. However, there is a rather wide variation in fiber size from one muscle to another, and the average normal diameter of muscle fibers in the thigh may exceed this figure.[22]

It has not been proved that hypertrophy is necessarily a desirable reaction. Some students are of the opinion that it may be simply a by-product of training, perhaps a noxious one.[23] Training of normal muscles utilizing progressive resistance exercise and weight lifting to produce hypertrophy does not increase strength per unit of weight.[24] Increases in circumference after weight training correlate with increases in strength by only r = 0.422. On the other hand, patients who have regained normal muscular strength but lack normal circumference are noted to lose their strength more rapidly than those who have also regained normal muscular circumference.[25]

Studies of the nature of hypertrophy have been made in an endeavor to further understand its significance. The massive increase in the number of capillaries as the result of training may account for some of the added bulk. An increase of as much as 45% has been noted in the muscles of guinea pigs after programs of exercise.[26] Other significant results were thickening of the sarcolemma, increase in the amount of connective tissue, increased phosphocreatine content, and increased glycogen and nonnitrogenous substances. Working muscles are richer in water than are resting ones, but it has been determined that the amount of fluid entering the muscles would hardly increase their water content by 1%. In another study of exercised and unexercised rats it was found that the water content of the skeletal muscle was essentially the same for both groups; no significant differences were noted in nitrogen content or creatine concentration, although the hemoglobin values of muscles were consistently higher in exercised animals.

When rats were injected with pituitary extracts, the quadriceps became 20 to 30% heavier and had a cross section 6 to 12% greater than untreated animals, but this did not confer any functional benefits. In fact the treated muscles gave less tension per gram of muscle weight than did those of the controls.[27]

Lack of use of muscles decreases the size of the fibers and increases the proportion of fat in the muscle tissues. The contractile strength of each fiber is diminished by disuse. Bed rest results in an almost immediate rise in the output of urinary nitrogen,[28] and it is probable that most of the nitrogen lost in atrophy comes from muscle cytoplasm.[29]

## Rationale for strength increases during training

Since hypertrophy is a questionable explanation for the increased strength in trained muscles, other reasons must be examined. Using as clues the events that occur during exercise, O'Connell[30] and Rasch and Morehouse[31] have designed experiments to elucidate the possible roles of such factors as oxygen deprivation, temperature, and alterations in the functions of the motor nervous system.

Noting that resistance exercise using heavy weights utilizes muscles in such a manner as to occlude blood flow, these investigators hypothesized that periods of hypoxia may stimulate gains in strength. Accordingly, 29 college students submitted to pressure occlusions of the upper arm using a blood pressure cuff 3 times weekly. Simultaneously 28 other students performed static exercise with heavy weights. An additional 29 subjects served as controls. After 6 weeks in this regimen the group using weights demonstrated significant gains in strength, whereas the strength of the group with pressure occlusions remained the same as that of the control group. Thus oxygen deficit did not appear to be an agent in increasing strength.[30]

Next, a similar experiment utilizing moist hot packs in place of pressure occlusion was performed in an attempt to duplicate the elevation of temperature during exercise. The purpose of this study was to see if periodic elevation of temperature would promote increases in strength. Six weeks of 3-times-weekly heating of muscles did not improve their strength. Thus elevated temperature does not appear to be an agent in increasing strength.

Of course, there are many other potential agents at the site of muscle which when brought into play during severe contractions act in some way to strengthen future contractions. This is a fertile field for exploration.

The large increases in the amount of weight that can be lifted during the first 2 or 3 weeks of training appear to be the result of the acquisition of skill rather than actual increases in the strength of muscle tissue. This conclusion is supported by the observation that when muscles were tested in the position in which they were exercised, they showed significant gains, but when they were tested in an unaccustomed position, the gains were not present.[31]

It is possible that just thinking about a movement brings about some strengthening of that movement. It is impossible even to imagine bending an arm and simultaneously keeping it perfectly relaxed.[32] However, one of the advantages of using maximal or near-maximal weights in strength training may be that this form of training helps "to bring some of the high threshold neurons within the orbit of voluntary activity."[33]

In a phenomenon as yet unexplained, called "cross education," when a limb on one side of the body is exercised regularly and intensely enough to yield strength gains, the strength of the corresponding opposite limb is likewise improved.[34]

## Deinhibition theory of strength training

A different set of hypotheses is constructed on the basis of the effect that strength training exercises may have on inhibitory mechanisms.[35] According to this theory, since the end point of a brief maximal strength effort may be set by inhibitory functions, training should be directed toward reducing the responsiveness of inhibitory controls. This lessening of inhibitory sensitivity would permit a higher degree of tension to occur, thus increasing the strength of movement. Two ways in which training may modify inhibitory mechanisms are suggested. One is morphological in nature; the other is behavioral.

A *morphological* result of muscular exercise of the repeated overload variety that improves strength is a thickening and toughening of the muscle's fibrous connective tissue. Embedded in the connective tissue throughout the muscle and its tendons are the Golgi sensory organs of inhibition. The Golgi organs are believed to discharge inhibitory impulses whenever muscle tension rises above their threshold level of stimulus. The resulting Golgi inhibitory impulses act as an emergency brake to bring further increases in muscle tension to a halt.

The thickening and toughening of the fibrous connective tissue may shield the Golgi tendon organs somewhat from the tension of maximal muscular contraction. This shielding may increase the extent to which the muscles can pull before the Golgi organs discharge their inhibitory impulses. This shielding may permit innervation of the muscle to proceed further without inhibition, and thus permit higher tension to be developed before the Golgi braking device is activated.

In a *behavioral* sense the whole organism seems to respond to maximal exertion to the degree of intensity that it interprets as the severity of threat to its integrity. This homeostatic force acts to preserve the organism.

Strength will be increased if the importance of the effort to the survival or well-being of the performer is believed to be great and if the effort is known by previous experiences to be nondestructive.

This deinhibition theory suggests implications for two principles of strength training. Exercises that exert repeated sharp pulls on the muscle and its tendons should be practiced to diminish the attenuating influence of the Golgi sensory organs of inhibition. The load of exercise in the training program should be progressive so as gradually to extinguish overly protective inhibitions.

## Muscular fitness

The optimum amount of muscular strength for a person is slightly above that needed to meet the requirements of daily activity. A reserve of strength allows for emergency physical activity and occasional prolonged periods when adequate nutrition and hours of rest are reduced. This reserve has a dual benefit. It also enables the daily tasks to be performed with greater ease and efficiency.

On the other hand, excessive strength, especially if accompanied by massive amounts of muscular tissue, is inefficient because of the work and time required to maintain it and because the extra bulk of tissue constitutes a superfluous load to be supported and moved. Although excessive muscle does not constitute the same health hazard as excessive fat, it has the same drawbacks from metabolic and mechanical points of view.

## Exercise for development of strength reserve

In order to acquire and maintain the extra strength needed for his fitness reserve, a person must engage frequently and regularly in extra physical activities.[36] This is true whether he is a professional athlete or an office worker. Fortunately for the office worker, who may find it inconvenient to fit physical exercise into his schedule of daily living, his physiological response to a small amount of exercise is of a large measure. It is the professional athlete or the heavy laborer who must work hard and frequently to keep his "edge."

Abdominal muscles are the ones most frequently needing attention since these are not brought into play in most work or sport activities. Moreover, they are difficult muscles to exercise because the action that brings them into play most strongly, that of flexing the hip, is usually dominated by the stronger flexor muscles of the hip—the sartorius, rectus femoris, psoas major, iliacus, and the adductors. A hook-lying position, in which the knees are at an angle of 65 degrees with the spine, tends to encourage the use of the abdominal rather than the hip flexor musculature.[37] Detailed accounts of programs of exercises for physical conditioning exercises and sports are found in textbooks on athletic training[15] and physical education.[38]

## Advanced study topics

1. Why are men stronger than women?
2. Review the recent literature on the subject of strength in the current issues of the *Research Quarterly*.
3. How can the hypertrophy of intact muscle be measured with greatest accuracy?
4. Observe the girth of muscles of various athletes and relate it to the athletes' specialty and joint mechanics.
5. Outline a strength training regimen.

## References

1. Steindler, A.: Kinesiology of the human body, Springfield, Ill., 1955, Charles C Thomas, Publisher.
2. Morris, C. B.: The measurement of strength of muscle relative to the cross section, Res. Quart. 19:295, 1948.
3. Merton, P. A.: Problems of muscular fatigue, Brit. M. Bull. 12:219, 1956.
4. Rose, D.: Discussing Hoag, D. G.: Physical therapy in orthopedics, with special reference to heavy resistance, low repetition exercise program, Physiotherapy Rev. 26:291, 1946.
5. Zuasmer, D. M.: The effect of cooling on muscle excitability, Ann. Phys. Med. 4:144, 1957.
6. Knowlton, G. C., and Hines, H. M.: Effect of growth and atrophy upon strength of skeletal muscle, Am. J. Physiol. 128:521, 1940.
7. Manzer, C. W.: An experimental investigation of rest pauses, Arch. Psychol., No. 90 14:1, 1927.
8. Payne, R. B., and Hauty, G. T.: Skill fatigue as a function of work-rest distribution, Report No. 57-140, Air University School of Aviation Medicine, U.S.A.F., July, 1957.
9. Clarke, H. H., Shay, C. T., and Mathews, D. K.: Strength decrements of elbow flexor muscles following exhaustive exercise, Arch. Phys. Med. 35:560, 1954.
10. Ikai, M., and Steinhaus, A. H.: Some factors modifying the expression of human strength, J. Appl. Physiol. 16:157, 1961.
11. Zhukov, E. K., and Zakhar'iants, Iu. Z.: Synchronized action potentials during muscular activity in man, Sechnov. Physiol. J. USSR 45:1053, 1959.
12. Zhukov, E. K., and Zakhar'iants, Iu. Z.: Electrophysiological data on some mechanisms for the overcoming of fatigue, Sechnov. Physiol. J. USSR 46:955, 1960.
13. Rasch, P. J.: Effect of position of forearm on strength of elbow flexion, Res. Quart. 26:333, 1956.
14. Provins, K. A., and Salter, N.: Maximum torque exerted about the elbow joint, J. Appl. Physiol. 7:393, 1955.
15. Morehouse, L. E., and Rasch, P. J.: Sports medicine for trainers, Philadelphia, 1963, W. B. Saunders Co.
16. Hunsicker, P. A., and Greey, G.: Studies in human strength, Res. Quart. 28:109, 1957.

17. Asmussen, E.: Muscular performance. In Rodahl, K., and Horvath, S., editors: Muscle as a tissue, New York, 1962, McGraw-Hill Book Company, chap. 8.

18. Hunsicker, P. A., and Donnelly, R. J.: Instruments to measure strength, Res. Quart. 26:408, 1955.

19. Clarke, H. H.: Recent advances in measurement and understanding of volitional muscular strength, Res. Quart. 27:263, 1956.

20. Tuttle, W. W., Janney, C. D., and Thompson, C. W.: Relation of maximum grip strength to grip strength endurance, J. Appl. Physiol. 2:663, 1950.

21. Steinhaus, A. H.: Strength from Morpurgo to Muller—a half century of research, J. A. Phys. & Ment. Rehab. 9: 147, 1955.

22. Adams, R. D., Denny-Brown, D., and Pearson, C. M.: Diseases of muscles, New York, 1954, Medical Book Division, Harper & Row, Publishers.

23. Maison, G. L., and Broeker, A. G.: Training in human muscles working with and without blood supply, Am. J. Physiol. 132:390, 1941.

24. DeLorme, T. L., West, F. E., and Schreiber, W. J.: Influence of progressive resistance exercises on knee function following femoral fractures, J. Bone & Joint Surg. 32-A:910, 1950.

25. DeLorme, T. L., and Watkins, A. L.: Progressive resistance exercise, New York, 1951, Appleton-Century-Crofts, Division of The Meredith Publishing Co.

26. Boyle, R. W., and Scott, F. H.: Some observations on effect of exercise on blood, lymph and muscle in its relation to muscle soreness, Am. J. Physiol. 44: 313, 1917.

27. Bigland, B., and Jehring, B.: Muscle performance in rats; normal and treated with growth hormone, J. Physiol. 116: 129, 1952.

28. Cuthbertson, D. P.: Influence of prolonged muscular rest on metabolism, J. Biochem. 23:1328, 1929.

29. Keys, A.: Caloric undernutrition and starvation, with notes on protein deficiency, J.A.M.A. 138:500, 1948.

30. O'Connell, E. R.: A physiological study of muscular strength, unpublished Master's thesis, June, 1956, University of California, Los Angeles.

31. Rasch, P. J., and Morehouse, L. E.: Effect of static and dynamic exercises on muscular strength and hypertrophy, J. Appl. Physiol. 11:29, 1957.

32. Jacobson, E.: Electrical measurements of neuro-muscular states during mental activities. IV. Evidence of contraction of specific muscles during imagination, Am. J. Physiol. 95:703, 1930.

33. Knowlton, G. C.: Physiological background for neuromuscular reeducation and coordination, Arch. Phys. Med. 35: 635, 1954.

34. Hodgkins, J.: Influence of unilateral endurance training on contralateral limb, J. Appl. Physiol. 16:991, 1961.

35. Morehouse, L. E.: Neurophysiology of strength, Proceedings of the First International Congress of Psychology of Sport, Rome, 1965.

36. Klumpp, T. G.: Control of fatigue in older persons, J.A.M.A. 165:605, 1957.

37. Walters, C. E., and Partridge, M. J.: Electromyographic study of the differential action of the abdominal muscles during exercise, Am. J. Phys. Med. 36: 259, 1957.

38. Mohr, D. R., and Vernier, E. L., editors: Physical education for high school students, Washington, D. C., 1955, American Association for Health, Physical Education, and Recreation.

# 8

# Connective tissue

The manner in which the pericardial sac affects heart function, discussed in Chapter 10, is only one example of the role of connective tissue in exercise. Connective tissue, which comprises a major portion of the total body mass, limits not only the range but also the speed of movement. The condition of the connective tissue is affected by exercise, and it is believed that the aches, pains, and sensitivities commonly associated with aging are more properly associated with inactivity. It is also postulated that the fatigue of sedentary work is in a large measure a connective tissue phenomenon.

It is, of course, difficult to study the functions of connective tissue in the living body, and thus there are many aspects that are as yet little understood. The body of knowledge on this subject is now growing because of the increasing recognition of its importance to physical performance and well-being.

Connective tissue consists of a fine, interlaced network of fibers lying within a plastic, gelatinous *ground substance* of varying consistency, thickness, and other characteristics. Some of the body components that are entirely or largely composed of connective tissue are bones, cartilage, joints, aponeuroses, tendons, ligaments, fasciae, the corium of the skin, the dura mater, the various tubes that must be kept open (such as the trachea and the bronchi), the fibrous neurilemma that sheaths the peripheral nerve fibers, and the sarcolemma, endomysium, and perimysium that surround the units of the muscular system.

The mucoid intercellular material comprising the ground substance is relatively inert chemically, but it is postulated that it is consumed in physiological function and removed through absorption of smaller molecular aggregates into the blood and lymph. It is renewed by the secretion of the fibroblastic cells.[1] Blood is a form of connective tissue in which the ground substance has become completely fluid.

### Fibers

There are three types of connective tissue fibers—*collagen,* *reticular,* and *elastic.* The nature of the three types is not well understood. Collagen appears to be a loose tissue of protein that tends to form large bundles of fine fibers. These are practically inextensible; excessive strains cause them to break rather than to stretch. Their great tensile strength and inelasticity makes them ideal for tendons, ligaments, aponeuroses, and fasciae. The pericardium surrounding the heart and the tunica adventitia surrounding the large blood vessels contain collagen fibers that serve to prevent overdistention of these organs. A prolonged steady tension may result in a weakening and stretching of these fibers. Collagen fibers are able to withstand great tensional stress but only comparatively small compressional stress. Collagen is insoluble in cold water, but if heated, it is converted into gelatin.

It has proved difficult to separate reticulin from collagen, but it appears to consist of very fine protein fibers combined with a high carbohydrate component. These fibers form an important constituent of lymph nodes and blood-forming organs. They do not become gelatin when heated.

Elastic connective tissue is believed to be composed of threads of sulfate polysaccharides in combination with protein lying in a shapeless matrix.[2]

### Cartilage

Cartilage comprises the gristle found in meat. It withstands compressional stress very well and tensional stress to a considerable extent. *Hyaline cartilage* consists of groups of cells lying in a structureless or faintly granular, pale blue matrix. It is found on the articular surfaces of bone joints and in the costal and laryngeal cartilages. The cartilage that ultimately becomes bone is of this type. *White fibrous cartilage* is made up of a mixture of white fibrous tissue and cartilaginous tissue. This is found in the attachment of ligaments and tendons to bone, at the symphysis pubis and certain other joints, and in the intervertebral disks. *Yellow fibrous cartilage* is composed of a mixture of yellow elastic fibers and cartilaginous tissue and is found in the external ear, the auditory tube, and in some of the cartilages of the larynx.

### Mechanical structure

The stresses to which articulations are exposed must be absorbed by a relatively small area of cartilage. The mechanical problem involved necessitates that the fibers be arranged in such a way that a sufficient number will always be at right angles to the imposed stresses. All articulating cartilages are fibrocartilages, and the density of the fibrous material is normally proportional to the customary pressures that it must withstand. According to Rauber[3] articular cartilage has a tension resistance of 0.17 kilogram per square millimeter and a compression resistance of 1.57 kilograms per square millimeter.

## Strength and elasticity

In animal tissues *hyaluronic acid,* a polysaccharide, seems to bind water in the interstitial spaces and to hold the cells together in a jellylike matrix. Certain functions of the skin, the ocular fluids, synovial fluid, and connective tissue in general appear to depend at least in part on the quantity and degree of aggregation of hyaluronic acid. The long-chain structures of chondroitin sulfuric acid and hyaluronic acid, together with the fiber proteins, may be the explanation for the tensile strength and elasticity of connective tissue.[4]

*Synovial fluid* consists of tissue fluids with a high hyaluronic acid content and appears to function as a lubricant and shock absorber. The synovial cavity of a joint normally contains only enough fluid to moisten and lubricate the synovial surfaces, but it may accumulate in painful amounts in an injured or inflamed joint. Other types of ground substances have different functions, but these are almost unexplored.

Hyaluronic acid is depolymerized by an enzyme, *hyaluronidase.* Hyaluronidase is found in the venom of bees, scorpions, and certain poisonous snakes. When it is injected into the knee joints of patients suffering from rheumatoid arthritis, it markedly reduces the viscosity of the synovial fluid.[5]

## Aging

There is a difference in the consistency and distribution of newly formed and adult connective tissue. Ground substance is abundant in an infant, less plentiful in an adult, and scanty in the elderly person. This reduction in ground substance and lean muscle mass in elderly persons may be correlated with their greater vulnerability to shock since diminution of ground substance results in a smaller area within which to meet changes in vascular volume. This makes it difficult for them to compensate for the rapid changes that occur in disease, injury, and surgery. Furthermore, as one grows older the quality of elasticity tends to disappear from connective tissue. The tendency of fascia to contract under certain conditions (to be discussed later) remains, and as elasticity decreases with advancing age, the range of movement is likely to become restricted.

However, during the aging process the hyaline covering of bone surfaces remains remarkably intact although localized areas of cartilage softening due to specific trauma or disease or to the wear and tear of abnormal joint mechanics may develop. These are usually found in the weight-bearing surfaces of the lower extremities. In normal aging of the musculoskeletal apparatus articular cartilage is the most stable element and the one least contributory to disability and dysfunction.[6]

## Stretching

Stretching exercises of various types have been used for at least 2,000 years for the relief of the discomforts associated with the menstrual period. These have proved of definite value, and a rather extensive literature has accumulated on this subject.[7] An example is shown in Fig. 15.

Other conditions of malfunction of connective tissue not associated with menstruation or pregnancy are common among both men and women, especially those leading a sedentary life. The most common of these is *fascial contraction*. Fibrocytic contracture of the fibrous elements of a muscle may result in shortening of the contractile muscle fibers and prevent them from extending to their normal relaxed length, hence limiting their power and

**Fig. 15.** Stretching the ligaments of the dorsolumbar spine. The abdominal and gluteal muscles are strongly contracted. The hips are moved slightly forward and inward toward the wall, assisted by pressure of the hand against the hip. (From Billig, H. E., and Loewendahl, E.: Mobilization of the human body, Stanford, 1949, Stanford University Press.)

placing them under tension. Afferent and efferent nerve pathways pass through various fascial and ligamentous planes in the muscle. If the fascia tightens abnormally (as may result from age, chilling, poor posture, inactivity, strain, and other causes), it constricts these nerve pathways, thus causing an abnormal pressure irritation of the nerves and resulting in neuralgia and other ailments. If the fasciae are stretched by gradual, repetitive, forcible, and progressive exercises, part of the elongation thus achieved remains after the exercise is completed. This affords an opportunity for the correction of bad mechanical alignment and for the elimination of compressions of peripheral nerves. Mobilizations of this type require specific techniques such as have been described by Billig and Loewendahl.[8]

## Exercise

Cartilage probably is always in a state of greater or lesser deformation during periods of activity, resuming its shape during rest. Fascia displays a tendency to contract during rest, and this is especially in evidence during inactivity following a period of activity. Thus after a night's rest a person awakes feeling stiff and with a natural tendency to stretch. Athletes, dancers, contortionists, and other performers of this type find it necessary to limber up carefully before engaging in their activities.

That this stiffness may have its basis in the viscosity and amount of synovial fluid is demonstrated by the following experiment. When one leg of an experimental animal was exercised and the other leg was left undisturbed, the exercised joint contained a larger amount of synovial fluid than did the unexercised joint. The longer the exercise, the greater was the amount of fluid present. The viscosity of the synovial fluid tended to increase, the hyaluronic acid concentration dropped to about 70% of that of the rested muscle, the total protein decreased to about 65%, and microscopically visible cellular elements were present in greater numbers. From this it was concluded that the increase in synovial volume was chiefly the result of the inflow of water. The larger number of particles probably resulted from abrasion of the articular cartilage and of the synovialis.[9]

Articular cartilage in growing animals that have been exercised is thicker than in animals that have been kept at rest.[10] During exercise articular cartilage increases in thickness, and during the rest period following exercise the thickness of the cartilage diminishes about 10%.[11] No direct connection exists between the joint cavities and the blood or lymph vessels. A layer of connective tissue always intervenes. Presumably the exercise creates an elevated intra-articular hydrostatic pressure, and the resistance of the synovial membrane is reduced so that there is an increased absorption of fluid into the cartilaginous tissues from joint cavities. Since in connective tissue water is bound in a gel, no free fluid exists in these tissues. It must be presumed that the structural conditions of the synovial membrane are changed in order to increase the absorption of fluid.

## Advanced study topics

1. How does connective tissue function during muscular activity?
2. Review the recent literature on the subject of connective tissue in the current issues of the *Journal of Bone and Joint Surgery.*
3. How is joint flexibility measured?
4. Measure the range of motion before and after various stretching exercises.
5. Prepare instructions for correction of joint stiffness.

## References

1. Gersh, I., and Catchpole, H. R.: The organization of ground substance and basement membrane and its significance in tissue injury, disease and growth, Am. J. Anat. **85**:457, 1949.
2. Asboe-Hansen, G.: Connective tissue in health and disease, New York, 1954, Philosophical Library, Inc.
3. Rauber, A. A.: Elastizitat und Festigkeit der Knocken, Leipzig, 1876. Cited in Steindler, A.: Kinesiology of the human body under normal and pathological conditions, Springfield, Ill., 1955, Charles C Thomas, Publisher.
4. Blix, G., and Snellman, O.: On chondroitin sulfuric acid and hyaluronic acid, Arkiv. Kemi. Min. och Geol. **19-A:**1, 1947. Abstracted in Biolog. Abst. **21:**24235, 1947.
5. Meyer, K.: The biological significance of hyaluronic acid and hyaluronidase, Physiol. Rev. **27:**335, 1947.
6. Vernon, S.: Connective tissue, hormones and aging, J. Am. Geriatrics Soc. **5:**786, 1957.
7. Golub, L. J., and Christaldi, J.: Reducing dysmenorrhea in young adults, J. Health, Phys. Ed. & Rec. **28:**24, 1957.
8. Billig, H. E., and Loewendahl, E.: Mobilization of the human body, Stanford, 1949, Stanford University Press.
9. Ekholm, R., and Norback, B.: On the relationship between articular changes and function, Acta Orthop. Scandinav. **21:**81, 1951.
10. Holmdahl, D. E.: Some results of an experimental investigation into the morpho-physiology of joints, Acta Orthop. Scandinav. **13:**13, 1948.
11. Gardner, E.: Physiology of movable joints, Physiol. Rev. **30:**127, 1950.

# 9

# Analysis of movement

The skeleton may be considered to be an arrangement of levers. These levers are moved by muscles. The type, range, and power of the movements are governed by the nature of the joints between the moving parts, the lengths of the bony levers, the size and arrangement of the muscles acting on the levers, and the weight of the load to be moved.

## Relation of the structure of bones and muscles to their functions

The structure of bones and of skeletal muscles adapts them to meet the terrific strains that occur during lifting, carrying, striking, pulling, and other movements.

A longitudinal section of one of the long bones reveals a fanlike arrangement of cancellous tissue with concentrations of latticelike *cancelli*. These add strength to the bone while minimizing its weight.

The arrangement of the fibers in a skeletal muscle likewise indicates a clear relation to function. When range of movement rather than power is the chief consideration, the bundles of fibers are spindle shaped and are arranged parallel to the long axis of the muscle with the tendons at each end. This is the *fusiform* arrangement (Fig. 16). When power is the principal requirement, the muscle fibers are short and are arranged in a *penniform* fashion, with the tendon at one side and the muscle fibers placed at an oblique angle with it. The maximal power is achieved in the *bipenniform* arrangement in which the muscle fibers are placed at an angle on either side of a central tendon.

## Partite action of muscles

Several of the larger muscles, such as the pectoralis major, trapezius, deltoid, latissimus dorsi, triceps brachii, and the quadriceps femoris, are so constructed and innervated that portions of each muscle may function *separately* as well as together. The actions of the various parts of a muscle

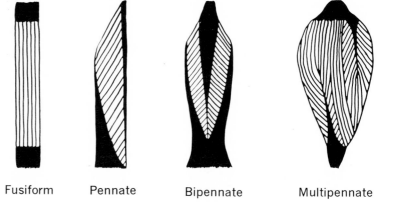

Fusiform        Pennate        Bipennate        Multipennate

**Fig. 16.** Fiber arrangement in skeletal muscles. Note that with the gain in power caused by the increased number of fibers in the pennate muscles there is a loss in the range of movement in comparison with the fusiform arrangement.

during an exercise may be analyzed by palpation or with greater accuracy by recording the electrical potentials associated with contraction.[1] The functions of the separate parts of the deltoid have been analyzed using the action current technique.[2] Electrodes were placed over the anterior, middle, and posterior parts of the deltoid, and the arm was raised forward. There was a strong contraction of the anterior deltoid, moderate contraction of the middle deltoid, and no observable contraction of the posterior deltoid. When the arm was raised diagonally backward-sideward, the contraction of the posterior deltoid seemed to initiate the movement and then to cease. The middle deltoid continued the contraction during the entire movement.

## Classification of muscular activity

Muscles act in teams during movement of the body. The direction of movement of any part is the result of a difference in tension of the muscles on either side of the joint that is moved. When the arm is flexed, tension exerted by the contraction of the biceps is greater than that exerted by the triceps. Muscles so arranged as to act against each other on opposite sides of a joint are known as *antagonistic muscles.* Muscles working in mutual assistance to move a joint in one direction are known as *synergic muscles.* The biceps and the brachialis help each other in flexing the elbow and are examples of synergic muscles.

Rapid, rhythmic activity is accomplished by an alternation of contraction and relaxation of the antagonistic flexors and extensors of the joints in motion. Such freedom and speed of motion is allowed by a reflex reduction in tension of the muscles that are lengthening at the same time; the tension is increased in the muscles that are shortening. This reflex reduction in tension of the muscles that are lengthening during rapid, light movement is brought about involuntarily by a reduction of the motor discharges from the central nervous system. This kind of coordination has its center in the spinal cord and is called *reciprocal innervation of antagonistic muscles.*

Unresisted shortening of a muscle, as in the rapid, light, rhythmic activity just described, is called *concentric contraction.* In slow, heavy work and in a controlled motion, such as steering an automobile, tension of antagonistic muscles during lengthening is called *eccentric contraction.* The synchronous tension of antagonistic muscles that commonly occurs during movement preceded by relaxation of both muscles is called *cocontraction.* Both concentric and eccentric contractions are called *isotonic contractions* because the increased muscular tonus results in a change in length. When antagonistic muscles contract against each other with equal tension so that no movement takes place, the fixation known as *static contraction* occurs. Such development of tension without change in length, such as that occurring in antagonistic muscles during static contraction, is known as *isometric contraction.*

It is practically impossible to hold the body still. Voluntary efforts to hold still by contracting groups of antagonistic muscles against each other, a fixation movement, will never fully succeed, and the distal portion of the segment will be observed to move to and fro. This movement is known as *tremor* and is caused by the unsteady muscle response caused by the synchronous nature of the volleys of nerve impulses stimulating the antagonistic muscles. An increase in muscular tension during fixation will increase tremor. Relaxation of tension will reduce tremor.

In a *slow tension movement* the antagonistic muscle groups are continuously in cocontraction, which serves to fix the joints involved in the action and to aid in accurate positioning. As slow tension movement continues, the body part moves in the direction of the group of muscles exerting the stronger pull, and there is a continual readjustment of tension of the groups of antagonistic muscles. A *rapid tension movement* such as shaking or tapping is one in which there is tension in all antagonistic muscles during the motion. Rapid tension movement is initiated by a sudden concentric contraction. There follows a contraction of the antagonists that stops the motion and reverses it. This is repeated and an oscillatory motion is set up. The maximal rate of tapping is limited by the rate of the tremor because it is not possible to modify the course of a movement except at the termination of each oscillation of the tremor. Thus, if the rate of the tremor is 10 per second, the tapping rate cannot exceed that value.

The *rapid ballistic* movement is one that is begun by a concentric contraction and proceeds unhindered by eccentric contraction of antagonists until near the end of the movement. If cocontraction of the antagonist becomes progressively intense toward the end of the movement, serving to arrest the motion, the movement is said to be *oscillatory.*

## Analysis of muscular action

The action of muscles during movement can be studied by simultaneous recordings of action currents occurring in the muscles under inves-

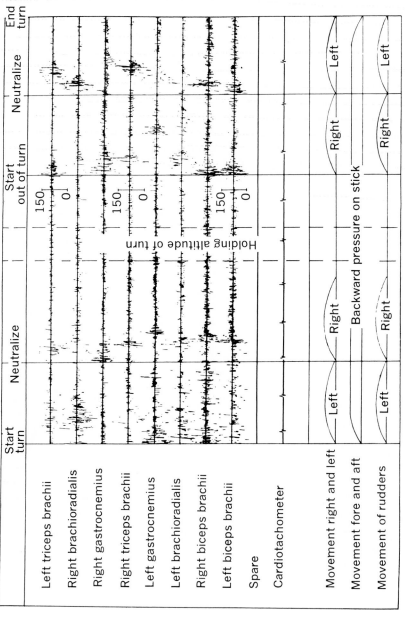

**Fig. 17.** Electromyogram of muscle interplay during a control movement in aircraft. The scale of 1-150 is an arbitrary calibration of amplitude of muscular activity. (From Wells, J. G.: Physical condition as a factor in pilot performance, unpublished doctoral dissertation.)

tigation. Electrical activity generated when muscles contract is detected either by a needle thrust into the muscle or by an electrode placed on the skin over the muscle and is conducted through a cable to an electromyograph, which amplifies the current and records changes as muscular tension is altered during activity. A sample electromyogram (record of action current alterations during activity) is presented in Fig. 17. Using this technique, analysis of golf,[3] tennis,[4] weight lifting,[5] and performance during acceleration in aircraft[6] has been accomplished. Recently multiple, simultaneous electromyographic records of muscular activity of aircraft pilots and changes in economy of effort, coordination, and accuracy of movement were made during each hour of a simulated 7-hour flight.[7] Poor performers were characterized by wasteful muscular activity, using forceful motions when only light ones were required. Muscular coordination during flight tasks was not observed to be affected by either a month of frequent and regular vigorous muscular exercise or a month in a hospital bed. The accuracy of muscular movements of subjects, both after bed rest and after normal duty, was observed to deteriorate during the latter portion of the long-range flight, but these errors in control were not gross enough to affect the scores of flight performance. Subjects whose physical condition was improved by exercise were able to make accurate muscular adjustments throughout the 7-hour flights.

The multiple electromyographic technique may possibly be employed as an objective measure of skill. Any muscular activity in excess of a minimum requirement for performance of standardized tasks would represent a measure of wasted effort. Performances accomplished with the least waste of effort would represent the highest standard of skill. Effects of training, drugs, fatigue, and other conditions upon skill could thus be quantitated by this method.

## Voluntary control of movement

Volition controls the whole movement, not the action of single muscles. Any movement, whether it is striking, jumping, lifting, pulling, throwing, or falling, requires a concentration on the movement and demands a disregard of the muscle action. The golf instructor who points out how the muscles should be acting during the swing of the club will soon have his pupil in the state of the centipede who "was happy quite, until a frog in fun said, 'Pray, which leg comes after which?' This wrought her up to such a pitch, she lay distracted in the ditch considering how to run."

## Mechanical efficiency

*Human body designed for speed.* The human body is designed for speed rather than for overcoming great loads. In most of the levers of the body the distance between the fulcrum and the point of application of power, the power arm, is relatively shorter than the distance between the fulcrum and the center of the weight, the weight arm. This is unlike most man-made mechanical levers in which the power arm is relatively long and the weight arm short so that great loads may be overcome by the application of a small force. The source of power in the body is placed at a great mechanical disadvantage, and extraordinarily strong forces must be applied through the short power arms and through the short distances. The muscles that are the source of power must be strong and efficient in order to work effectively at such mechanical disadvantage.

*Factors affecting mechanical efficiency.* In general the mechanical efficiency of muscular movements is affected by the following mechanical conditions: (1) the length of the power arm, (2) the length of the weight arm, (3) the load and the speed of movement of the load, (4) momentum, (5) the angle of the pull by the muscle as affected by the attachment to the lever, (6) the stretched condition of the pulling muscle, and (7) the action of synergic and antagonistic muscles.

*Length of the power arm.* A *long* power arm in comparison with the length of the weight arm gives the lever a mechanical advantage that enables heavy loads to be lifted. A *short* power arm results in a mechanical disadvantage in lifting heavy loads but imparts speed to the movement if the muscular power is sufficient. The calcaneus presents a long power arm that enables a person to rise on his toes while carrying a heavy weight. The olecranon is a short power arm that allows great speed in throwing.

*Length of the weight arm.* A *long* weight arm is a disadvantage in lifting heavy loads but is an advantage in movements of speed and in imparting momentum to light objects. A *short* weight arm in relation to the power arm gives the lever a mechanical advantage in lifting loads.

*Load and speed of movement of the load.* The closer a load is placed to the fulcrum, the greater is the mechanical advantage. The further a light object is held from the fulcrum, the greater is the advantage for speed. A lightweight ball is thrown with the arm extended, whereas the heavy shot is put from close to the shoulder.

The magnitude of the load determines the speed at which the lever can be moved. The heavier the load, the slower is the movement. In the case of heavy loads the amount determines the distance through which a load can be lifted. The importance of the most effective application of muscular power and mechanical efficiency becomes greater as the load to be lifted becomes heavier. A load that is difficult to lift by the use of inefficient movements becomes less difficult if efficient mechanical principles are applied. Heavy loads are best moved by the arm through a flexion of approximately 150 to 160 degrees or through an extension from approximately 45 to 90 degrees.

The speed of the movement of the load affects the maximum load that can be moved. Heavy loads can only be lifted slowly. If a fast movement is required, the weight must be light. A heavy weight can be moved faster if it is held closer to the fulcrum (for example, the shot put).

*Momentum.* Momentum affects the amount of power that must be applied in moving a load. A greater amount of power must be applied to overcome the inertia of a stationary object than to maintain the speed of a moving object. Likewise, a greater amount of power is needed to stop a moving object quickly than to stop it by gradually reducing the speed. A greater momentum can be imparted to a movable object if the weight arm is lengthened. Less power is necessary to change the direction of a moving object if the object is kept moving than if the object is brought to a stop before it is moved in the new direction. The turn in swimming is a continuous motion through a short circle, not an abrupt reversal of the direction of movement.

*Angle of pull.* A pull at a right angle to the lever gives the maximum mechanical efficiency. The greater the deviation from the right angle, the less efficient is the angle of pull. In a flexion of a fully extended arm most of the force is wasted by pulling the radius and ulna against the humerus.

If the pull of a muscle is not directly away from its point of insertion, additional muscles must be called into activity in order to hold the lever in the desired position during the movement. Most arm movements in swimming, for example, are angular and require the contraction of synergic muscles.

*Stretched condition of the pulling muscle.* One of the general properties of all types of muscle is that the force developed during contraction is greater if the muscle is under stretch at the time of contraction. In the case of skeletal muscle, the optimal degree of stretching corresponds roughly to the natural or resting length of the muscle in the body (that is, the muscle must be stretched about 25% to bridge the distance between its origin and its insertion).

*Action of synergic and antagonistic muscles.* The reciprocal action of synergic and antagonistic muscles increases the steadiness and accuracy of a movement. The greater the number of muscles engaged in a movement, the more accurate and graceful is the movement. The more complete the relaxation of the antagonistic muscles, the more rapid and powerful is the movement. The more angular the direction of pull, the greater is the importance of the action of the synergic muscles in controlling the direction of the movement.

*Motion economy.* There is a best way to perform any task, and it is the job of the coach in athletics and the time-and-motion specialist in industry to find it. A few of the principles that have been found to be of importance in improving performance are as follows:

1. Momentum should be employed to overcome resistance.
2. Momentum should be reduced to a minimum if it must be overcome by muscular effort.
3. Continuous curved motions require less effort than straight-line motions involving sudden and sharp changes in direction.
4. Movements in which the muscles initiating movement are unopposed, allowing free and smooth motion, are faster, easier, and more accurate than restricted or controlled movements.
5. Work arranged to permit an easy and natural rhythm is conducive to smooth and automatic performance.

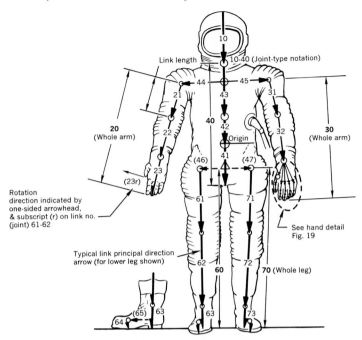

**Fig. 18.** Link diagram and numerical notation system. (From Roebuck, J. A., Jr.: NASA study presented at AAHPER Council on Kinesiology, Chicago, Ill., March, 1966 [unpublished data].)

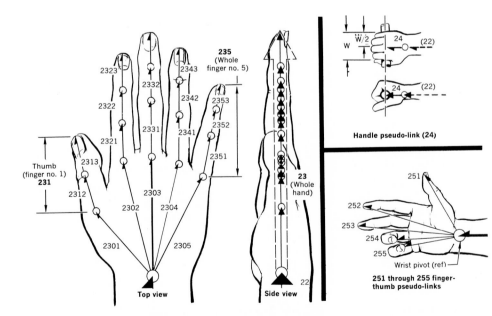

**Fig. 19.** Basic hand link details. (From Roebuck, J. A., Jr.: NASA study presented at AAHPER Council on Kinesiology, Chicago, Ill., March, 1966 [unpublished data].)

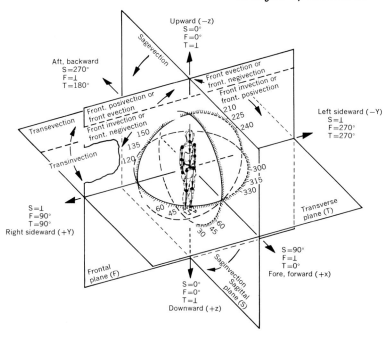

**Fig. 20.** Mobility terminology. Triplanar angular coordinate system. (From Roebuck, J. A., Jr.: NASA study presented at the AAHPER Council on Kinesiology, Chicago, Ill., March, 1966 [unpublished data].)

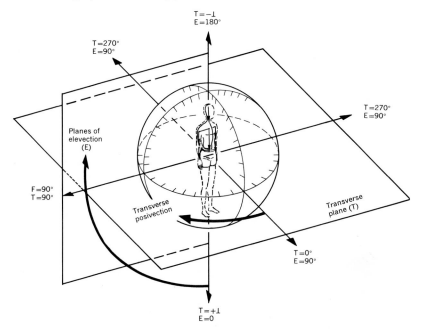

**Fig. 21.** Global coordinate system. (From Roebuck, J. A., Jr.: NASA study presented at the AAHPER Council on Kinesiology, Chicago, Ill., March, 1966 [unpublished data].)

6. Hesitation or the temporary and often minute cessation from motion should be eliminated from the performance.

Textbooks with a more detailed discussion of body movement in relation to the performance of work and sport are available to the reader.[8, 9]

*Movement description and measurement.* The exacting requirements for the design of astronauts' space suits have led engineers[10] to standardize a system of describing and measuring body movement in the suit. This system of movement notation is useful to students of exercise physiology who need descriptions of movement that are clear, simple, and reproducible. The system is compatible with common methods of engineering analysis, including machine computation.

The mobility models shown in Figs. 18 and 19 are concepts of man as a collection of mechanical linkages. The links are connected by joints having a variety of freedoms of motion. Every movement can be described in terms of numbers.

Looking at Fig. 18, the first digit for right limbs is even (2 or 6), and left is odd (3 or 7). Segment numbers, with few exceptions, increase from head to toe.

The direction and range of movement is described in three planes, using

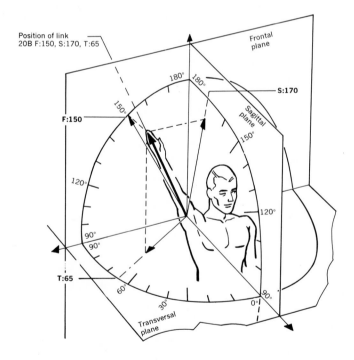

**Fig. 22.** Example of shorthand notation. (From Roebuck, J. A., Jr.: NASA study presented at the AAHPER Council on Kinesiology, Chicago, Ill., March, 1966 [unpublished data].)

a 360-degree circle scale as shown in Figs. 20 and 21. An example of numerical notation shorthand is given in Fig. 22. The zero direction for both the sagittal and frontal planes is always the same as that of link 41 (or link 40 when the trunk is considered as one single link).

## Movement terminology

Except for the term "vection," used to describe rotary movements, root words are common to kinesiology and are shortened for use in combination to describe decreasing and increasing angular readings as movements progress. The following set of words describe all mobility performances. With these the exercise physiologist can relate the phenomena of his discipline, such as strength and metabolic requirements, to movements described precisely in terms of their type and direction.

1. Terms denoting type of movement

| | |
|---|---|
| (a) Vection (vek'shun) | Pivoting or revolving a link director (the principal director unless otherwise noted), or its projection on a principal plane, about an axis perpendicular to itself |
| (b) Rotation | A rotatory movement of a link about its major axis, or principal director. Described as an angular direction change (vection) of the rotary director |
| (c) Torsion | Twisting of a link about its major axis, described as an angular direction change (vection) of the rotary director assuming the tail of the principal director is fixed |

2. Terms denoting direction of movement—single links

| | |
|---|---|
| (a) Posivection (pos'i-vek-shun) | Vection in any plane producing an increasing angular reading in that plane. The plane in which action is measured must be specified by a preceding term; i.e., frontal, sagittal, transversal |
| (b) Negivection | Opposite of posivection |
| (c) Positive rotation | As seen from the tail of the principal director, rotation resulting in clockwise vection of the rotary director |
| (d) Negative rotation | Opposite to positive rotation |
| (e) Positive torsion | As seen from the tail of the principal director, torsion resulting in clockwise vection of the rotary director |
| (f) Negative torsion | Opposite to positive torsion |

3. Terms denoting direction of movement—dual links

| | |
|---|---|
| (a) Frontevection (frunt'e-vek-shun) | As seen from the front, clockwise vection of the right limb together with counterclockwise vection of the left limb about axes perpendicular to the frontal plane |
| (b) Frontinvection (frunt'in-vek-shun) | Opposite to frontevection |
| (c) Sagevection (saj'e-vek-shun) | As seen from the right, counterclockwise vection of the limbs about an axis perpendicular to the sagittal plane |
| (d) saginvection (saj'in-vek-shun) | Opposite to sagevection |

(e) Transevection
(trans'e-vek-shun)

As seen from above, clockwise vection of the right limb together with counterclockwise vection of the left limb about axes perpendicular to the transverse plane

(f) Transinvection
(trans'in-vek-shun)

Opposite to transevection

(g) Fronterotation
(frunt'e-roh-tay-shun)

Frontevection of the rotary directors of the limbs. *Positive fronterotation* implies that the principal director is pointing in the positive X direction, or forward. *Negative fronterotation* implies that the principal director is pointing aft, or in the minus X direction

(h) Frontinrotation
(frunt'in-roh-tay-shun)

Opposite to fronterotation. Frontinvection of the rotary directors of the limbs. As in above, *positive* implies that the principal director points forward; *negative* implies that the principal director points aft

(i) Sagerotation
(saj'e-roh-tay-shun)

Sagevection of the rotary directors of dual links. *Positive* implies that the principal director of the right limb is pointing to the right, or in the positive Y direction, and opposite for the left limb. *Negative* implies that the right limb is pointing left and the left limb is pointing right

(j) Saginrotation
(saj'in-roh-tay-shun)

Saginvection of the rotary directors of dual links. The terms *positive* and *negative* apply as in sagerotation above

(k) Transerotation
(trans'e-roh-tay-shun)

Transevection of the rotary directors of the limbs. *Positive* implies that the principal director of the links points downward, in the direction of the plus Z axis, *negative* implies the opposite

(l) Transinrotation
(trans'in-roh-tay-shun)

Transinvection of the rotary directors of limbs. The terms *positive* and *negative* apply as in transerotation above

(m) Frontetorsion
(frunt'e-tor-shun)

Frontevection of the rotary directors of the limbs with the tail end of the principal directors held fixed. The terms *positive* and *negative* apply as for fronterotation

(n) Frontintorsion
(frunt'in-tor-shun)

Opposite of frontetorsion

(o) Sagetorsion
(saj'e-tor-shun)

Sagevection of the rotary directors of the limbs with the tail end of the principal directors held fixed. The terms *positive* and *negative* apply as for sagerotation

(p) Sagintorsion
(saj'in-tor-shun)

Opposite of sagetorsion

(q) Transetorsion
(trans'e-tor-shun)

Transevection of the rotary directors of the limbs with the tail end of the principal directors held fixed. The terms *positive* and *negative* apply as for transerotation

(r) Transintorsion
(trans'in-tor-shun)

Opposite to transetorsion

4. Combinations

The major terms for dual links are formed by combining the three terms denoting type of movement with the following prefix elements indicating direction:

(a) -E-   A positive upward- or outward-tending movement (from the standard position) or any motion resulting in an increasing angular coordinate of the right limb

(b) -IN-      Opposite to -E-, an inward or downward movement
(c, d, e)     The first syllable of each of the names for the principal planes (front, sag, trans)

Additional necessary distinctions for attitude of the limbs when performing rotational and torsional movements are defined by the terms *positive* and *negative*, which also serve to indicate direction for single links.

## Advanced study topics

1. What sport or other physical activity employs the human body most efficiently?
2. Review the recent literature on the subject of analysis of movement in the current issues of *Human Factors*.
3. Describe the techniques of time and motion study.
4. Evaluate a tool and its arrangement for human use.
5. Describe the best way to use a shovel or other implement.

## References

1. Hubbard, A. W.: An experimental analysis of running and of certain fundamental differences between trained and untrained runners, Res. Quart. Am. A. Health Phys. Ed. & Rec. **10**:28, 1939.
2. McCloy, C. H.: Some notes of differential actions of partite muscles, Res. Quart. Am. A. Health Phys. Ed. & Rec. **17**:254, 1946.
3. Slater-Hammel, A. T.: Action current study of contraction movement relationship in golf strokes, Res. Quart. Am. A. Health Phys. Ed. & Rec. **19**:164, 1948.
4. Slater-Hammel, A. T.: Action current study of tennis stroke, Res. Quart. Am. A. Health Phys. Ed. & Rec. **20**:424, 1949.
5. Payne, B., and Davis, R. C.: The role of muscular tension in the comparison of lifted weights, J. Exper. Psychol. **27**:227, 1940.
6. Wells, J. G., and Morehouse, L. E.: Electromyographic study of the effects of various headward accelerative forces upon the pilot's ability to perform standardized pulls on an aircraft control stick, J. Aviation Med. **21**:49, 1950.
7. Wells, J. G.: Physical condition as a factor in pilot performance (unpublished data).
8. Handbook of human engineering data for design engineers, Office of Naval Research, Special Devices Center Technical Report 199-1-1, December, 1949.
9. Morehouse, L. E., and Cooper, J. M.: Kinesiology, St. Louis, 1950, The C. V. Mosby Co.
10. Roebuck, J. A., Jr.: NASA study presented at the AAHPER Council on Kinesiology, Chicago, Ill., March, 1966, (unpublished data).

# Part two

# Circulatory and respiratory adjustments during exercise

# 10

# The heart

## General features of the circulation

The tissues of the body require for their normal functioning a reasonable degree of constancy with respect to certain factors.

Among these factors are temperature, acidity, food supply, and oxygen. The primary function of the circulation of the blood is to ensure the preservation of this constant internal environment by transporting oxygen, food materials, and hormones to the tissue cells and by removing the waste products of activity. The interchange of materials between the blood and the tissues occurs in the thin-walled *capillaries*. The rest of the circulatory system, including the heart, exists solely for the purpose of maintaining the capillary exchange. The heart is a muscular pump that imparts sufficient kinetic energy to the blood to move it through the capillaries. The arteries conduct the blood from the heart to the capillaries, and the veins conduct the blood from the capillaries back to the heart again. As will be seen in later chapters, the arteries and veins are not simply passive conducting tubes but are also responsible, through alterations in their diameters, for the proper distribution of the blood to various organs and tissues in accordance with their metabolic requirements.

From the standpoint of the physiology of exercise the heart is primarily a respiratory organ. In the periods of rest between bouts of exercise the muscles are able to store sufficient food materials to initiate exercise and to maintain it until reserves can be mobilized. There is, however, no mechanism for the storage of oxygen in the tissues. Any increase in the oxygen requirement must be satisfied by a corresponding increase in the transport of oxygen to the tissues. This is accomplished in two ways: (1) by diverting blood to the contracting muscles from less active regions and (2) by increasing the volume of blood pumped by the heart per minute. Not only is the flow of blood to the muscles increased when they become active but also a larger volume of oxygen is removed from each volume of blood. This is made possible by certain peculiar properties of hemoglobin that will be discussed in Chapter 16.

The increased pumping action of the heart has long been regarded as the most important of the adaptive responses that increase the delivery of oxygen to contracting muscles and as the factor that ordinarily sets the upper limit to the capacity for exercise. There is mounting evidence that peripheral vascular changes, which increase the capacity of the muscle blood vessels to receive the increased blood flow, may be of equal importance. Nevertheless, the increase in cardiac output remains a key factor in the physiological response to exercise.

## General description of the heart

The salient anatomical features of the heart will be reviewed. The heart is a hollow muscular organ subdivided internally into four chambers—the right and left *atria* (or auricles) and the right and left *ventricles*. The atria are thin-walled collecting chambers. They have little contractile power and serve primarily to store the blood brought to them by the veins during the contraction, or *systole*, of the ventricles and then to pass this blood on to the ventricles during their period of relaxation, or *diastole*. The ventricles, on the other hand, are thick-walled muscular chambers that exert considerable force during contraction. This contractile force imparts the necessary kinetic energy to the blood to maintain its circulation.

From a functional standpoint the heart may be divided into the right heart (right atrium and ventricle) and the left heart (left atrium and ventricle). The right heart receives venous blood from all the systemic veins of the body and pumps it through the pulmonary arteries into the lungs where oxygen is absorbed and carbon dioxide eliminated. The oxygenated blood is returned through the pulmonary veins to the left heart, which in turn pumps it through the aorta into the systemic arteries of the body. The orifices between the atria and their corresponding ventricles and the exit of the pulmonary artery and the aorta from their respective ventricles are guarded by valves that permit the flow of blood in one direction only.

The heart muscle itself is not nourished by the blood contained within its chambers but is supplied by the coronary arteries that leave the aorta just beyond the aortic valves.

The stimulus that causes contraction of the heart muscle at each beat arises within the heart itself in a specialized muscle mass known as the sinoatrial (S-A) node, or pacemaker. The impulse is conducted to all parts of the heart muscle by way of a specialized conducting system, the atrioventricular (A-V) node and bundle (Fig. 23). The rate of beating of the heart is regulated by two sets of nerves—the *vagus* nerves, which slow the rate, and the *accelerator* nerves, which increase the rate. The adjustment of the heart rate to the metabolic requirements of the body will be discussed in Chapter 11.

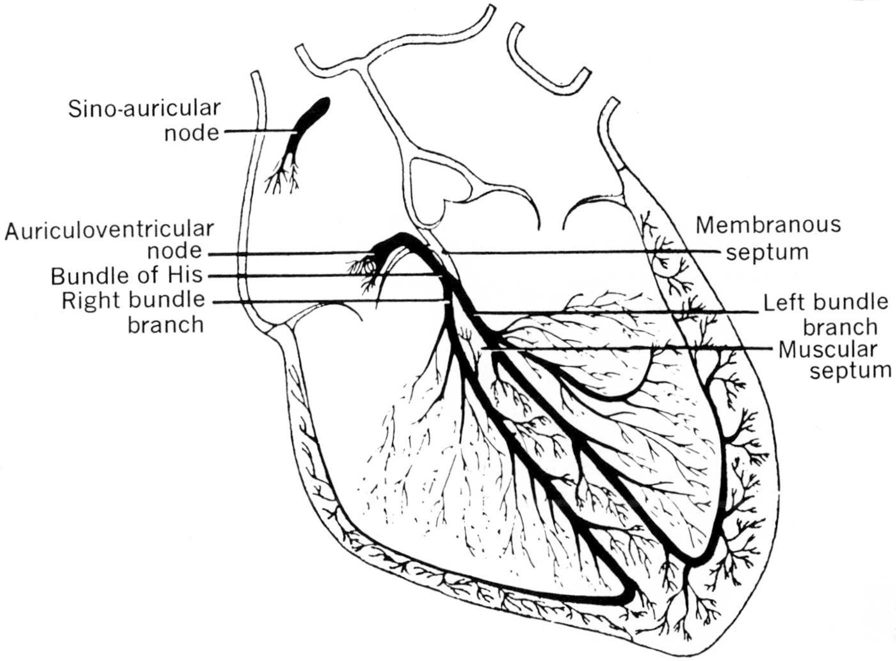

**Fig. 23.** Diagram of the conduction system of the heart. (From Sigler, L. H.: The electrocardiogram, New York, 1944, Grune & Stratton, Inc.)

The heart is enclosed in a fibrous sac called the pericardium. A thin film of fluid (the pericardial fluid) separates the heart from the pericardium and minimizes the friction that otherwise would occur during contraction and relaxation of the heart. The pericardium probably serves a protective function in preventing dangerous overdistention of the heart. Although the pericardium is relatively nondistensible and hence resists attempts at sudden stretching, it can be stretched very slowly to permit the normal increase in heart size often present in athletes or the pathological dilatation of the heart that occurs in certain types of heart disease.

## The cardiac cycle

The cardiac cycle includes all the events (pressure changes, volume changes, and valve action) that occur during one complete period of contraction and relaxation of the heart. Since the complete cycle takes place in a period of 1 second or less, it is no wonder that early physiologists despaired of ever solving its mysteries. Modern methods of recording rapid changes in volume and pressure have, however, permitted a very exact analysis of events.

A description of the cardiac cycle may begin at any point in the cycle (Figs. 24 and 25). For convenience we will start with the phase of *diastasis,* the period during which the whole heart is completely relaxed. Blood is entering the right atrium from the venae cavae and the left atrium from the pulmonary veins. The atrioventricular (A-V) valves that guard the orifice between the atrium and the ventricle on each side are open, and the blood that enters the atria flows freely through into the relaxed ventricles. The valves leading from the ventricles to the pulmonary artery and the aorta are closed, so that none of the blood entering the ventricles is able to leave. The period of diastasis ends abruptly with the onset of *systole* (contraction) of the atria. Filling of the ventricles is already virtually complete when atrial systole occurs, so that it is of minor importance so far as ventricular filling is concerned. Almost immediately after atrial systole is completed, ventricular systole begins. Contraction of the ventricular muscle results in a rapid rise in the pressure of the blood in the ventricle. This very quickly exceeds the atrial pressure (which is always low) and causes a sudden closure of the A-V valves on both sides. The vibrations of these valves as they close set up waves that are transmitted to the surface of the chest where they may be heard as the *first heart sound*. As the ventricles continue their contraction, the pressure exerted on their contained masses of blood rises steeply, but since all the valves of the heart are closed, no blood is pumped out. Since the heart muscle cannot shorten during this period, it is referred to as the *isometric phase* of systole. As soon as the

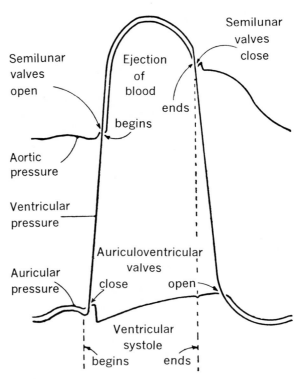

**Fig. 24.** Pressure changes and valve action during the cardiac cycle. (From Carlson, A. J., and Johnson, V. E.: The machinery of the body, ed. 2, Chicago, 1941, University of Chicago Press.)

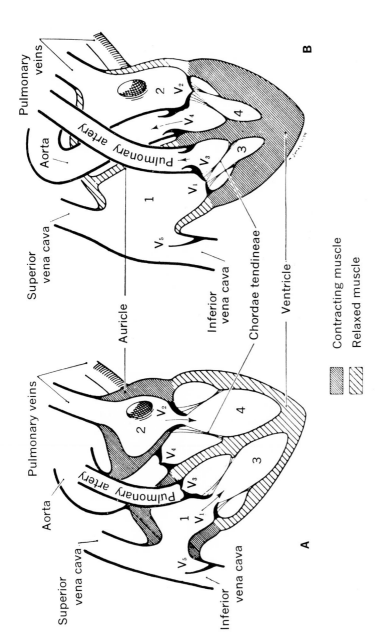

**Fig. 25.** Blood flow and valve action during auricular and ventricular systole. (From Amberson, W. R., and Smith, D. C.: Outline of physiology, Baltimore, 1939, The Williams & Wilkins Co.)

ventricular pressure rises above the pressure in the pulmonary artery and the aorta, the valves guarding these vessels open and blood is rapidly ejected. During the ejection phase the ventricular muscle is able to shorten (resulting in a decrease in the size of the ventricular cavities) so that it represents an *isotonic* contraction.

The termination of ventricular systole marks the onset of ventricular *diastole*, or relaxation. As the ventricular muscle relaxes, intraventricular pressure falls. When it drops below the pressure in the aorta and the pulmonary artery, the valves guarding their orifices close, giving rise to the *second heart sound*. The intraventricular pressure continues to fall and eventually drops below intra-atrial pressure, resulting in the opening of the A-V valves. As blood begins to pour from the atria into the ventricles, the period of diastasis, with which this description of the cardiac cycle began, is reached once more.

A typical cardiac cycle consists, then, of three phases: (1) diastasis* (resting period), (2) systole (contraction period), and (3) diastole (relaxation period). Most of the filling of the ventricle occurs during the early part of diastole. Since the increase in heart rate during exercise occurs primarily through shortening of the period of diastasis, there is little interference with the proper filling of the ventricles.

**Heart murmurs.** Sometimes the action of the heart valves is impaired because of congenital malformation or disease. The valve orifices may be narrowed so that the normal flow of blood is impeded, and the valve leaflets may fail to close completely, allowing a leakage of blood in the reverse direction. This abnormal valve action results in distortion of the normal heart sounds or in the appearance of additional sounds. These abnormal heart sounds are called *murmurs*. The particular valve involved may be determined from the point on the chest wall at which the murmur is heard most clearly. In the case of so-called functional murmurs, there is no structural defect to account for the abnormal heart sounds. The significance of heart murmurs and their underlying valvular defects in the physiological adjustments to exercise and especially in the estimation of the maximal tolerance for exercise will be discussed later.

## Cardiac output

From a functional standpoint the most important index of heart function is the cardiac output, that is, the volume of blood pumped by *each* ventricle per minute. Two factors, each of which may vary within wide limits, determine the size of the cardiac output. These are the heart rate and the stroke volume. The heart rate is very easily determined. The stroke volume, on the other hand, must be calculated from the values of the cardiac output and the heart rate. For example, a subject with a cardiac output of 4.2 liters and a heart rate of 70 has a stroke volume of 4,200/70 or 60 ml.

---

*Diastasis is often considered to be the final portion of the period of diastole.

The fundamental importance of the cardiac output as an index of heart function has led to many attempts to devise a method for its measurement. Most of these methods depend on some modification or other of the original *Fick principle.* Fick, many years ago, reasoned that the cardiac output could be calculated from the experimentally determined values of the oxygen content of the mixed venous blood (that is, the venous blood from all parts of the body after it has been mixed in the right heart), the oxygen content of the arterial blood, and the oxygen consumption of the body. Suppose, for example, that the oxygen content of the mixed venous blood is 15 vol.% and that of the arterial blood 20 vol.% and the oxygen consumption is 250 ml. per minute. It is obvious that each 100 ml. of blood yields 5 ml. of oxygen to the tissues, so that $\frac{250}{5} \times 100 = 5,000$ ml. of blood is required to furnish 250 ml. of oxygen to the tissues. Since this amount of blood must be pumped by each ventricle per minute, it represents the cardiac output. Formerly this method was not used for studies on human subjects because of the difficulty in obtaining samples of mixed venous blood. Various procedures for determining the gaseous content of the mixed venous blood by indirect methods have been devised (for details see textbooks of physiology), but all are open to criticism, especially when attempts are made to measure the cardiac output during exercise. The direct Fick principle may now be used to determine cardiac output in human subjects by means of the technique of cardiac catheterization.[1] A plastic catheter is inserted into an arm vein and carefully threaded up the vein and into the right heart. Samples of mixed venous blood are thus obtained and their oxygen content determined. The oxygen content of the arterial blood is determined by analysis of samples obtained by arterial puncture, and the oxygen consumption of the body is measured with the ordinary clinical apparatus used to measure basal metabolism. From these data the cardiac output is calculated as just described.

*Resting values.* In textbooks, values for resting cardiac output are somewhat variable because of the differences in the conditions of measurement. For average subjects resting cardiac output is about 5 to 6 liters per minute in the recumbent position and 4 to 5 liters per minute in the sitting position.[2] It is usually reduced further when the subject stands. These differences are largely due to decrease in stroke volume in the sitting and standing positions. The values for stroke volume are about 100 ml., recumbent, and 60 ml., sitting. It obviously makes a great deal of difference whether the recumbent or the standing stroke volume is used as the baseline for observations on the changes in stroke volume in exercise.

*Cardiac output during exercise.* Because of technical difficulties cardiac output has been measured only in stationary exercises (bicycle ergometer, treadmill, etc.).[2] Trained athletes may achieve a maximal cardiac output of 30 liters per minute at an oxygen uptake of 4 liters per minute. Average subjects may have a maximal cardiac output of about 22 liters at an oxygen uptake of 3.3 liters per minute. Since the maximal heart rate during exercise is about the same in athletes and nonathletes, the greater cardiac output of athletes is caused by the greater stroke volume of their more powerful hearts (maximal stroke volume values as high as 150 to 170 ml. have been recorded, as compared with maximal values of 100 to 125 ml. in nonathletes).

## Regulation of the stroke volume of the heart

The cardiac output (amount of blood pumped by each ventricle per minute) is the product of two factors, the stroke volume and the heart rate. The stroke volume cannot be measured directly in the human being but must be calculated from measured values of cardiac output and heart rate as follows:

$$\text{Stroke volume (ml.)} = \frac{\text{Cardiac output (ml. per minute)}}{\text{Heart rate (beats per minute)}}$$

This means, of course, that stroke volume estimates are only as accurate as the cardiac output determinations on which they are based.

The increased cardiac output that occurs in exercise is the result of an increase in heart rate and stroke volume, but the relative increase in each factor depends on the nature of the exercise and on the physical condition of the subject. Since increased cardiac output is one of the key adjustments in exercise, it is appropriate that its regulation should be considered at some length. The regulation of stroke volume will be discussed in this chapter and the regulation of heart rate in Chapter 11.

*Starling's law of the heart.* It has been known for many years that the force of contraction of both skeletal muscle and heart muscle is increased if the muscle is slightly stretched at the moment when contraction begins. In the case of the heart the greater the volume of blood contained in the ventricles at the end of diastole, the greater is the degree of stretching of the cardiac muscle fibers, and hence the more powerful the next contraction (systole). If the heart empties completely, it means that an increase in the filling of the heart (end-diastolic volume) automatically results in a greater stroke volume. The famous British physiologist, Starling, called this the law of the heart.[3]

The uncritical application of a basic discovery sometimes retards the growth of knowledge, and this has happened in the case of Starling's law. Starling, in his classical experiments, used the "heart-lung preparation," which consists essentially of the heart and lungs isolated from the body and perfused with warm, oxygenated blood at any desired rate. The heart is thus removed from the influence of the chemical and nervous regulation to which it is subject in the body. Under these conditions the stroke volume increases and decreases with the increase and decrease in the volume of blood that fills the ventricles during diastole. By analogy it has been supposed that the stroke volume of the heart under normal conditions is likewise determined by its diastolic filling volume so that, for example, the increased stroke volume observed in exercise would be the result of a greater diastolic filling caused by the greater venous return of blood to the heart.

This application of Starling's law to heart function during exercise rests on two basic assumptions: (1) that the diastolic size of the heart is increased in exercise and (2) that the heart empties itself completely at each beat.

The belief that the stroke volume is increased during exercise through the operation of Starling's law has been so firmly entrenched in the physiological literature that evidence to the contrary, some dating back to the turn of the century, has been disregarded. In recent years with the use of better techniques it has been clearly demonstrated that the diastolic size of the heart actually *decreases* during exercise,[4] so that the increased stroke volume cannot be caused by greater stretching as described by Starling's law. Also, if the greater stroke volume in exercise is not the result of greater filling, it must be due to more complete emptying. This implies that during rest the ventricle does not empty itself completely, leaving a *systolic residue* to which is added an additional amount of blood during the succeeding diastolic filling period. As exercise increases in severity, the heart ejects larger proportions of its contained blood, and the upper limit of stroke volume is reached when the ventricle empties itself completely at each beat. The validity of these newer concepts has been firmly established by a variety of methods, including x-ray films of the heart taken during exercise[4, 5] that permit the calculation of both systolic and diastolic volumes of the heart.

The modern view, then, is that Starling's law is a valid description of *one* of the factors that *can* modify the force of contraction of heart muscle. Since the heart does not dilate during exercise, Starling's law cannot explain the increased force of contraction of the heart during exercise. It is probable that several factors interact to bring this about. Thus it is known that epinephrine (adrenaline) increases the force of contraction of heart muscle and that epinephrine secretion is increased during exercise. Increased nervous stimulation of the heart via the sympathetic (accelerator) nerves and rise in body temperature may also contribute to the increased stroke volume during exercise. More experimental work is needed for a final answer to this very important problem.

The traditional view that the increased cardiac output in exercise necessarily involves an increase in stroke volume and in heart rate has been questioned. Rushmer[6] claims that improved modern techniques for measuring cardiac output demonstrate that exercise is not accompanied by an increase in stroke volume in normal human subjects or in unanesthetized dogs. He believes that the traditional view is subject to criticism because it is based on results obtained with the use of indirect methods of measuring cardiac output and largely on experiments performed on trained athletes who often have a very slow resting heart rate and relatively little increase in heart rate in exercise. Data showing both types of response are illustrated in Fig. 26. Horvath[7] has criticized Rushmer's experiments on technical grounds and has reported that the stroke volume may be increased as much as twofold or threefold in strenuous exercise.

In a study[8] on 25 unselected male college students subjected to graded exercise on a treadmill it was observed that while cardiac output correlated

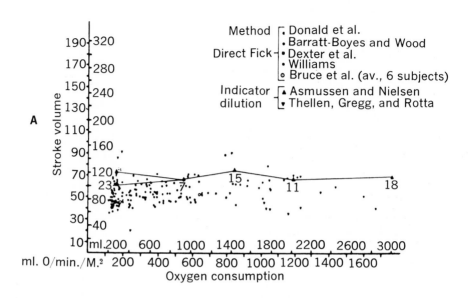

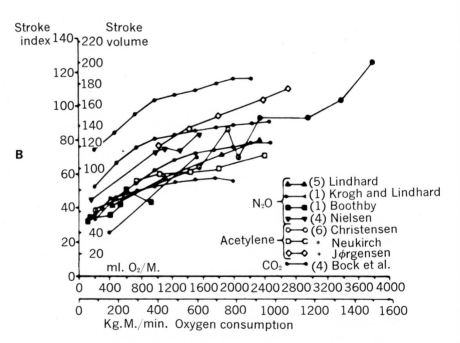

**Fig. 26.** Stroke volume response to exercise. **A,** Stroke volume computed by Fick or dye dilution techniques was not consistently increased in normal subjects. **B,** The traditional concept that stroke volume increases during exercise was based on the use of indirect methods applied largely to athletes. (From Rushmer, R. F.: Constancy of stroke volume in ventricular responses to exertion, Am. J. Physiol. **196:**745, 1959.)

fairly well with work load, there was absolutely no relation between stroke volume and work load. This implies, of course, that the increase in cardiac output in exercise is caused mainly (perhaps entirely) by the concomitant increase in heart rate. The important question about the relation of stroke volume changes to the increased cardiac output in exercise must be considered to be still unanswered. It should be pointed out, however, that even if the stroke volume is not increased in exercise the fact that it is not decreased suggests that the ventricle has contracted more forcefully, since the ejection period is much shorter when the heart rate is very high.

The current status of the problem has been analyzed by Rushmer.[9] Stroke volume is definitely increased during the transition from quiet standing to any level of exercise, but it increases by about the same amount on changing from the standing to the supine position. The problem, then, essentially may be one of selecting the proper control baseline from which to measure exercise changes in stroke volume. If the standing value is used, then stroke volume is increased in exercise; if the recumbent stroke volume is used, there seems to be no significant increase in exercise.

*Cardiac dilatation and hypertrophy ("athletic heart").* There is a great deal of misunderstanding about the effects of athletic endeavors on the heart. In heart disease there is frequently a gradual increase in the size of the heart with consequent thinning of the walls similar to the inflation of a rubber balloon. This process is known as dilatation, and the increased stretch of the cardiac muscle fibers through the operation of Starling's law is supposed to increase the force of contraction of the heart sufficiently to permit an adequate stroke volume despite the weakness of the heart muscle or the presence of valve defects. The dilated heart is mechanically and metabolically inefficient and has little reserve to call on during exercise— hence the limited capacity for exercise in patients with heart disease.

Since x-ray films of athletes sometimes reveal a somewhat larger heart than is present in nonathletes, it has been thought that strenuous exertion may actually cause dilatation of the heart similar to that occurring in heart disease. The condition has been called "athletic heart." If this were true, it would constitute a strong indictment of strenuous athletics. It appears, however, that this is a false interpretation. The increased heart size sometimes present in athletes, especially those competing in endurance rather than speed events, is now believed to be the result of an actual hypertrophy or increase in thickness of the heart muscle entirely comparable to the hypertrophy of skeletal muscles resulting from weight lifting and similar exercises. The end result is a more powerful heart, capable of greater increase in stroke volume during exercise. There is no medical evidence that strenuous exercise can harm the healthy heart of a young adult. The modifying effects of age are discussed in a later chapter.

## Venous return to the heart

*Factors that maintain the venous return.* In a cylinder of water the pressure at the surface is atmospheric, but it increases in proportion to the depth below the surface because of the weight of the overlying column of water. This pressure, caused by the action of gravity on a column of fluid, is called hydrostatic pressure and has important effects on the circulation of blood in the body. When a person is standing, the pressure in the right atrium is approximately atmospheric. The hydrostatic pressure increases progressively in the veins below the level of the heart, reaching a pressure of about 90 mm. Hg in the veins of the feet because of the weight of the column of blood extending from the feet to the heart. If there were no compensatory mechanisms, blood would tend to pool in lower parts of the body, and the fluid would exude from the capillaries into the tissue spaces, causing swelling of the tissues (edema). This does happen to some extent during prolonged standing, especially in persons with inadequate venous valves (as in varicose veins). Normally, however, this does not happen because (1) the veins of the extremities have valves that permit the flow of blood only toward the heart and (2) the contractions of skeletal muscles and the pressure changes associated with respiration act as "booster pumps" in promoting the flow of blood from the lower part of the body toward the heart. As a result of these factors, which are discussed in greater detail in the following paragraphs, the pressure of blood in the veins of the feet during normal standing and walking is only about 10 mm. Hg.

*Massaging action of skeletal muscles.* The veins are thin-walled, easily collapsible vessels. When the muscle mass surrounding one of these vessels contracts, the vein is collapsed and its contained mass of blood is forced out. When the muscles relax, the vein is filled with blood. Contraction of the muscles might force blood out of the vein in both directions, that is, toward the heart and toward the capillaries, if it were not for the presence of *valves* in the veins that prevent the backward flow of blood. As a result muscular contraction squeezes the blood in the veins onward toward the heart, and relaxation of the muscles allows the veins to fill with blood from the capillaries. In this way the contracting muscles act as a "booster pump." This mechanism is constantly active to varying degrees. Even when the subject is standing at attention the muscle contractions that maintain muscle tone aid somewhat in the venous return. The fact that the mechanism may be inadequate under these conditions is indicated by the reduction in venous return, often sufficient to produce fainting by curtailment of the blood flow to the brain, which sometimes occurs in subjects standing at attention too long.

The quantitative importance of this pumping mechanism varies considerably according to the intensity and type of exercise. It is obvious that for a given type of exercise greater intensity results in a more rapid and more powerful massaging effect. During different types of exercise of the same intensity, the effect on venous return is correlated with the position of the muscles relative to the main venous channels and with the frequency of alternation between contraction and relaxation. For example, in comparing two almost equally exhausting sports, running and rowing, the movements are more rapid and rhythmical in running, and the volume flow of blood is correspondingly greater. Maintained static contractions of the muscles, as in weight lifting, may actually hinder the venous return of blood to the heart and make such activities exhausting out of all proportion to the amount of energy expended.

*Respiratory movements.* The veins of the abdominal and thoracic cavities constitute a venous cistern largely unsupported by skeletal muscles and capable of holding 400 to 500 ml. of blood. This cistern is closed at its lower end by the valves of the femoral veins and at its upper end by the valves of the jugular and subclavian veins. The outlet of least resistance is into the right heart. Respiratory movements exert a pumping action on the blood contained in this cistern in the following way. During inspiration the thoracic cavity is enlarged in all dimensions by the movements of the ribs and diaphragm. This results in a fall in pressure in the thoracic cavity, which is transmitted to the thin-walled veins in that cavity. At the same time the descent of the diaphragm results in a rise in pressure in the abdominal cavity, only partly offset by the bulging of the anterior abdominal wall. This increased pressure is also exerted on the thin-walled vena cava, and since the blood is not only prevented from flowing backward by the iliac and femoral vein valves but also is aspirated into the thoracic veins by the decreased pressure in the thorax, its onward flow to the heart is promoted. During expiration the pressure effects are reversed, and the venous cistern tends to fill from the veins that feed into it. Alternate inspiration and expiration tend to create a pumping device very similar to that caused by contraction and relaxation of the skeletal muscles. During exercise this influence is increased by the greater depth and frequency of the respiratory movements.

The mechanical pumping action of respiration is not present in all forms of activity. In weight lifting and other forms of exertion in which "straining" is present, both intrathoracic and intra-abdominal pressures are elevated by the forced expiration against a closed glottis and the contraction of the abdominal muscles. As a result the blood is unable to enter the abdominal and thoracic veins and the veins of the limbs and face are engorged. The decrease in venous return no doubt accounts for the sudden fall in blood pressure that may follow the initial rise in such activities.

*Contraction of limb veins.* The veins are thin walled and distensible and might be capable of pooling much of the increased blood flow that results from decreased vascular resistance in exercising muscles. It has been observed,[10] however, that the limb veins both in exercising and nonexercising limbs undergo reflex vasoconstriction during exercise, so that the blood is returned promptly to the heart rather than pooling in the veins.

### Advanced study topics

1. How does the heart increase its output in exercise?
2. Review the recent literature on the heart in the current issues of the *American Journal of Cardiology*.
3. Describe methods of measuring cardiac output during exercise.
4. Compare the effects of leg elevation with exercise of the foot and leg in reducing swelling of the ankles after prolonged quiet standing.

5. What measures can be used to promote venous return to the heart during static exercise?

## References

1. Cournand, A., Riley, R. L., Breed, E. S., Baldwin, E. deF., and Richards, D. W., Jr.: Measurement of cardiac output in man using the technique of catheterization of the right auricle or ventricle, J. Clin. Invest. **24**:106, 1945.

2. Asmussen, E., and Nielsen, M.: Cardiac output during muscular work and its regulation, Physiol. Rev. **35**:778, 1955.

3. Starling, E. H.: Linacre lecture on the law of the heart, New York, 1918, Longmans, Green & Co.

4. Gauer, O. H.: Volume changes of the left ventricle during blood pooling and exercise in the intact animal. Their effects on left ventricular performance, Physiol. Rev. **35**:143, 1955.

5. Chapman, C. B., Baker, O., and Mitch-ell, J. H.: Left ventricular function at rest and during exercise, J. Clin. Invest. **38**:1202, 1959.

6. Rushmer, R. F.: Constancy of stroke volume in ventricular responses to exertion, Am. J. Physiol. **196**:745, 1959.

7. Horvath, S. M.: Cardiac performance. In Rodahl, K., and Horvath, S. M., editors: Muscle as a tissue, New York, 1962, McGraw-Hill Book Company.

8. Tabakin, B. S., Hanson, J. S., Merriam, T. W., Jr., and Caldwell, E. J.: Hemodynamic response of normal men to graded treadmill exercise, J. Appl. Physiol. **19**:457, 1964.

9. Rushmer, R. F.: Control of cardiac output. In Ruch, T. C., and Patton, H. D., editors: Physiology and biophysics, ed. 19, Philadelphia, 1965, W. B. Saunders Co.

10. Bevegård, B. S., and Shepherd, J. T.: Changes in tone of limb veins during supine exercise, J. Appl. Physiol. **20**: 1, 1965.

# 11

# *Heart rate during exercise*

### Resting heart rate

The rate of beating of the heart is influenced by many factors, including posture, exercise, emotion, and body temperature. Normal heart rate under presumably controlled conditions shows a wide range in different persons. The American Heart Association suggests that the normal range should be 50 to 100 beats per minute, and in an examination of 1,000 healthy young aviators during World War II,[1] the range was 38 to 110 beats per minute. It is difficult to say whether the variation in heart rate from person to person is actually this great or whether it indicates lack of rigid control of the factors that modify heart rate. It emphasizes, however, the importance of careful determination of the resting heart rate in experiments and tests involving changes in heart rate during exercise.

There is said to be a tendency for the heart rate to be lower in subjects who are in good physical condition than in nonathletic subjects, but numerous tabulations of heart rate as related to physical fitness fail to show any clear correlation if the exceptionally slow rates in certain highly trained athletes are excluded. There seems to be little relation between heart rate and body weight, stature, or body type, although the rate is ordinarily 5 to 10 beats per minute higher in women than in men.

During sleep there is a progressive slowing of the heart rate during the first 7 hours, followed by an increase before awakening. During waking hours wide variations in heart rate are associated with random activity. The average heart rate under resting (but not basal) conditions is about 78 beats per minute for men and 84 beats per minute for women. The heart rate diminishes progressively from birth (when it is around 130 beats per minute) to adolescence but increases slightly again in old age.

### Postural changes affecting heart rate

An extensive study by Schneider and Truesdell[2] indicated postural changes affecting heart rate. These data do not support the widespread be-

*Table 2.* Postural changes affecting heart rate*

|  | Heartbeats per minute | | |
|---|---|---|---|
|  | Lying | Standing | Difference |
| Average subject | 74 | 92 | 18 |
| Athletes | 66 | 83 | 17 |

*Based on data from Schneider and Truesdell: Am. J. Physiol. **61**:429, 1922.

lief that greater physical fitness is associated with a smaller difference between reclining and standing heart rates, which has led to its inclusion in numerous physical fitness tests.

Actually the increase in heart rate upon changing from the recumbent to the standing position is a favorable compensatory reaction. It balances the decrease in stroke volume caused by gravity interference with filling of the heart and prevents a serious decrease in cardiac output. An excessive increase in heart rate upon standing, however, indicates inadequate compensation for the effects of gravity on the circulation and is often present in persons who stand after prolonged periods of bed rest and as the primary defect in one type of circulatory disease. Excessive postural increase in heart rate may then distinguish obviously abnormal people from normal people but probably not normal sedentary people from athletes. Its value as a component of physical fitness tests is very doubtful.

## Heart rate changes during exercise

The fact that the heart rate is increased during exercise is a matter of common observation. The ease with which the pulse rate may be counted has led to a tremendous number of investigations on the changes in the heart rate resulting from different types, intensities, and durations of exercise. Most of these studies have suffered from the defect that the period of observation usually began after the cessation of exercise. However, since the advent of the recording cardiotachometer[3] it has been possible to record the heart rate continuously during exercise and recovery.

The maximal heart rate reached during exercise and the rapidity with which the maximal value is attained vary with a number of factors, including the type of exercise (its intensity and duration), the emotional content of the exercise, environmental temperature and humidity, and the physical condition of the subject. Heart rates of more than 200 beats per minute have been reported in well men during exercise.

The acceleration of the heart rate begins immediately after the commencement of exercise; it may, in fact, begin *before* exercise starts, coincident with the tensing of the muscles, as in "getting set" for a sprint. This preliminary increase in heart rate is believed to be caused by the influence of the cerebral cortex on the controlling center of the heart rate in the medulla. The preliminary rise in heart rate usually shows a tendency to level off after a few seconds and is followed by a more gradual rise to the final maximal level, which may be reached only after 4 or 5 minutes. This time course is subject to very considerable variation. In some persons the maximal rate may be attained within less than 1 minute; in others the rate may continue to rise slowly for more than 1 hour.

The rapidity with which the heart rate returns to normal at the cessation of exercise is often used as a test of cardiovascular fitness (see Chapter 27). Less attention has been devoted to the study of the heart rate changes during the transition from rest to exercise and in the early period of exercise. In one study[4] measurements of heart rate and oxygen consumption were made during 8-minute periods of treadmill exercise of graded severity. The pulse deficit (PD) was defined as the number of beats by which the pulse count during the first 4 minutes of exercise fell short of the count during the second 4 minutes of exercise. The oxygen consumption per minute ($\dot{V}_{O_2}$) was corrected to the calculated value for a man weighing 65 kilograms and expressed as $\dot{V}_{O_2}{}^{65}$. From these data, the pulse deficit index (PDI[65]) was taken to be the lowest $\dot{V}_{O_2}{}^{65}$ at which the pulse deficit showed a decided upward swing, when PD was plotted against $\dot{V}_{O_2}{}^{65}$. The higher the value of the pulse deficit index, the higher was the maximal oxygen intake (generally accepted as the best independent index of cardiovascular-respiratory fitness); the correlation was good enough to make it possible to calculate either factor from measured values of the other. It is interesting to speculate that the point at which the pulse deficit increases abruptly probably marks the threshold of work intensity at which oxidations suffer and lactic acid begins to accumulate in the blood.[5] The significance of this interpretation will be examined later in connection with the concept of the oxygen debt, but the pulse deficit may be presumed to reflect the deficit in cardiac output in the early stages of exercise (especially if the reported absence of a stroke volume increase in exercise is accepted).

In a given subject the maximal heart rate reached during exertion, especially if the subject is in a steady state, correlates fairly closely with the *work load*. Table 3 gives the relation between heart rate and work load in the case of a man working on a bicycle ergometer. The successive increases in heart rate were 30, 27, 22, 23, and 21, respectively. It is a common observation that the successive increments in heart rate may become smaller as the limiting value of the heart rate (about 200 for most persons) is approached.

*Table 3.* Relation between work load and heart rate*

| Work load (foot-pounds per minute) | Heart rate per minute | Heart rate increment |
|---|---|---|
| Resting | 75 | — |
| 2,000 | 105 | 30 |
| 4,000 | 132 | 27 |
| 6,000 | 154 | 22 |
| 8,000 | 177 | 23 |
| 10,000 | 198 | 21 |

*From Schneider: Physiology of muscular activity, ed. 2, Philadelphia, 1939, W. B. Saunders Co.

The *type* of exercise influences the amount of increase in the heart rate. McCurdy[7] found the greatest acceleration in exercises of speed (sprinting) and the smallest acceleration in exercises of strength (weight throwing). In exercises of endurance (distance running) the heart rate was intermediate between those of speed and strength but remained elevated for longer periods of time following cessation of exercise. Exercises of strength do not invariably increase the heart rate; McCurdy cites an instance of a man who lifted 220 kilograms without changing his standing heart rate of 72 beats per minute.

For a given work load the increase in heart rate is less in a physically fit subject than in an unfit subject. If both physically fit and unfit subjects work to the point of exhaustion, the maximal heart rates will be approximately the same in each, but the total work load performed will be much greater in the case of the more fit subject. In other words the greater stroke volume of a trained person enables him to achieve the necessary cardiac output with a smaller increase in heart rate. This involves less strain on the heart since an increase in heart rate is brought about primarily by cutting short the rest period of the heart, that is, the pause between beats.

The influence of emotional and environmental factors on heart function during exercise is considered in later chapters. It is sufficient to point out here that emotion increases the heart rate at rest and in light exercise but probably has little influence on the maximal heart rate. The same is true, to a lesser degree perhaps, of an elevation in environmental temperature and humidity.

## Return of the heart rate to normal after exercise

The time required for the heart rate to return to normal after exercise depends on the work load of the exercise period and on the physical condition of the subject. In men in good physical condition, recovery occurs more rapidly than in fatigued or poorly trained subjects. The return to normal occurs more slowly during very exhausting exercise, sometimes requiring as long as 1 to 2 hours.

The physiological factors that determine the time course of the recovery of the heart rate after exercise are not clearly understood. They probably include the following:

1. A persistence during recovery of some of the same factors that increase the heart rate during exercise, for example, rise in body temperature and increased blood concentrations of adrenaline and lactic acid

2. Reflex responses to the sudden cessation of exercise with the consequent pooling of blood in the dilated muscle vessels → decreased venous return → decreased stroke volume → decreased blood pressure → increased heart rate (carotid sinus reflex)

In support of suggestion 2 is the fact that heart rate recovers more rapidly if the limbs used in the exercise are firmly bandaged at the beginning of the recovery period.[8]

## Regulation of the heart rate

The heart rate during rest and exercise is regulated by a complex mechanism involving both nervous and chemical factors. It has long been known that the mammalian heart will continue to beat for hours after its removal from the body if it is kept warm and supplied with food and oxygen. This can only mean that the origin of the heartbeat is in the heart itself. It has been demonstrated that the impulse that initiates contraction of the heart muscle originates in a small node of specialized muscle, the sinoatrial node, or pacemaker, which is located in the wall of the right atrium at the entrance of the superior vena cava. The impulse spreads through the network of atrial muscle, causing contraction of the atria. It is then picked up by a second node, the atrioventricular, or A-V node, located in the lower part of the septum that separates the two atria, and is conducted along a bundle (the A-V bundle or bundle of His), which is a continuation of the A-V node. This bundle splits into two branches that ramify along the inner wall of each ventricle and conduct the impulse to all parts of the ventricular muscle.

The pacemaker discharges rhythmic impulses that cause a rhythmic beating of the heart. The cardiac nerves, which terminate in the heart in close association with the pacemaker, belong to the autonomic division of the nervous system and are of two types: (1) the vagus nerves, which *slow* the rate of beating of the heart and (2) the sympathetic or accelerator nerves, which *increase* the heart rate. It is believed that these nerves exert their characteristic influence on the heart rate by direct action on the pacemaker. Under resting conditions the pacemaker is constantly bombarded by impulses reaching it by way of the vagus nerves, which slow the heart rate. This continuous arrival of vagal impulses is due to the constant discharge of the nerve cells in the medulla from which the vagus nerves arise. This group of nerve cells is called the cardioinhibitory center.* A nervous center that is continuously discharging impulses is said to be *tonically* active or to exhibit *tone*. Thus the constant influence on the heart of the vagus nerves is referred to as *vagal tone*. If the vagus nerves are cut or their endings in the heart paralyzed with atropine, this vagal tone is abolished and the heart rate immediately increases. It is believed that much of the increase in heart rate in exercise is the result of a decrease in the inhibitory action of the vagus nerve on the heart (decrease in vagal tone). However, complete abolition of the vagal influence on the heart by the injection of atropine results in an increase in heart rate of only 30 to 40 beats per minute, whereas the increase in heart rate during exercise may amount to 100 beats per minute.[9] Obviously decreased vagal action cannot be the only cause of the increased heart rate during exercise. There is good evidence that, especially during very strenuous exercise, increased stimula-

---

*A nervous center is a group of nerve cells whose corresponding nerve fibers control or adjust the activity of some particular organ or system. Thus the respiratory center controls the breathing movements, and the vasomotor center controls the caliber of the blood vessels.

tion of the heart by way of its sympathetic (accelerator) nerves is of equal or perhaps even greater importance.[10] Additional factors include increased body temperature and increased secretion of adrenaline, both of which act directly on the heart.

The slow heart rate often present in well-trained athletes is believed to be caused by an increase in vagal tone. It is not entirely clear to what extent this is due to training; it may be partly inherent.

The existence of tonic activity of the accelerator nerves to the heart has been vigorously debated for many years. It now seems probable that a certain amount of accelerator tone exists, but its influence on the heart is much less important than is that of the vagal mechanism.

The discharge of impulses from the vagal or cardioinhibitory center is due to the arrival at the center of afferent impulses from several sources; in other words the control of the heart rate is predominantly through *reflexes*, the cells of the cardiac centers corresponding to the motor nerve cells in the spinal cord in the case of spinal reflexes. The most important sources of afferent impulses for the cardiac reflexes are specialized nerve endings located in the walls of the great vessels near the heart and perhaps to some extent in the walls of the heart itself. The *carotid sinus*, a small dilatation of the internal carotid artery at its origin from the common carotid about the level of the angle of the jaw, is richly supplied with receptors that are sensitive to stretch. The ordinary level of arterial blood pressure is sufficient to stretch the walls of the sinus somewhat, so that a stream of impulses is constantly being sent over the sinus nerve to the cardioinhibitory center in the medulla. This results in tonic discharge of the cardioinhibitory center over the vagus nerves to the heart. If the nerve endings in the carotid sinus are experimentally destroyed, the heart speeds up just as though the vagus nerves had been cut. A rise in blood pressure in the carotid artery, by causing greater stretching of the walls of the sinus, increases the flow of impulses to the cardioinhibitory center and thus reflexly slows the heart rate. This probably protects the heart from excessive increase in rate when the blood pressure rises, as during exercise. The reverse of this reaction also occurs; when the arterial blood pressure falls, the stretching of the sinus walls and hence the discharge of impulses to the cardioinhibitory center is diminished and the heart rate is increased by the removal of vagal tone. The *aortic sinus*, similar in structure and function to the carotid sinus, is located in the arch of the aorta.

Nerve endings sensitive to stretch are also found in the walls of the venae cavae at their entrance into the right atrium and in the walls of the heart chambers themselves. Bainbridge,[11] many years ago, reported that a rise in blood pressure in the venae cavae and the right atrium produced a reflex increase in heart rate, and he believed that this reflex was the principal cause of the increased heart rate during exercise. Since the rise in right atrial pressure was presumed to be caused by the increased venous return resulting from the muscular activity, this mechanism (Bainbridge reflex) in effect would permit an automatic control of heart rate by the muscles. However desirable such a response might be, it has not been supported by recent research. It now appears that the so-called Bainbridge reflex is not a factor in the increase of heart rate during exercise for two reasons:

1. The right atrial pressure does not usually rise during exercise (it may actually fall), so that stretch receptors would not be stimulated.

2. Other evidence indicates that stimulation of the stretch receptors in the right atrium may cause an increase, a decrease, or no change in the heart rate and that the effect is not altered by cutting both vagus nerves.[12]

Pathak[12] suggests that alteration in the heart rate in response to increased right atrial pressure may be caused by stretch-induced alterations in impulse generation in the pacemaker of the heart (S-A node). In support of this view he cites his experiments that demonstrate a definite relation between right atrial pressure and heart rate in the isolated, perfused hearts of frogs, dogs, and several other mammals. Jones[13] has reported that the change in heart rate produced by the intravenous infusion of blood or saline solution is related to the heart rate before infusion, resulting in a change in the heart rate to the optimal value for increasing the cardiac output and thereby restoring the venous pressure to its initial level. The conflicting opinions about the existence and significance of the Bainbridge reflex are reviewed in the literature.[14, 15]

The heart rate can also be altered by nervous influences originating in the cerebral cortex and other higher brain centers. This psychic increase in heart rate is seen in the first few seconds of exercise and, in fact, may anticipate the exercise. It is uncertain to what extent an emotional factor during exercise influences the heart rate in this way and how much of the effect is due to increased secretion of epinephrine.

It has been known for many years that the rate of secretion of epinephrine by the adrenal glands is increased during various emotional states (fear, anger, excitement, etc.) and during muscular exercise. The increased secretion of epinephrine during exercise may be due partly to the emotional component of the exercise. The hormone is transported in the bloodstream and upon reaching the heart increases both its force of contraction and its rate of beating.

Other nonnervous factors that have been shown experimentally to cause an increased heart rate include a rise in the carbon dioxide content and in the temperature of the blood and a fall in the blood oxygen content. The extent to which these changes contribute to the heart rate increase in exercise is uncertain.

In recent years reflexes originating in contracting muscles have been suggested as contributing to the increases in both heart rate and respiration during exercise.[14-16] The stimulus that sets off this reflex may be the stretching of sensory receptors in the moving joints or in the contracting muscles or the stimulation of chemical receptors in the muscles (or in their blood vessels) by the acid metabolic products of muscular activity.

It should be obvious from the preceding discussion that a complete explanation of the increase in heart rate that occurs during exercise is not yet possible. A number of factors are known to be capable of increasing the heart rate under experimental conditions, but their quantitative importance in exercising human subjects is uncertain. At the very beginning of exercise the increase in heart rate is probably chiefly psychic in origin. As exercise continues, other factors come into operation, including perhaps acid metabolites liberated from the working muscles, reflexes originating in contracting muscles and moving joints, and the secretion into the bloodstream of much larger amounts of epinephrine.

## Advanced study topics

1. How does heart rate correlate with other physiological responses to exercise such as oxygen consumption and pulmonary ventilation?
2. Review the recent literature on heart rate in the current issues of the *Journal of Applied Physiology.*
3. Describe a cardiotachometer and its uses.
4. Observe the heart rate during rest and various activities throughout the day.
5. Describe how the heart rate can be used to calibrate the intensity of work during endurance training.

## References

1. Graybiel, A., McFarland, R. A., Gates, D. C., and Webster, F. A.: Analysis of the electrocardiograms obtained from 1,000 healthy young aviators, Am. Heart J. **27**:524, 1944.
2. Schneider, E. C., and Truesdell, D.: A statistical study of the pulse rate and the arterial blood pressure in recumbency, standing and after a standard exercise, Am. J. Physiol. **61**:429, 1922.
3. Boas, E. P., and Goldschmidt, E. F.: The heart rate, Springfield, Ill., 1932, Charles C Thomas, Publisher.
4. Davies, C. T. M., and Harris, E. A.: Heart rate during transition from rest to exercise, J. Appl. Physiol. **19**:857, 1964.
5. Margaria, R., Edwards, H. T., and Dill, D. B.: The possible mechanisms of contracting and paying the oxygen debt and the role of lactic acid in muscular contraction, Am. J. Physiol. **106**:681, 1933.
6. Schneider, E. C.: Physiology of muscular activity, ed. 2, Philadelphia, 1939, W. B. Saunders Co.
7. McCurdy, J. H.: Adolescent changes in heart rate and blood pressure, Am. Phys. Ed. Rev. **15**:421, 1910.
8. Herxheimer, H.: Heart rate in recovery from severe exercise, J. Appl. Physiol. **1**:279, 1948.
9. Robinson, S., Pearcy, M., Brueckman, F. R., Nicholas, J. R., and Miller, D. I.: Effects of atropine on heart rate and oxygen intake in working man, J. Appl. Physiol. **5**:508, 1953.
10. Craig, F. N.: Effects of atropine, work and heat on heart rate and sweat production in man, J. Appl. Physiol. **4**:826, 1952.
11. Bainbridge, F. A.: The influence of venous filling upon the rate of the heart, J. Physiol. **50**:65, 1915.
12. Pathak, C. L.: Alternative mechanism of cardiac acceleration in Bainbridge's infusion experiments, Am. J. Physiol. **197**:441, 1959.
13. Jones, J. J.: The Bainbridge reflex, J. Physiol. **160**:298, 1962.
14. Aviado, D. M., Jr., and Schmidt, C. F.: Reflexes from stretch receptors in blood vessels, heart and lungs, Physiol. Rev. **35**:247, 1955.
15. Aviado, D. M., Jr.: Some controversial cardiac reflexes, Circulation Res. **10**:831, 1962.
16. Asmussen, E., and Nielsen, M.: Cardiac output during muscular work and its regulation, Physiol. Rev. **35**:778, 1955.

# 12

# Circulation of the blood

During exercise the increased oxygen requirement of the contracting muscles is met by an increased flow of blood through the muscles. This is made possible by an increase in the amount of blood pumped by the heart each minute and by circulatory adjustments that divert a large fraction of the blood from less active tissues to the muscles. The circulatory adjustments of exercise are not, however, confined to the skeletal muscles. The oxygen requirement of the heart is increased, and the diversion of blood from the brain to the muscles must be prevented. The blood flow through the lungs must, of course, be increased in the same proportion as the flow through the systemic portion of the circulation and without an increase in the velocity of flow sufficient to prevent adequate exchange of gases. These widespread circulatory adjustments are the result of the interaction of numerous factors, both nervous and chemical, many of which are still incompletely understood. An attempt is made in this chapter to analyze the basic factors involved in the regulation of the flow of blood, and Chapter 13 will deal with the adjustments that occur during exercise.

## General outline of the circulation

*Anatomy of the blood vessels.* The blood vessels in different regions of the circulatory system have characteristic anatomical features that are definitely correlated with their function. The *arteries*, especially the larger ones, have a predominance of elastic tissue in their walls. During systole, blood is pumped into the large arteries at a greater rate than can be accommodated by the rate of flow out of the arteries into the capillaries. As a result the walls of the arteries are distended by the excess blood, and during diastole, when the ejection of blood by the heart has ceased, the walls of the vessels recoil and force the excess blood onward toward the capillaries. The elastic properties of the arterial walls are thus largely responsible for the maintenance of blood flow during diastole. The smaller arteries have less elastic tissue and more smooth muscle than do the large arteries. This is particularly noticeable in the arterioles, the small terminal arteries through which the blood passes into the capillaries. In the arterioles the smooth muscle is arranged in definite circular layers, so that its contraction results in a narrowing of the lumen of the vessel, a process known as *vaso-constriction*. In this way the flow of blood into the capillaries beyond can be regulated according to the metabolic requirements of the tissues in that region. Widespread vasoconstriction as opposed to localized vasoconstriction is an important factor in the regulation of the general level of arterial blood pressure. The *capillaries* are characterized by their extremely small size (0.01 mm. or less in diameter and about 0.5 mm. in length) and by their very thin walls. The elastic tissue and smooth muscle of the arterial walls are absent in the capillaries, only the thin internal lining membrane or endo-thelium persisting. The structure of the capillaries obviously adapts them for the performance of their important function—the exchange of materials between the blood and the tissues. The general structural features of the *veins* are the same as those of the arteries, but the walls of the veins are thinner, softer, and less elastic. They are easily collapsible and exert very little recoil when distended. The veins are further characterized by the presence of valves whose function of preventing a backward flow of blood has already been discussed.

**Velocity of blood flow in different portions of the circulatory system.** The velocity with which the blood flows through the various types of ves-sels is governed by physical laws. As a river flows along its course its veloc-ity is increased if its channel becomes narrow and is decreased if the channel widens again. In the same way the velocity of blood flow through a given *type* of vessel is inversely proportional to the total cross-sectional area of all the vessels of that type. It must be emphasized that the velocity of flow in an individual vessel is not controlled by the diameter of that vessel but rather by the combined diameters of all the vessels of that type. Reverting to the example of the river, the velocity of flow may be dimin-ished when the stream breaks up into a number of separate channels, as sometimes happens in a delta, even though the diameter of any one of the branches is much less than that of the parent stream.

The cross-sectional area of the aorta in man is about 2.7 sq.cm., and the mean velocity of blood flow during rest is approximately 24 cm. per second. Little change in velocity occurs in the smaller arteries and the arterioles in spite of their progressive decrease in individual size because their combined cross-sectional areas do not differ greatly from that of the aorta. In the capillaries the rate of flow is dramatically decreased because of the tre-mendous increase in total cross-sectional area. Although each capillary is only about 1/100 mm. in diameter, the combined cross-sectional area of all the capillaries is about 800 times that of the aorta, and so the velocity of flow is about 1/800 that in the aorta or roughly 0.3 mm. per second. Since the average capillary is about 0.5 mm. long, the time spent by a single red blood cell in traversing a capillary is a little more than 1 second. The total cross-sectional area of the veins at any level is about twice that of the corresponding arteries, so that the velocity of flow is roughly one half that in the arteries.

Although these relations determine the *average* velocity of flow in a given type of vessel, the rate of flow in an individual vessel may vary widely from the prevailing average. For example, exposure to external warmth dilates the blood vessels in the skin and increases the velocity of flow in these vessels above the general average. In this case the increased rate of blood flow is a part of the mechanism for the control of body temperature and is compensated by a decreased rate of flow in some other portion of the circulation. As a general rule circulatory adjustments in one part of the body are thus balanced by reciprocal adjustments in some other part.

## Blood pressure

The blood pressure is the force with which the blood distends the walls of the vessels and with which it would escape if the vessel were cut. Blood flows from one point to another along the circulatory system because of a difference in the blood pressure between the two points. The pressure thus diminishes progressively as the blood flow away from the heart and has fallen almost to zero by the time the blood reaches the right heart, completing its circulation. This is in contrast to the *velocity* of flow, which reaches a minimum in the capillaries and then increases again in the veins. The progressive fall in blood pressure along the circulatory system is caused by the loss of energy in overcoming the frictional resistance to flow offered by the walls of the vessels. The amount of friction between two moving surfaces is proportional to the area of contact and to the velocity with which one surface moves past the other. As applied to the circulation, this means that the pressure will fall most rapidly at the points of greatest friction. Inspection of Fig. 27 reveals that the blood pressure declines very little in the arteries, falls very steeply in the arterioles, and then falls more gradually in the capillaries and the veins. The great frictional resistance in the arterioles is due almost entirely to the tremendous surface of contact since a single artery gives rise to many arterioles. In the capillaries the surface of contact is still greater, but this factor, which tends to increase frictional resistance, is offset by the extreme slowing of the velocity of flow which tends to diminish friction. As a result the fall in pressure in the capillaries is much less than that in the arterioles. The rate of loss of pressure as the blood flows through the veins toward the heart is very low due partly to the additional energy imparted to the blood by the massaging action of the skeletal muscles and the siphoning effect of the respiratory movements discussed earlier.

*Arterial blood pressure.* A high level of blood pressure in the arteries is essential if blood is to be driven through the arterioles with their great frictional resistance and into the capillaries beyond. The ultimate source of energy for the maintenance of arterial blood pressure is, of course, the

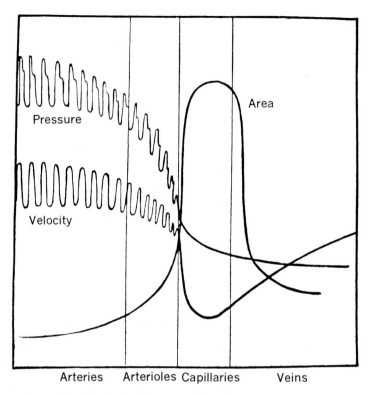

Pressure

Area

Velocity

Arteries    Arterioles Capillaries        Veins

**Fig. 27.** Diagram showing the pressure and velocity of the blood in different parts of the circulatory system. (From Best, C. H., and Taylor, N. B.: The physiological basis of medical practice, Baltimore, 1945, The Williams & Wilkins Co.)

pumping action of the heart. There are, however, subsidiary factors of considerable importance for which the blood vessels themselves are responsible. Among the most significant of these are the elasticity of the large arteries, the high resistance offered by the arterioles (the so-called "peripheral resistance"), and the relation that exists between the capacity of the vascular system and the total volume of the blood that it contains. An additional factor of minor importance under most conditions is the viscosity of the blood.

When the ventricle of the heart contracts, it ejects a mass of blood into the aorta. This vessel is already full of blood that must be displaced by onward flow through the smaller arteries and arterioles into the capillaries. Because of the high resistance offered by the arterioles the flow into the capillaries cannot keep pace with the flow into the aorta. As a result the pressure in the arteries rises steadily, distending the elastic arterial walls, until the increased velocity of flow through the arterioles is great enough to balance the inflow into the aorta. This maximal level of arterial blood pressure is called the *systolic pressure*. With the onset of ventricular relaxation and the closure of the aortic valve, the arterial pressure begins to fall since the outflow into the capillaries is no longer balanced by an inflow into the aorta. The distended arterial walls now recoil and force onward the extra mass of blood accommodated during the ejection period of the heart. The elasticity of the large arteries is thus the primary factor that ensures a flow of blood into the capillaries in the interval between beats of the heart. The fall in arterial pressure as the force of the recoil is gradually spent continues until it is checked by the next systolic ejection of blood. The lowest level reached by the arterial pressure in this decline is referred to as the *diastolic pressure*. The difference between the systolic and the diastolic pressure at any moment is the *pulse pressure*.

The distention of the arterial walls at the beginning of the systolic ejection of blood is not confined to the aorta but travels down the arteries as a wave followed by a wave of recoil. In arteries that lie close to the surface of the body such as the radial artery at the wrist, the arrival of the wave of distention and subsequent recoil may be felt as a distinct throb, the *pulse*, which affords a convenient method of counting the heart rate.

If all the blood vessels in the body were to relax at the same time, the total volume of blood would be insufficient to fill them completely. This would result in an immediate fall in blood pressure since pressure implies some distention of the vessel walls. Accordingly it is essential that a large fraction of the vessels be partly constricted at all times in order to reduce the capacity of the vascular system to a point at which the available blood volume can fill and slightly distend it. A common example of the result of a sudden widespread vasodilatation is fainting, in which the fall in blood pressure induced by dilatation of the splanchnic vessels reduces the blood flow to the brain, resulting in loss of consciousness.

An increase in the viscosity of the blood raises the general level of blood pressure since viscosity is a measure of internal resistance to flow. This factor is probably of minor importance in all but extreme cases.

An elevation of the arterial blood pressure is one of the important adjustments during exercise, providing the driving force for increasing the blood flow through the muscles. At the same time an excessively high resting blood pressure may seriously reduce the tolerance of a person for exercise. It is worthwhile then to consider briefly the influence on blood pressure of variations in the basic controlling factors just discussed. All fluctuations in blood pressure, both at rest and during exercise, are the result of alterations in one or more of these factors.

An increase in the *stroke volume* of the heart results in the ejection of a larger volume of blood into the aorta during the period of systole. If the peripheral resistance of the arterioles remains the same, the distention of the arteries must be increased to accommodate this larger mass of blood, and the systolic blood pressure rises to a higher level before outflow can be made to balance inflow. The diastolic pressure is increased to a lesser degree because the greater systolic distention of the vessel walls results in a more rapid diastolic recoil, so that the pressure may fall almost to the normal diastolic level before the next systole. An increase in the *heart rate,* on the other hand, predominantly elevates the diastolic pressure by curtailing the time available for the diastolic fall in pressure.

The *elasticity of the arterial walls* tends to diminish with advancing age. As a result the blood ejected into the aorta in systole is less completely accommodated by distention of the arterial walls, and the systolic pressure rises. On the other hand, the diminished recoil of the arterial walls during diastole may result in a lowered diastolic pressure. These effects are greatly intensified in the pathological "hardening of the arteries" associated with hypertension. In this disease, involvement of the arterioles frequently results in elevation of the diastolic as well as the systolic pressure.

An increase in the *peripheral resistance* because of widespread constriction of arterioles elevates both the systolic and the diastolic pressures. Constriction of the arterioles diminishes the rate of outflow from the arteries. This in turn increases the systolic distention of the arterial walls and limits the speed of their recoil during diastole. If elevated arterial blood pressure due to widespread vasoconstriction is associated with localized vasodilatation in a particular organ, the conditions are ideal for an increased blood flow through that organ. It will be shown that this is, in fact, the basis of the increased blood flow through active muscles.

*Measurement of arterial blood pressure in man.* The measurement of the arterial blood pressure is one of the most common of clinical procedures and is part of every physical examination. An indirect method based on the measurement of the pressure that just suffices to collapse an artery is ordinarily used. The pressure is applied to the main artery of the arm by inflating an airtight rubber cuff that is wrapped around the upper arm, and a stethoscope is placed over the brachial artery below the cuff. The pressure in the cuff is rapidly raised above systolic pressure. No blood enters the artery below the cuff and no sound is heard. The cuff pressure is lowered slowly, and when it falls just below the systolic level, a spurt of blood escapes into the artery below the cuff at the peak of each systole. The impact of the small spurts of blood upon the stationary column of blood sets up vibrations that are detected as thumping sounds. The pressure indicated on the manometer is recorded as the systolic pressure. As the cuff pressure is lowered still further, more blood escapes beyond the cuff at each systole, and the sounds become louder. When the diastolic pressure is reached, blood flows through the artery under the cuff throughout the cardiac cycle, and the sounds suddenly become muffled and then disappear entirely. Direct blood pressure measurements obtained from a needle inserted in the artery indicate that indirect blood pressure measurements are accurate during rest but not during exercise.[1] If the exercise is at all strenuous, systolic pressure may be underestimated by 8 to 15 mm. Hg and overestimated during the first few minutes of recovery by 16 to 38 mm. Hg. The errors are even greater in the measurement of diastolic pressure, and as a matter of fact, it cannot be determined at all in some subjects. As a result of this unfortunate state of affairs much of the work on changes in

*Table 4.* Influence of age on blood pressure[*]

| Age | Systolic pressure | Diastolic pressure | Pulse pressure |
|---|---|---|---|
| 6 mo. male | 89 | 60 | 29 |
| 6 mo. female | 93 | 62 | 31 |
| 4 yr. male | 100 | 67 | 33 |
| 4 year female | 100 | 64 | 36 |
| 10 yr. | 103 | 70 | 33 |
| 15 yr. | 113 | 75 | 38 |
| 20 yr. | 120 | 80 | 40 |
| 25 yr. | 122 | 81 | 41 |
| 30 yr. | 123 | 82 | 41 |
| 35 yr. | 124 | 83 | 41 |
| 40 yr. | 126 | 84 | 42 |
| 45 yr. | 128 | 85 | 43 |
| 50 yr. | 130 | 86 | 44 |
| 55 yr. | 132 | 87 | 45 |
| 60 yr. | 135 | 89 | 46 |

[*]Based on data from Allen-Williams: Arch. Dis. Childhood **20:**125, 1945; and from Ponder: In Fulton, editor: Howell's textbook of physiology, ed. 15, Philadelphia, 1946, W. B. Saunders Co.

blood pressure during exercise and recovery must be accepted with reservation until it has been confirmed by direct blood pressure measurements.

*Normal arterial blood pressure standards.* At birth the arterial blood pressure is only about 20 to 60 mm. Hg, but at the end of the first month of life it is 70 to 80 mm. Hg. It increases steadily thereafter, so that the average normal systolic pressure of young male adults is about 120 mm. Hg, and the average diastolic pressure is about 80 mm. Hg (this is usually recorded as 120/80).

The influence of *age* on the systolic, diastolic, and pulse pressure is shown in Table 4. It will be noted that there is a sharp increase in the systolic pressure about the time of puberty. After the age of 20 years there is a steady rise in both systolic and diastolic pressures as age advances, probably because of a gradual decrease in the elasticity of the arterial walls. *Sex differences* in the way in which the arterial pressure varies with age have been observed. In girls the sharp increase at puberty is less marked and is often followed by a decrease until 18 years of age, after which the increase is steady as age advances, although the absolute values are about 10 mm. Hg less than in the male.

*Emotional states* such as excitement, fear, and anxiety increase the arterial blood pressure and may cause falsely high results in the first of a series of blood pressure determinations. It is uncertain to what extent the effects of emotion are due to the liberation of epinephrine; a flow of nerve impulses from the cerebral cortex to the medullary centers must also be considered a possible factor.

As in the case of the heart rate, the arterial blood pressure is affected by *posture.* When a reclining subject stands up, there is a momentary fall in blood pressure caused by the diminished venous return. In most subjects the carotid sinus reflex brings about a prompt vasoconstriction in the splanch-nic vessels, with a resulting rise in arterial pressure that ensures an adequate blood flow to the brain. This compensation usually overshoots the mark, and the arterial pressure is ordinarily 10 or 15 mm. Hg higher than in the reclining position. In some otherwise normal persons the compensatory vasoconstriction is inadequate or delayed, so that the blood pressure may fall when the erect posture is assumed. These persons often feel faint or dizzy upon first standing or if standing is maintained for a considerable period.

The postural changes in heart rate and blood pressure are items in several tests of physical fitness. A minimal or no rise in heart rate and a moderate increase in blood pressure are interpreted as favorable circula-tory adjustments, while an undue increase in heart rate and a fall in blood pressure upon assuming the standing posture are considered to indicate poor vasomotor stability. It is uncertain to what extent these postural cir-culatory adjustments correlate with general physical fitness.

## Control of the blood flow to organs

The capacity of the fully relaxed vascular system is greater than the total volume of blood in the body. This means that a considerable fraction of the blood vessels must at all times be partially or completely constricted so that the available volume of blood may fill the remainder of the system. Constriction of the arterioles by increasing the peripheral resistance also places the blood in the arteries under sufficient pressure to ensure an ade-quate driving force for maintaining a flow of blood through the capillaries.

When organs become more active, they require a greater volume of blood flow. This is achieved primarily by a dilatation of the arterioles sup-plying the active organ and a compensatory constriction of the arterioles in less active regions, so that blood is shunted from resting to active tissues. When large muscle masses are contracting during exercise, the vasodilata-tion in the muscles may be so profound that total peripheral resistance is decreased in spite of the compensatory vasoconstriction in less active re-gions. This means that the rise in blood pressure during exercise is probably due entirely to the increased cardiac output.

All the tissues of the body do not take part in the vasoconstriction that diverts blood to active regions. The blood vessels of the skin and abdomi-nal organs normally store large amounts of blood and can undergo the greatest amount of vasoconstriction when blood is required elsewhere. Such organs as the heart and brain, on the other hand, require a rich supply of blood at all times and hence do not participate in the compensatory vaso-constriction in exercise.

In brief, the adjustment of blood flow to the metabolic requirements of the tissues involves two distinct though interrelated processes: (1) dila-tation of the arterioles in the active tissues and (2) compensatory constric-tion of the arterioles in certain of the less active tissues. (When necessary, blood flow through the active tissues may be still further increased by an increase in cardiac output.) The changes in caliber of the arterioles in active and inactive tissues are the result of nervous, chemical, and mechanical factors that must now be considered.

## Control of the blood flow through skeletal muscles

The vasomotor control of the blood vessels in skeletal muscles has been extensively investigated in recent years, but the situation is not yet entirely clear. The blood flow through resting muscles is very small because of the high degree of constriction of the blood vessels in muscles. This constriction persists after removal of the vasomotor nerve supply,[4] so that it appears to be due to the normal intrinsic tone of the smooth muscle in blood vessels in muscles. It follows that increased blood flow in muscles during exercise must result from factors that overcome this normal constriction and bring about vasodilatation.

The blood vessels in skeletal muscle receive vasomotor fibers exclusively from the sympathetic division of the autonomic nervous system. Some of these fibers liberate norepinephrine at their endings and hence are called *adrenergic* fibers. These resemble typical vasoconstrictor nerve fibers in other parts of the body, and they are believed to exert a weak vasoconstrictor action on the blood vessels in muscle. In addition the blood vessels of skeletal muscle receive a rich supply of vasodilator fibers from the sympathetic nervous system. These fibers release acetylcholine at their endings (in this regard resembling parasympathetic fibers elsewhere) and hence are called *cholinergic* fibers. The increased discharge of impulses over the sympathetic vasodilator nerves may be a significant factor in increasing the blood flow through muscles during exercise. However, experiments[5] have shown that although stimulation of the sympathetic vasodilator pathway in the hypothalamus does indeed increase the total blood flow through muscle, it diminishes the oxygen consumption of the muscle and presumably the blood flow through the capillaries, perhaps by shunting the blood through direct arteriovenous shunts. The degree to which the blood flow through muscle capillaries during exercise is increased by the action of the sympathetic vasodilator nerves cannot be determined from the evidence available at this time.

## Effect of local chemical changes on muscle blood flow during exercise

It was mentioned previously that the blood vessels in resting skeletal muscles show a considerable degree of constriction largely independent of nervous control and that the increased blood flow through the muscles in exercise is brought about by a decrease in this intrinsic constriction. There is a large amount of evidence which indicates that this is due to the direct action on the blood vessels of local chemical changes. Among the agents suggested for this role are lack of oxygen, increased concentrations of carbon dioxide and lactic acid, liberation of intracellular potassium and histamine, adenine compounds resulting from the breakdown of ATP (adenosine triphosphate), and the specific vasodilator compound bradykinin. The subject has been reviewed by Hilton[6] and by Barcroft.[7] A strong argument for the predominant role of potassium (released from muscle cells) in the production of dilatation of the muscle vessels during exercise has been presented by Kjellmer.[8]

## Site of the compensatory vasoconstriction during exercise

In a normal, resting man with a cardiac output of 5.4 liters per minute, the abdominal organs (gastrointestinal tract, liver, kidneys, and spleen) receive about 2.8 liters per minute, the skin about 0.5 liter, and the skeletal muscles about 0.8 liter. During exercise, along with the dilatation of the blood vessels of muscles, there is constriction of the blood vessels in the abdominal organs, so that their blood flow is decreased below resting levels despite the increase in cardiac output. The blood flow through the kidney, for example, has been shown to suffer a decrease of 50 to 80% in exercising human subjects.[9, 10] The blood vessels of the skin initially constrict in the same manner, but as the exercise continues, they ordinarily dilate as a part of the mechanism for eliminating the excess heat produced in the contracting muscles. The end result is a shunting of blood from the abdominal organs to the exercising muscles, heart, and skin and little change in the blood flow through other regions of the body. This shunting mechanism, together with the increased cardiac output, increases the blood flow through contracting muscles to such a degree that the oxygen consumption (milliliters of oxygen used per 100 grams of muscle per minute) may be increased from a resting value of 0.16 to an exercise value of 12, or 75 *times* the resting rate of oxygen consumption.

### Advanced study topics

1. What is the mechanism by which blood is shunted to active muscles during exercise?
2. Review the recent literature on heart rate in the current issues of *Circulation*.
3. Describe an automatic blood pressure recorder and its uses.
4. Measure the blood pressure of a person at rest and immediately after various activities throughout the day.
5. Illustrate how blood pressure is used with other physiological responses to postural changes and exercise as a measure of physical fitness.

### References

1. Henschel, A., de la Vega, F., and Taylor, H. L.: Simultaneous direct and indirect blood pressure measurements in man at rest and work, J. Appl. Physiol. 6:506, 1954.
2. Allen-Williams, G. M.: Pulse rate and blood pressure in infancy and early childhood, Arch. Dis. Childhood 20: 125, 1945.
3. Ponder, E.: The velocity and pressure of blood flow. In Fulton, J. F., editor: Howell's textbook of physiology, ed. 15, Philadelphia, 1946, W. B. Saunders Co.
4. Stein, I. D., Harpuder, K., and Byer, J.: Effect of sympathectomy on blood flow in the human limb, Am. J. Physiol. 152:499, 1948.
5. Uvnäs, B.: Sympathetic vasodilator system and blood flow, Physiol. Rev. (supp. 4) 40:69, 1960.
6. Hilton, S. M.: Local mechanisms regulating peripheral blood flow, Physiol. Rev. (supp. 5) 42:265, 1962.
7. Barcroft, H.: Circulation in skeletal muscle; In Field, J.: Handbook of Physiology. Section 2, Circulation, vol. 2,

Washington, D. C., 1963, American Physiological Society, p. 1353.

8. Kjellmer, I.: Studies on exercise hyperemia, Acta Physiol. Scand. (supp. 244) 64:1-27, 1965.

9. White, H. L., and Rolf, D.: Effects of exercise and of some other influences on the renal circulation in man, Am. J. Physiol. 152:505, 1948.

10. Radigan, L. R., and Robinson, S.: Effects of environmental heat stress and exercise on renal blood flow and filtration rate, J. Appl. Physiol. 2:185, 1949.

# 13

# *Circulatory adjustments during exercise*

## Blood flow through active muscles

Very few data on the blood flow through muscles during exercise are available. Attempts to measure the blood flow through single muscles during tetanic contraction induced by stimulation of the motor nerve have yielded conflicting results. Some workers[1, 2] have described a decreased blood flow during the period of contraction followed by an increased flow after the contraction was over. Others[3, 4] have reported increased blood flow during as well as after the contraction. These divergent viewpoints are partly reconciled by the experiments of Barcroft and Millen[5] who measured the blood flow through the plantar flexor muscles of human subjects during rhythmic contraction of the leg muscles and during various degrees of static work. These authors found that for rhythmic contraction and for low intensities of static work blood flow increased; for high degrees of static work blood flow was impaired. It was also found in these experiments that with high intensities of static work the amount and duration of work were not influenced by cutting off the circulation with a cuff, emphasizing the normally anaerobic nature of this type of work. The discrepancies in the results obtained by the earlier workers are probably caused by the differences in the type and intensity of the contractions studied. It can be stated then that light muscular work or rhythmic contraction increases the blood flow during the exercise and for some time afterward but that heavy static work decreases or stops the blood flow during the exercise and only increases it afterward. During periods of diminished blood flow in static work, the contracting muscles are forced to utilize anaerobic sources of energy.

The increased blood flow through muscles engaged in rhythmic or light static work is due partly to the increase in cardiac output and in arterial blood pressure (discussed in previous chapters) and partly to the dilatation of the muscle vessels. In the gracilis muscle of the dog Martin and co-workers[6] found 1,050 open capillaries per square millimeter in the resting muscle and 2,010 open capillaries per square millimeter in the exercised muscle. In a similar area there were 1,690 muscle fibers. Therefore there is more than one open capillary per muscle fiber during exercise. The opening of previously closed capillaries is probably due primarily to the nervous and chemical factors described in the previous chapter and not to mechanical force derived from the increased arterial blood pressure.

The amount the blood flow through skeletal muscles increases during exercise is very difficult to measure directly;[7] it varies not only with the type and intensity of the exercise but also with the relative proportion of the total musculature that is involved. Assuming maximal involvement of muscles and maximal intensity of exercise (of a rhythmic nature), some rough calculations can be made. Under resting conditions the cardiac output may be 5 liters per minute, and it may rise to 20 liters per minute during exercise. At rest, about 0.8 liter of the cardiac output goes to the skeletal muscles, and since the net flow to nonmuscular tissue probably changes little in exercise, perhaps as much as 16 liters of the cardiac output may go to the muscles during exercise. Thus the total muscle blood flow during exercise would be about 20 times greater than the muscle blood flow at rest (this relative increase might be even greater when only small muscle masses participate in the exercise). The actual increase in the delivery of oxygen to the working muscles is even greater (perhaps as much as 75 times the resting value), since a larger fraction of the oxygen is removed from each volume of blood flowing through the muscle capillaries.

One of the results of athletic training is reported[8] to be a decrease in the cardiac output during submaximal exercise, which is attributed to more effective shunting of blood to the muscles. Another result of training is an increase in the blood flow through working muscles involved in standard, rhythmic exercise.[9]

## *Blood flow through the heart, lungs, and brain during exercise*

It has been emphasized repeatedly that muscular exercise involves widespread physiological adjustments over and above the actual contractions of the skeletal muscles. The functional activity of the heart is tremendously increased, and since the heart has a very limited capacity for anaerobic contraction, the blood flow through the coronary vessels, which nourish the heart muscle, must be correspondingly augmented. The blood flow through the lungs must keep pace with the venous return or blood will accumulate in the lungs; at the same time the *velocity* of flow through the lungs must not be increased unduly if the exchange of gases in the pulmonary capillaries is to be reasonably complete. The oxygen requirement of the brain presumably varies little from rest to exercise, but it must at all times be adequate; there must be no diversion of blood from the brain to the contracting muscles. Adequate blood flow through the heart, brain, and lungs is achieved primarily by virtue of the fact that the arterioles in these organs do not participate in the compensatory vasoconstriction that diverts blood to the muscles. In the heart and the brain the principal factor determining blood flow is the level of arterial blood pressure. In addition the coronary vessels are dilated by release of vasoconstrictor tone; local dilatation by acid metabolites is probably of minor importance. The blood flow through the lung is determined by the output of the right ventricle and hence ultimately by the venous return. Dilatation of lung vessels probably results passively from the increased inflow of blood.

*Blood flow through the heart.* The factor of greatest importance in the control of coronary blood flow is the level of blood pressure in the aorta. The coronary arteries originate as lateral branches from the aorta just beyond the aortic valve, so that any rise in aortic blood pressure is transmitted directly to the blood in the coronary arteries. The great increase in aortic pressure during exercise thus ensures a corresponding increase in the inflow of blood into the coronary vessels. It was believed at one time that the contraction of the heart muscle in systole compresses the coronary vessels and stops the flow of blood, just as in static contraction of skeletal muscles. It now seems that this is true only for the brief isometric phase of systole when no blood is being ejected into the aorta. During the major portion of systole and throughout diastole, the blood flow in the coronary vessels is proportional to the aortic pressure.[10]

It is technically very difficult to determine the influence of the sympathetic and vagus nerves on the coronary blood vessels because these nerves also influence the heart directly, which in turn alters the aortic blood pressure and the inflow of blood in the coronary vessels. Stimulation of the sympathetic nerves to the heart increases coronary blood flow, and stimulation of the vagus nerves decreases coronary blood flow. However, the injection of norepinephrine directly into the coronary arteries decreases coronary flow while acetylcholine increases it. It thus seems probable that the effects of stimulation of the cardiac nerves on coronary flow are indirect, by way of the influence on the rate and force of contraction of the heart.

A decrease in the oxygen content of the blood results in a prompt dilatation of the coronary vessels and an increase in coronary blood flow, which tends to compensate for the low oxygen content. Increased carbon dioxide content of the blood has little effect on the coronary blood vessels. Thus it appears that the increased oxygen requirement of the heart during exercise is met by an increase in coronary blood flow that is due primarily to the rise in aortic blood pressure.

*Blood flow through the lungs.* The blood flow through the lungs during exercise is increased in proportion to the increase in venous return to the heart. In spite of the considerable increase in blood flow there is no significant rise in pulmonary arterial pressure, indicating that a decrease in the peripheral resistance in the pulmonary circuit must occur. This is probably due to the passive opening of capillaries that previously were partially or completely closed. Since all lobes of the lung are qualitatively identical, there is no need for a vasomotor mechanism for diversion of blood from one part to another, and the vasomotor nerves to the pulmonary vessels seem rather to regulate the total capacity of the pulmonary system.

Heavy static exercise such as weight lifting frequently involves straining, that is, forced expiration against a closed glottis. There is a considerable increase in pressure in the abdominal and thoracic cavities that may hinder the venous return to the heart, and as a direct consequence the blood flow through the lungs may be diminished rather than increased as in the case of rhythmic exercise.

*Blood flow through the brain.* The blood flow through the brain is steadier and more carefully safeguarded than is the flow through any other organ. The brain is enclosed within a rigid bony case, in which the total volume of contents cannot vary; hence a dilatation of the vessels in one portion of the brain must be balanced by a constriction in some other portion. Actually there is little evidence for any very significant alteration in the *caliber* of cerebral vessels except under extreme conditions. There is no positive evidence of the existence of a significant vasomotor control of the cerebral vessels in man. Vasodilatation results from a rise in the carbon dioxide content or a fall in the oxygen content of the arterial blood. It is probable that the cerebral vessels have a high level of intrinsic tone which normally is reduced by the usual amount of carbon dioxide in the blood.

Cerebral vascular resistance and cerebral blood flow are relatively unaffected by the increase in cardiac output that occurs in exercise.[11]

## Blood pressure changes during exercise

The rise in systolic arterial pressure during exercise is one of the most important of the several factors that increase the blood flow through the contracting muscles, the heart, and the brain. The causes of the elevated arterial blood pressure have been discussed in the preceding chapters; briefly they are as follows:

1. Increased stroke volume of the heart, resulting in greater systolic distention of the aorta and the large arteries
2. Increased heart rate, allowing less time for the arterial pressure to fall in diastole
3. Compensatory vasoconstriction in less active tissues, especially the skin and abdominal organs

Accurate data on the changes in blood pressure during many types of exercise are almost impossible to obtain because of technical difficulties. It is obvious that special techniques would be required to obtain measurements of blood pressure during such activities as swimming and sprint running. Most of our knowledge is derived from measurements made shortly after the termination of such exercises. Since the systolic blood pressure falls rapidly immediately after the cessation of exercise, such measurements are of doubtful value as indications of the actual changes *during* exercise. It has been possible to record the changes in blood pressure during exercise for static work such as weight lifting and for stationary rhythmic work such as pedaling on a bicycle ergometer or running on a treadmill. In all of these studies the results must be interpreted with caution in view of the demonstrated unreliability of indirect measurements of blood pressure during exercise and recovery.

It is impossible to generalize about the changes in blood pressure during exercise because of the variety of modifying factors; among the most important of these are the type, speed, and duration of the activity and the physical condition of the subject.

Very moderate exercise may fail to influence the systolic pressure; it may even show a slight fall after a slow walk. As the exercise becomes more strenuous, however, the systolic pressure usually rises. One of the earliest careful studies of changes in blood pressure during exercise is that of Bowen[12] who made continuous records of the heart rate and systolic pressure during work on a bicycle ergometer. The results of a typical experiment are shown in Fig. 28. Bowen observed a rapid rise in pressure at the beginning of exercise followed by a more gradual secondary rise to a maximum that was reached in 5 to 10 minutes. The pressure then remained fairly steady although it showed a slight tendency to fall during the remainder of the exercise period. An abrupt fall almost to the resting level took place as soon as the exercise ceased. The heart rate increased more abruptly at the beginning of exercise than did the blood pressure but returned to normal more slowly after exercise than did the blood pressure. Bock and Dill[7] explain this as follows: At the beginning of exercise the heart rate is immediately increased through inhibition of the cardioinhibitory (vagus) center by impulses from the cerebral cortex. The more gradual rise in sys-

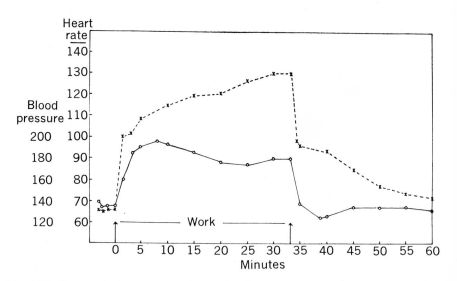

**Fig. 28.** Changes in heart rate and systolic blood pressure during and after exercise. (Redrawn from Bowen, W. P.: Changes in heart rate, blood pressure and duration of systole resulting from bicycling, Am. J. Physiol. **11:**59, 1904.)

tolic blood pressure results from the steadily increasing venous return brought about by the contractions of the working muscles. Note that this implies increased filling of the heart during exercise, which probably does not occur. (See discussion of Starling's law of the heart, Chapter 10.) At the end of exercise the forces sustaining the blood pressure are suddenly withdrawn, whereas the heart rate continues for a time to be influenced by secondary factors. The tendency for the systolic pressure to decrease as exercise is prolonged probably reflects such vascular readjustments as dilatation of the blood vessels of the skin coincident with the rise in body temperature.

The systolic blood pressure may fall abruptly in the first few seconds after exercise ceases only to rise steeply again, reaching a maximum 20 to 60 seconds later.[13] Bock and Dill explain the abrupt fall as being caused by a sudden decrease in venous return and momentary stagnation of blood in the capillaries when the pumping action of the contracting muscles ceases; this is rapidly succeeded by restoration of the venous inflow to the heart as the capillaries gradually empty themselves into the great veins.

McCurdy[14] made a careful study of the changes in blood pressure associated with weight lifting, an exercise of *strength* having a large static component. He found a sudden rise in blood pressure without any great change in pulse rate at the onset of exercise and an equally abrupt return of the pressure to normal upon cessation of exercise. This is in sharp contrast to the gradual rise of the blood pressure in moderate rhythmic exercise and its slow return to normal. McCurdy believed that the sharp rise in pressure during weight lifting was due to the accompanying increase in pressure in the thoracic and abdominal cavities resulting from straining. Karpovich[15] verified these results and found in addition that the blood pressure may drop rapidly below normal even *during* the expiratory effort of lifting, presumably due to the decreased cardiac output that results from interference with the venous return to the heart. This may explain the fainting sometimes observed during weight lifting and formerly attributed to the great increase in blood pressure. The great and sudden rise in arterial blood pressure during exercises of strength subjects the heart and blood vessels to considerable strain and makes this type of activity inadvisable for persons with cardiovascular disease or weakness.

During exercises of *endurance* McCurdy found that the rise in blood pressure was greater than during exercises of speed but less than in exercises of strength. The systolic pressure always fell below normal within 10 minutes after long races (marathon) and continued to fall gradually for periods of 1 to 4 hours. The diastolic pressure, on the other hand, usually returned to normal within 35 minutes. The heart rate returned to normal very slowly and usually remained above normal throughout the period of observation. The subnormal postexercise systolic blood pressure, in spite of a persistent elevation in heart rate, indicates a diminished stroke volume of the heart. This may be due to the slowness with which the dilated vascular bed in the muscles and the skin returns to normal, so that blood tends to pool in these regions.

The changes in diastolic pressure during exercise have received much less attention than have the systolic pressure changes partly, perhaps, because of the greater inaccuracies in diastolic pressure measurements by the indirect method during exercise. Direct measurements made by needles inserted into the subject's arteries show that the diastolic pressure usually changes very little in exercise, indicating that the increased cardiac output, which would elevate the pressure, is balanced by the extensive vasodilatation in the muscles, which would lower the diastolic pressure.

The nature of the response of blood pressure to exercise depends not only on the rate, intensity, and duration of work but also on the state of training of the subject. Bock and associates[16] compared the changes in blood pressure of DeMar, a trained marathon runner, with those of an untrained subject when each performed work on a bicycle ergometer. DeMar had a rise of 60 mm. Hg in his systolic pressure when his metabolic rate was 2 liters of oxygen per minute, whereas the untrained subject had a similar rise in systolic pressure with one half the work load.

The circulatory changes occurring during muscular exercise in man have recently been studied in great detail by Holmgren.[17] His results, using the best modern techniques, confirm the general conclusions just stated.

Nevertheless, it should not be thought that our information concerning the circulatory changes in exercise is at all satisfactory. For example, in a recent study[18] involving exercise at a level of 75% of the maximal oxygen transport capacity, for a period of 90 minutes, there was observed a gradual fall in the mean arterial blood pressure and the stroke volume of the heart throughout the period of exercise. The cardiac output was increased, despite the decline in stroke volume, because of the great increase in heart rate.

### Advanced study topics

1. Explain how alterations in systolic and diastolic blood pressure compensate for the circulatory needs of various types of exercise.
2. Review the recent literature on circulatory adjustments during exercise in the current issues of the *American Journal of Physiology*.
3. Describe a direct method of blood pressure determination.
4. Compare the effect of continued light exercise with quiet standing after exercise, using blood pressure measurements to observe the responses.
5. What is the best kind of exercise to stimulate the opening of previously closed capillaries?

### References

1. Verzar, F.: The gaseous metabolism of striated muscle in warm blooded animals, J. Physiol. 44:243, 1912.
2. Anrep, G. V., and v. Saalfeld, E.: The blood flow through skeletal muscle in relation to its contraction, J. Physiol. 85:375, 1935.
3. Rein, H., Mertens, O., and Schneider, M.: Die Blutversorgung des Muskels bei aktiver Dauerverküngung, Pflüger's Arch. ges. Physiol. 236:636, 1935.
4. Millikan, G. A.: Experiments on muscle hemoglobin in vivo; the instantaneous measurement of muscle hemoglobin, Proc. Roy. Soc., London, sB 123:218, 1937.
5. Barcroft, H., and Millen, J. L. E.: The blood flow through muscle during sustained contraction, J. Physiol. 97:17, 1939.
6. Martin, E. G., Wooley, E. C., and Miller, M.: Capillary counts in resting and active muscle, Am. J. Physiol. 100:407, 1932.
7. Bainbridge, F. A.: Physiology of mus-

cular exercise, rewritten by Bock, A. V., and Dill, D. B., ed. 3, London, 1931, Longmans, Green & Co.

8. Andrew, G. M., Guzman, C. A., and Becklake, M. R.: Effect of athletic training on exercise cardiac output, J. Appl. Physiol. **21**:603, 1966.

9. Rohter, F. D., Rochelle, R. H., and Hyman, C.: Exercise blood flow changes in the human forearm during physical training, J. Appl. Physiol. **18**: 789, 1963.

10. Gregg, D. E., and Green, H. D.: Registration and interpretation of normal phasic inflow into a left coronary artery by an improved differential manometric method, Am. J. Physiol. **130**:114, 1940.

11. Zobl, E. G., Talmers, F. N., Christensen, R. C., and Baer, L. J.: Effect of exercise on the cerebral circulation and metabolism, J. Appl. Physiol. **20**:1289, 1965.

12. Bowen, W. P.: Changes in heart rate, blood pressure and duration of systole resulting from bicycling, Am. J. Physiol. **11**:59, 1904.

13. Cotton, T. F., Lewis, T., and Rapport, D. L.: After-effects of exercise on pulse rate and systolic blood pressure in cases of "irritable heart," Heart **6**:269, 1917.

14. McCurdy, J. J.: The physiology of exercise, ed. 2, Philadelphia, 1928, Lea & Febiger.

15. Karpovich, P.: Quoted by McCurdy.[14]

16. Bock, A. V., van Caulaert, C., Dill, D. B., Fölling, A., and Hurxthal, L. M.: Studies in muscular activity. III. Dynamical changes occurring in man at work, J. Physiol. **66**:136, 1928.

17. Holmgren, A.: Circulatory changes during muscular work in man, Scandinav. J. Clin. & Lab. Invest. (supp. 24) **8**:1, 1956.

18. Saltin, B., and Stenberg, J.: Circulatory response to prolonged severe exercise, J. Appl. Physiol. **19**:833, 1964.

# 14

## Body fluid changes
## in exercise

### Fluid balance

*Fluid compartments and their measurement.* The body of the average person has a water content of about 70%. The actual amount of water in a given individual (expressed as percent of body weight) varies inversely with his fat content, since fat is simply added to the body without the addition of a corresponding amount of water.

The body fluids can be considered to occupy several anatomical compartments separated by barriers and having characteristic differences in composition. The primary subdivisions are intracellular and extracellular compartments. The extracellular compartment, in turn, may be subdivided into vascular and interstitial compartments, the latter including all the fluids outside the cells and outside the vascular system. It includes the fluid that surrounds and bathes the tissue cells and certain localized collections of fluid such as the cerebrospinal fluid, the synovial fluid of the joints, and the intraocular fluid.

The total amount of water in the body ("total body water") can be measured by injecting intravenously a known amount of some substance that diffuses freely through all the body water. From its measured concentration in the blood plasma after distribution is complete, the "volume of distribution" (in this case the total body water) can be calculated. For example, suppose that 5 grams of the test substance is injected, and its concentration in the blood plasma is found to be 0.1 gram per liter; then the total volume of distribution is 5/0.1 = 50 liters. This would be the total water content of the body. Among the substances that have been used to measure total body water are isotopically labeled water, urea, antipyrine, and antipyrine derivatives.

Since the fat-free portion of the body has a reasonably constant water content (about 72%), measurement of total body water permits the calculation of the fat content of the body. For example, if the measured water content of an individual is 54% and letting X = percent fat, then

$$(100) (0.54) = (100 - X) (0.72) + (X) (0)$$
$$X = 25 \text{ or the fat content is 25\% of the body weight}$$

The total extracellular fluid volume can be measured in a similar manner from the volume of distribution of a substance that diffuses throughout the extracellular compartment but does not enter the cells. Thiocyanate is a convenient (although not very accurate) test substance. Better test substances are inulin, sucrose, mannitol, thiosulfate, and radioactive sodium or chloride. The spaces measured by these different substances vary somewhat, but they usually fall within the range of 15 to 19% of body weight (except for thiocyanate, which has a "space" of about 23 to 24%). The plasma volume, measured by the volume of distribution of substances that do not leave the blood or that leave it a slow and measurable rate, is about 5% of body weight.

The intracellular volume cannot be measured directly, but it can be calculated by subtracting the extracellular fluid volume from the total body water. Thus, if total body water is 50 liters and if extracellular volume is 15 liters, the volume of the intracellular fluid is 35 liters.

The fluids in the various compartments differ in chemical composition, which indicates that free movement of chemical substances (electrolytes, proteins, etc.) from one compartment to another may be restricted, whereas water appears to move freely. In the extracellular fluids sodium is the most important cation, and chloride is the most important anion; in the intracellular fluids potassium is the predominant cation, and the prominent anions include phosphate and organic anions. For further details textbooks of biochemistry should be consulted.

*Fluid exchange in the tissue capillaries.* The exchange of fluids (including dissolved components other than proteins) between the blood and the interstitial fluid occurs in the tissue capillaries. The basic mechanisms involved in this exchange were described many years ago by the English physiologist E. H. Starling and are commonly referred to as Starling's hypothesis. According to Starling, fluid leaves the capillary at the arterial end and is reabsorbed at the venous end because of a progressive change in the balance between filtration and reabsorption forces as the blood passes through the capillary. This may be illustrated by the following example.

The blood pressure in the arterial end of the capillary, which causes fluid to pass out into the tissue spaces, is about 35 mm. Hg. It is opposed by the colloid osmotic pressure of the plasma proteins, amounting to about 25 mm. Hg, which tends to draw fluid into the capillary from the tissue spaces. The net result is a force of 35 − 25 = 10 mm. Hg that causes fluid to leave the capillary. The blood pressure falls progressively along the capillary, reaching a level of about 15 mm. Hg at the venous end. This is less than the colloid osmotic pressure of the plasma proteins, and a force of 25 – 15 = 10 mm. Hg is available to bring about reabsorption of fluid at the venous end of the capillary. Minor corrections for the tissue fluid pressure and colloid osmotic pressure do not materially affect this picture. Thus under normal conditions in resting subjects, filtration and reabsorption of fluid at the arterial and venous ends of the capillaries balance each other, and the volume of the tissue fluid is maintained constant. (This is an oversimplification that indicates the net result of opposing forces; actually the outward filtration of fluid may occur throughout the length of some capillaries, while the reabsorption of fluid occurs throughout the length of other capillaries.) This balance may be disturbed by a variety of conditions, including exercise and exposure to heat (to be discussed later). If the filtration of fluid out of the capillaries exceeds its reabsorption, the volume of interstitial fluid is increased, resulting in *edema*. If reabsorption exceeds filtration, the interstitial (and eventually the intracellular) fluid is diminished and the state of *dehydration* results.

**Fluid exchange between cells and interstitial fluid.** The volume and composition of the intracellular fluid are carefully guarded, but if extreme changes occur in the water content of the interstitial fluid, water may pass into or out of the cells because of osmotic imbalance. This is especially likely to occur if the body gains or loses water in excess of salts or salts in excess of water. For example, as a result of excessive sweating, water is lost in excess of salt. This increases the concentration of salts in the plasma and interstitial fluid, and water is drawn from the cells.

**Regulation of volume and composition of fluid compartments.** The total water content of the body is determined by the balance between the intake of water (including the water content of the food and the water produced during the metabolism of foodstuffs) and the loss of water in the urine, feces, sweat, and expired air. This balance is normally maintained by appropriate adjustments among these various factors when one or more is disturbed. For example, if excessive water is lost in sweating, the excretion of water in the urine is diminished, and if water intake is excessive, the excretion of water in the urine is correspondingly increased. The two major regulatory factors in the maintenance of water balance are the voluntary intake of water controlled by the sense of thirst and the excretion of water in the urine controlled by the antidiuretic hormone of the posterior pituitary gland. The secretion of the antidiuretic hormone is thought to be regulated by the osmotic effect of changes in the salt content of the blood acting on special osmoreceptors in the hypothalamus. The hormone acts by increasing the reabsorption of water from the renal tubules, thus decreasing the amount of water appearing in the urine.

**Alterations in fluid balance under various conditions.** Posture and acute exercise are conditions that alter fluid balance.

*Posture.* When a previously recumbent person stands up, the blood pressure in the lower parts of the body rises, and fluid leaves the capillaries in these regions. This results in the well-known "dependent edema" experienced by many people after long periods of standing. This is less marked if the person is able to walk about since the muscular contractions increase the reabsorption of fluid in the lower legs into the lymphatic vessels for eventual return to the blood.

*Acute exercise.* During a single bout of exercise fluid leaves the blood, as shown by the increased concentration of erythrocytes, hemoglobin, and plasma proteins in the blood. This condition is known as hemoconcentration, and it is a sign that plasma volume has decreased. In moderate exercise the change may be no greater than that on changing from the recumbent to the standing posture, but in more strenuous exercise it is more striking. The basic mechanism is the loss of fluid from the blood into the tissue spaces because of the increased blood pressure in the capillaries associated with the rise in systolic blood pressure in exercise. If excessive sweating occurs during the exercise, the resulting water loss, unless balanced by decreased excretion of water by the kidney (or by voluntary intake of water), will contribute to the hemoconcentration. Finally, there is evidence that increased metabolism in the cells, by breaking down large molecules into smaller ones with consequent increase in the number of particles, may cause the osmotic absorption of fluid into the cells at the expense of the water of the interstitial and vascular compartments. As would be expected compensatory changes in the other regulatory factors tend to restrain or correct the tendency for water to be lost from the blood during exercise. This probably accounts for the fact that if moderate exercise is continued, there may occur a return of fluid to the blood.

*Chronic exercise.* Sustained training or habitual exercise appears to result in no permanent shifts in body fluid.

## Dehydration

*Acute dehydration.* Acute dehydration is an important problem in sports because of the greatly increased loss of water in the sweat and the expired air and failure to replace the water during the exercise period. Replacement may be impossible because of the nature of the activity or because of the belief of coaches and trainers that it is harmful. Surprisingly large water losses may occur during a period of strenuous activity, especially in hot climates,[1, 2] and one of the results of the decreased blood volume is an elevation of the rectal temperature, sometimes to dangerous levels.[2, 3] Extensive laboratory and field studies stimulated by the problems of desert warfare during World War II clearly demonstrated a deterioration in performance associated with dehydration, which could be reduced by the continual replacement of water loss during the period of exercise[1, 4] (Figs. 29 to 31). This deterioration is manifested by a rise in rectal temperature and pulse rate( indicating additional strains on the cardiovascular and temperature-regulating adjustments required in exercise) and by the earlier onset of exhaustion. Except for those persons who experience slight nausea when they drink water during exercise, there seems to be no contraindication to the continual replacement of water during strenuous exercise and much

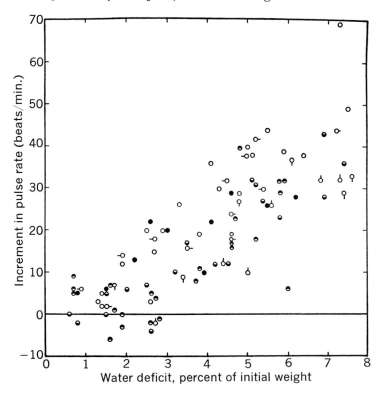

**Fig. 29.** Increments in pulse rate of standing subjects at various water deficits. Each symbol represents one subject. (From Adolph, E. F., and associates: Physiology of man in the desert, New York, 1947, Interscience Publishers, Inc.)

to recommend it. Unless the amount of sweating is extreme, as during prolonged exercise in hot environments, salt loss may be compensated by increasing the amount of salt used at meals. The use of salt tablets between meals is rarely necessary, and it may lead to gastric irritation and nausea unless accompanied by copious amounts of water.

*Chronic dehydration.* Acute dehydration is usually corrected by increased water intake in the hours following the period of exercise, and compensation is ordinarily complete by the next day. If dehydration persists longer than 24 hours, it may be considered to be chronic. This is not a common occurrence, but it may be seen in athletes who restrict their food and water intake in order to meet weight requirements. It is occasionally enforced by coaches and trainers as part of a training regime in the belief that performance is thereby improved. The situation appears to differ in some respects from that of acute dehydration, perhaps because of more effective compensatory reactions.[3, 5] The decrement in work performance may be considerably lessened even though the expected effect of dehydration on pulse rate and rectal temperature is present. It is not clear whether this represents increased tolerance to dehydration or improved fitness due

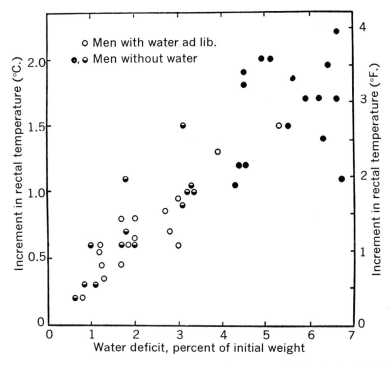

**Fig. 30.** Increments in rectal temperature at various water deficits induced by hiking 10 to 14 miles in the desert at air temperatures of 90° to 100° F. (From Adolph, E. F., and associates: Physiology of man in the desert, New York, 1947, Interscience Publishers, Inc.)

to training. The increased tolerance to dehydration is seen only when the dehydration is developed under cool environmental conditions and not at all in men who become dehydrated in the heat.[1]

## Kidney function in exercise

The alterations in kidney function associated with exercise may be considered from two aspects: (1) the influence of exercise on kidney function and (2) the contribution of the kidney to the homeostatic adjustments to exercise.

The alteration in kidney function due to exercise is largely the consequence of the cardiovascular response that shunts blood from the visceral organs and skin to the working muscles. The amount of blood flowing through the kidneys is regularly decreased during exercise and for periods as long as 1 hour after exercise, and the magnitude of the decrease is related to the severity of the exercise and the degree of exhaustion produced. In order to appreciate the effect on the kidney of this decrease in renal blood flow, certain details of the histology of the kidney and of the arrangement of its blood vessels should be recalled. The blood flowing

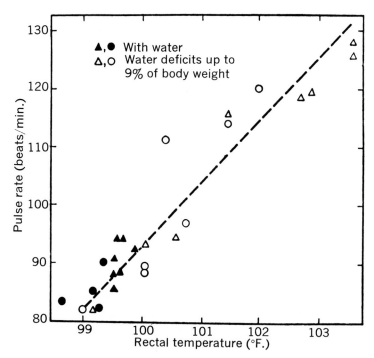

**Fig. 31.** Relation between pulse rate and rectal temperature of subject at work while dehydrating. (From Adolph, E. F., and associates: Physiology of man in the desert, New York, 1947, Interscience Publishers, Inc.)

through the kidney passes through two sets of capillaries arranged in series. The first set of capillaries includes those of the glomeruli, where water and dissolved materials filter from the capillaries into the lumen of the renal tubules. After leaving the glomeruli the blood traverses a second set of capillaries surrounding the renal tubules, where water is reabsorbed from the tubular fluid into the blood, and various dissolved substances may be either reabsorbed from the tubular fluid or secreted into the tubular fluid from the blood. Furthermore the glomerular capillaries are provided with two sets of arterioles, the afferent arterioles located proximal to the capillaries and the efferent arterioles distal to the capillaries. The constriction of either set of arterioles decreases the blood flow through the kidney, but if the afferent arterioles are predominantly involved, the blood pressure in the glomerular capillaries falls, and filtration of fluid in the glomerulus (glomerular filtration rate or G.F.R.) decreases. If, however, the efferent arterioles are primarily involved, the blood pressure in the glomerular capillaries rises and a greater proportion of the blood plasma is filtered into the renal tubule (the proportion of fluid extracted from each volume of plasma passing through the glomeruli is called the filtration fraction). In exercise the reduction in renal blood flow is greater than the reduction in G.F.R., so that the filtration fraction rises. This indicates a proportionately greater constriction of the efferent than of the afferent arterioles.

The volume of urine formed per minute depends on the balance between the rate of filtration of fluid in the glomeruli and the amount of the filtered fluid that is reabsorbed as it passes down the renal tubules. From each 100 ml. of plasma passing through the glomerular capillaries, about 20 ml. of fluid is filtered into the renal tubules. The amount of fluid thus filtered in 1 minute (the G.F.R.) amounts to about 120 ml. in an average resting person. Most of this fluid is reabsorbed as it passes down the tubules, so that only about 1 or 2 ml. of urine is formed each minute under ordinary conditions, but after the ingestion of large amounts of water, the rate of urine formation may exceed 10 ml. per minute. The factor that determines the amount of water reabsorbed in the kidney tubules is the action of the antidiuretic hormone (ADH) secreted by the posterior pituitary gland. This hormone causes the reabsorption of a greater proportion of the water from the fluid in the renal tubules and hence diminishes the rate of urine formation. The ingestion of large amounts of water results in a decreased rate of secretion of ADH, and a larger proportion of the water filtered in the glomeruli escapes reabsorption in the tubules. The result is a larger flow of urine and eventual elimination of the extra water ingested. In dehydration, on the other hand, the hormone secretion is increased, and a greater proportion of the filtered water is reabsorbed, thus conserving the body's water supply.

In exercise there is believed to be an increased secretion of ADH due initially to stress and emotional stimuli and perhaps later to the dehydration that may result from increased sweating. The result is a greater reabsorption of fluid from the renal tubules and a decrease in the rate of urine formation.

It is apparent that the decreased rate of urine formation commonly observed in exercise may be due to one or both of the following factors: (1) decrease in glomerular filtration rate caused by decreased renal blood flow and (2) increased tubular reabsorption of filtered fluid caused by increased secretion of antidiuretic hormone. The relative importance of these two factors has not been established.

The contribution of the kidney to the homeostatic adjustments to exercise is easy to state but difficult to explain in detail. In addition to the conservation of body water already described, the kidney plays an important role in eliminating much of the excess acid produced during strenuous exertion. This is readily demonstrated by measurements of the pH of the urine, which may fall dramatically during and especially following severe exercise. Since the urine is usually more acid (that is, has a lower pH) than the blood, it is normally concerned with the excretion of acid metabolites and thus with the maintenance of a normal pH in the blood and tissues. The response to exercise probably consists largely in an exaggeration of this normal activity of the kidney with the result that the increase in acidity of the blood and tissues due to the production of lactic and pyruvic acids during exercise is diminished and normal acidity is more rapidly restored. The details of the mechanisms involved in the acidification of the urine are beyond the scope of this book but are described in textbooks of medical physiology. The adjustments occurring during and after exercise have been analyzed by Wesson.[6]

### Advanced study topics

1. What is the mechanism of blood volume changes in prolonged bed rest and exercise training?
2. Review the recent literature on body fluid changes in exercise in current issues of the *Journal of Aerospace Medicine.*
3. Describe a method of measuring body fluid volume.
4. Record weight loss during various physical activities.
5. What is the best way to replace water lost during prolonged heavy exercise?

### References

1. Adolph, E. F., and associates: Physiology of man in the desert, New York, 1947, Interscience Publishers, Inc.
2. Barach, J. H.: Physiological and pathological effects of severe exertion (the marathon race), Am. Phys. Ed. Rev. **16:** 200, 1911.
3. Monagle, J. E., Grande, F., Buskirk, E., Brozek, J., Taylor, H. L., and Keys, A.: Body temperature during work in man on restricted water intake and low caloric carbohydrate diet, Fed. Proc. **15:** 132, 1956.
4. Pitts, G. C., Johnson, R. E., and Consolazio, F. C.: Work in the heat as affected by intake of water, salt and glucose, Am. J. Physiol. 142:253, 1944.
5. Grande, F., Taylor, H. L., Anderson, J. T., Buskirk, E., and Keys, A.: Water exchange in men on a restricted water intake and a low caloric carbohydrate diet accompanied by physical work, J. Appl. Physiol. 12:202, 1958.
6. Wesson, L. G., Jr.: Kidney function in exercise. In Johnson, W. R., editor: Science and medicine of exercise and sports, New York, 1960, Harper & Row, Publishers.

# 15

# *Pulmonary ventilation*

The term respiration in the broadest sense includes all the processes that contribute to the exchange of gases between the organism and its environment. Even resting tissues require a continuous supply of oxygen and the continuous removal of carbon dioxide. Activity increases both of these needs, so that the overall level of respiratory function must be adaptable to the changing metabolic requirements of the body.

In unicellular organisms such as the ameba the exchange of gases occurs directly across the cell membrane. In higher multicellular animals most of the tissue cells are no longer in immediate contact with the external environment, and a transportation system, the bloodstream, serves to connect the two. There are two surfaces across which the respiratory gases must diffuse: (1) the surface of contact between air and blood in the lungs and (2) the surface of contact between blood and tissue fluid in the systemic capillaries. There are two prerequisites for an efficient diffusion system: (1) a large surface of contact between the two media and (2) a very thin membrane that offers minimal resistance to diffusion. These essential features are secured in the tissues by the tremendous surface area and the extremely thin walls of the capillaries. In the lungs the air surface to which the blood in the pulmonary capillaries is exposed is greatly increased by a complex folding of the pulmonary epithelium. As a result of the peculiar structure of the lung, the air that takes part in gas exchange is located in the depths of the lung in the tiny pulmonary alveoli. This *alveolar air* is constantly losing oxygen and gaining carbon dioxide by exchange with the blood in the pulmonary capillaries. In order to maintain a constant composition of the alveolar air, there must be some provision for periodic ventilation of the alveoli by outside air. This is achieved by breathing movements under the control of the central nervous system.

For convenience of discussion, respiration may be thought of as involving three separate processes: (1) pulmonary ventilation or breathing, (2) the exchange of gases in the lungs and tissues, and (3) the transport of gases in the bloodstream. This chapter is concerned with the first of these processes, pulmonary ventilation.

## Mechanics of breathing

*Structure of the lung.* Functionally the lung consists of two portions— the alveoli in which gas exchange occurs and the conducting system by means of which outside air reaches the alveoli during inspiration. Air is conducted to the lungs by the trachea, which divides into two main bronchi, one going to each lung. Inside each lung the bronchus divides into smaller bronchioles, each of which divides into still smaller bronchioles, and so on until the terminal bronchioles are reached. These are tiny tubes surrounded by a circular layer of smooth muscle in a manner reminiscent of the arterioles (Fig. 32). Each terminal bronchiole branches to form a number of respiratory bronchioles, thin-walled tubes in which a certain amount of gas exchange probably takes place (Fig. 33). Each respiratory bronchiole leads by way of an alveolar duct into an expanded air sac. The alveoli are small dilatations of the walls of the air sac, the whole having the appearance of a cluster of grapes (Fig. 34). Since gas exchange occurs only in the terminal ramifications of the respiratory tree (the respiratory bronchioles, air sacs, and alveoli), the remainder of the air-conducting tubes constitutes a dead space which, during inspiration, is filled with air that takes no part in gas exchange. The volume of this dead space in the normal resting adult is about 150 ml. It increases in volume when the depth of breathing is increased, as in exercise.[1]

Expansion of the lungs during inspiration results in the drawing in of fresh air as far as the terminal bronchioles. Lung expansion consists primarily of a lengthening and dilatation of the air passages (Fig. 35). The alveoli themselves probably do not expand during inspiration but are ventilated by diffusion currents in the fresh air that reaches the terminal bronchioles.

The pulmonary capillaries form a network surrounding each alveolus, so that air in the alveolus is separated from blood in the capillary by a very thin double membrane that offers little resistance to the free exchange of gases. An idea of the enormous surface of diffusion thus made available may be gained from the calculation made by Zuntz that the total number of alveoli in both lungs in a human being is about 750 million. The total surface of diffusion has been variously estimated at 40 to 90 sq.M. (the surface area of the human body is about 1.5 sq.M.).

*Inspiration and expiration.* The two lungs lie completely enclosed within the chest cavity or thorax, one lung lying on either side of the heart. The sides and dome of the thorax are made up of the chest wall, which is rendered rather rigid by the ribs. Below, it is bounded by the diaphragm, a domelike sheet of skeletal muscle that separates the thoracic and abdominal cavities. The lungs are covered externally by a thin membrane, the pleura,

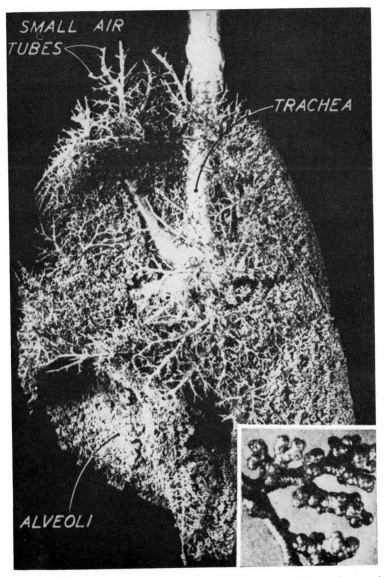

**Fig. 32.** Metal cast of the air passages of the lungs of a dog. Where the metal filled the alveoli well, the metal forms an almost solid mass. Where the metal failed to fill the alveoli, the small branching air tubes can be seen. The inset (lower right) shows a cast of clusters of alveoli at the termination of tiny air tubes. (About ×11.) (From Carlson, A. J., and Johnson, V. E..: The machinery of the body, ed. 2, Chicago, 1941, University of Chicago Press.)

which is reflected from the root of the lungs onto the inner surface of the chest wall. A thin film of fluid fills the potential space between the two layers of pleura.

The size of the chest cavity is increased during inspiration as a result of the contraction of the respiratory muscles. The ribs and sternum are elevated by contraction of the intercostal muscles, with resulting enlargement

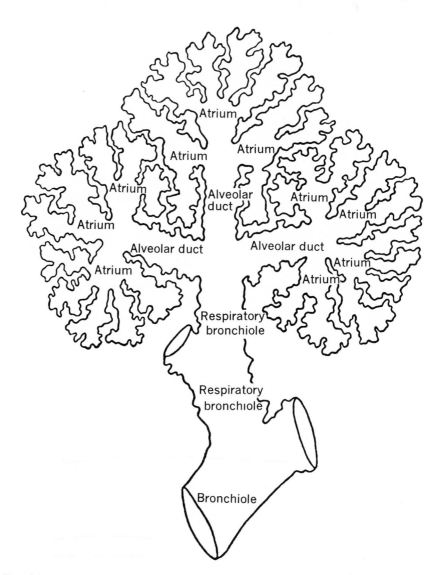

**Fig. 33.** Diagram showing a terminal bronchiole and the structures derived from it. Each atrium leads into several air sacs. The individual alveoli are small, blind pouches in the walls of an air sac. (From Haldane, J. S., and Priestley, J. G.: Respiration, New Haven, 1935, Yale University Press.)

**Fig. 34.** Portion of a metal cast of a human lung showing the arrangement of alveoli and alveolar sacs (air sacs) and the branching alveolar duct. (After Bender; from Maximow and Bloom: A textbook of histology, ed. 4, Philadelphia, 1944, W. B. Saunders Co.)

of the anteroposterior and lateral diameters of the chest cavity. Contraction of the diaphragm increases the vertical dimensions of the thorax. Since the chest is a closed cavity with only one opening to the outside (the trachea), it follows that the increase in size of the cavity will aspirate a corresponding quantity of air into the lungs by way of the trachea. Relaxation of the respiratory muscles permits the chest walls to return to their normal position with the expulsion of air from the lungs. Expiration is thus a passive process under normal resting conditions. During exercise, when the rate and depth of breathing are increased, the expiratory decrease in the size of the chest cavity is hastened by the contraction of certain expiratory muscles. During exercise additional respiratory muscles come into play; they make expiration an active process and also increase the force and velocity of inspiration. The increased activity of the respiratory muscles may result in a considerable increase in the energy cost of breathing.

The respiratory muscles are ordinary skeletal muscles and hence contract only in response to nerve impulses arriving over motor nerve fibers. The intercostal muscles are innervated by the intercostal nerves, and the

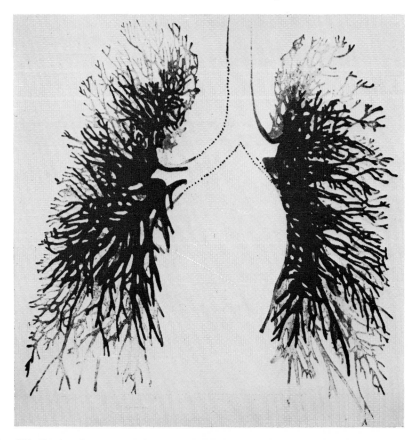

**Fig. 35.** Tracing from x-ray shadows of human lungs in deep inspiration (gray) and forced expiration (black). (After Macklin; from Bloom, W., and Fawcett, D. W.: A textbook of histology, ed. 8, Philadelphia, 1962, W. B. Saunders Co.)

diaphragm is innervated by the phrenic nerves. The fact that contraction and relaxation of the respiratory muscles alternate rhythmically with a frequency and strength proportional to the oxygen requirement of the body indicates the existence of a coordinating mechanism. This is the respiratory center located in the medulla in close proximity with the cardiac and vasomotor centers.

## Respired air

In quiet breathing about 500 ml. of air is drawn into the lungs at each inspiration and expelled at each expiration. This volume is referred to as the *tidal volume*. It is a matter of common experience that the depth of breathing may be much greater than this in exercise and can be increased at rest by a voluntary effort. The greatest volume of air that can be inhaled from the *resting respiratory level* (position of the chest at the end of a normal quiet expiration) is called the inspiratory capacity. It amounts to 2 to

3 liters. In the same way a considerable volume of air (about 1.5 liters) can be forcibly exhaled; this is the *expiratory reserve volume*. The sum of the inspiratory capacity and the expiratory reserve volume is called the *vital capacity*. It is usually measured by requiring the subject to make the deepest possible inspiration, followed by a maximal expiration into a measuring spirometer. The vital capacity varies considerably with a person's body build and, to a lesser degree, the physical condition of the subject, with a range of about 3.5 to 6 liters. Its significance as an index of respiratory efficiency is discussed later.

A maximal expiratory effort by no means empties the lungs completely but leaves a volume of air amounting to about 1.5 liters (this is called the *residual volume*). At the end of a normal expiration the volume of air remaining in the lungs is the sum of the expiratory reserve and residual volumes. This volume of about 3 liters is called the *functional residual capacity*; it is of importance because it represents the volume of air with which the incoming tidal volume mixes at each inspiration.

*Influence of dead space on the efficiency of ventilation.* It was mentioned that the nonrespiratory air-conducting portions of the respiratory tract constitute a dead space having an average capacity of 150 ml. in the resting subject. This means that of the 500 ml. of air in normal inspiration only 350 ml. actually mixes with the 2,000 to 3,000 ml. of air in the alveoli; the remaining 150 ml. of air must fill the dead space. With the onset of expiration, the first portion of air to be expelled is that filling the dead space. Since it has not participated in respiratory exchange, its composition is essentially the same as that of atmospheric air. The rest of the air exhaled comes from the depths of the lungs where gas exchange has occurred, presumably for the most part from the respiratory bronchioles, the alveolar ducts, and the air sacs since the alveoli themselves apparently do not contract in expiration. By convention this air, which has participated in respiratory exchange, is called *alveolar air*. It is believed to approximate the composition of the air in the alveoli very closely; the air in the alveoli cannot be obtained for direct analysis. The expired air is thus a mixture of atmospheric (dead space) air and alveolar air, and its composition is intermediate between the two.

*Alveolar air.* As just mentioned, the term "alveolar air" is used to identify the air in those portions of the respiratory tree in which gas exchange occurs. It is with this air and not with that of the outside atmosphere that the blood flowing through the capillaries of the lungs comes into diffusion equilibrium. The average composition of the alveolar air is oxygen, 14.5%; carbon dioxide, 5.5%; and nitrogen, 80%.[*] This composition remains reasonably constant in a given subject at rest, indicating that ventilation of the alveoli is so adjusted as to balance the gas exchange between the alveolar air and blood in the pulmonary capillaries.

---

[*]The composition of atmospheric air is oxygen, 20.93%; carbon dioxide, 0.03%; and nitrogen, 79.04%. The rare gases are included in the nitrogen fraction.

It is of considerable significance that the alveolar air is not completely flushed out at each inspiration. If this did occur, the composition of the alveolar air would fluctuate widely from inspiration to expiration, with a corresponding fluctuation in the gaseous composition of the blood leaving the lungs. This would have serious effects on certain tissues that are delicately responsive to alterations in their gas exchange with the blood. The normal composition of the alveolar air is such that the blood leaving the lungs is about 98% saturated with oxygen and has lost a volume of carbon dioxide equivalent to that gained in the tissue capillaries.

During exercise, changes occur in the composition of the alveolar air that afford considerable information concerning the adequacy of the respiratory and circulatory adjustments. These are described in the discussion that follows.

*Expired air.* The expired air is a mixture of atmospheric air from the dead space and alveolar air. Its composition varies with fluctuations in that of the alveolar air and in the depth of breathing. It is obvious that the smaller the tidal volume (that is, the shallower the breath), the more closely will the expired air approach the composition of atmospheric air. For example, with a tidal volume of 450 ml. and a dead space of 150 ml., the expired air will consist of one-third atmospheric air and two-thirds alveolar air, whereas a reduction of the tidal volume to 300 ml. would result in an equal mixture of atmospheric and alveolar airs in the expired air. Since the composition of the expired air and the alveolar air and the volume of the dead space are mutually dependent variables, if the values of any two are known, that of the third may be calculated. This is a valuable procedure in many types of research dealing with the physiological adjustments to exercise.

## Pulmonary ventilation during exercise

*Minute volume of breathing.* The observations of Lindhard and others indicate that ventilation of the lungs during exercise is probably always adequate for normal saturation of the blood flowing through the lungs. Hence it is to be expected that in moderate exertion there will be a linear relation between the minute volume of breathing and the amount of oxygen absorbed. This is illustrated in Fig. 36.

The approximately linear relation between work load and minute volume of breathing is maintained as the work load is increased until the intensity of work is so great that a steady state cannot be achieved. With the accumulation of lactic acid, pulmonary ventilation becomes excessive and no longer bears a constant relation to oxygen consumption. This excessive ventilation serves no useful purpose since the delivery of oxygen to the tissues is now limited by the maximal output of blood by the heart. It does indicate, however, that pulmonary ventilation is capable of further increase at a time when the limit of circulatory adjustment has been reached, emphasizing the fact that the minute volume of breathing is unlikely to be a limiting factor in exercise.

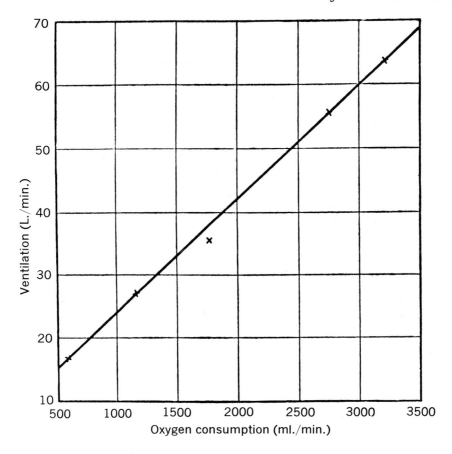

**Fig. 36.** Relation between oxygen consumption and pulmonary ventilation during exercise. (From Bainbridge: The physiology of muscular exercise, rewritten by Bock and Dill, London, 1931, Longmans, Green & Co.)

The minute volume of breathing in exercise is influenced by the physical condition of the subject and by training. This is manifested in two ways:

1. By a decrease in the minute volume of breathing required for the performance of a given load, indicating an improvement in the *efficiency* of ventilation
2. By an increase in the maximal respiratory minute volume that can be achieved during very strenuous exertion

Schneider and Ring[2] followed the changes in breathing in two subjects during a period of moderate training. They found that the decrease in breathing came about so gradually that it was impossible to say just when it began, although it was slightly in evidence by the end of the second week of training. The maximum reduction was reached in from 4 to 6 weeks. One subject had a reduction of 17% in the minute volume of breathing for a work load of 8,000 foot-pounds per minute; the reduction in the other subject was even greater, 23.3% for a work load of 6,000 foot-pounds per minute. Within 4 to 6 weeks after training was discontinued, the minute volume of breathing during work was nearly back to the pretraining level.

It is difficult to evaluate the influence of training on the maximal minute volume of breathing that can be achieved by a subject engaging in strenuous exertion. The evidence from several studies indicates that regular exercise may result in an increase in the vital capacity, especially in adolescent children and young adults.[3] On the other hand, it was found that the vital capacity was normal in most of the runners participating in the Boston marathon of 1924.[4] Furthermore, there was no direct relation between the vital capacity and the order in which the runners finished.

It is probable that the respiratory superiority of the trained athlete lies not so much in a larger vital capacity as in a greater ability to utilize his maximal lung capacity. As the depth of breathing approaches the limit imposed by the vital capacity, subjective feelings of discomfort develop. This stage is reached sooner by an untrained man than by a trained man, and the subject is said to be "out of breath" or "winded." The physiological basis of this phenomenon is not clearly understood. It may be correlated with certain differences in the breathing patterns of trained and untrained men. In an untrained man there is a tendency toward a greater frequency of breathing to attain a given minute volume of ventilation. This may be caused by his inability to achieve both rapid and maximal enlargement of the thoracic cage because of the lesser strength of his respiratory muscles. Another difference in the respiratory pattern of untrained men is the relatively greater role of costal as opposed to diaphragmatic enlargement of the chest. Since costal enlargement is executed against a greater resistance as the elastic limits of the chest wall are approached, fatigue of the respiratory muscles and the accompanying subjective feelings of distress appear more quickly than in predominantly diaphragmatic breathing.

The cause of the stabbing pain in the side, called by some a "stitch," is not definitely known. The most likely cause is lack of oxygen in the diaphragm. It is said to be relieved by bending over toward the affected side, with the hand in the region of the pain.[5]

*Time relations of the respiratory changes during exercise.* With the beginning of exercise an immediate augmentation of breathing occurs (Fig. 37). When the excitement of competition is involved, there may occur an anticipatory increase in breathing just before the work is started. For a given work load there are two phases to the respiratory response, the rapid initial increase just mentioned, followed by a slow rise to the final value which is maintained throughout the exercise. Since the onset of the initial phase is very rapid, occurring before any metabolic products from the contracting muscles could possibly reach the respiratory center, Krogh and Lindhard[6] have suggested that it is the result of impulses from the cerebral cortex influencing the respiratory center.

There may be a considerable lag in the attainment of the final maximal level of breathing (Fig. 38), indicating a steadily mounting chemical and

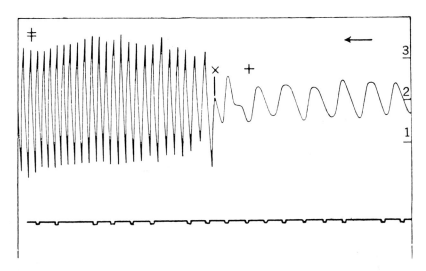

**Fig. 37.** Respiratory response to exercise, showing the transition from rest to work. The record is read from right to left. The scale is in liters of air, time in one-tenth minute. + = ready; X = begin; ‡ = stop. (After Krogh and Lindhard; from Bainbridge: The physiology of muscular exercise, rewritten by Bock and Dill, London, 1931, Longmans, Green & Co.)

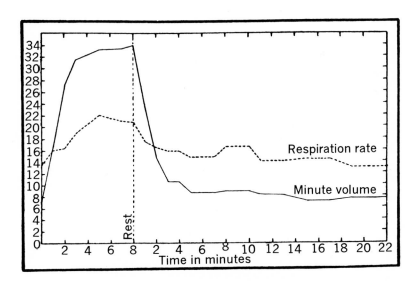

**Fig. 38.** The minute volume and frequency of breathing during and after 8 minutes of work on a bicycle ergometer (load, 4,000 foot-pounds per minute). Note the lag of 5 minutes before the maximum is reached during work and the rapid drop within the first 2 minutes after work. (From Schneider, E. C.: Physiology of muscular activity, Philadelphia, 1939, W. B. Saunders Co.)

reflex drive to the respiratory center. With moderate exertion a steady state is usually reached in 3 to 5 minutes, which is approximately the same as the time required for completion of the circulatory adjustments. This suggests that certain factors of control must be common to both types of adjustment.

When exertion is severe, both the minute volume and the frequency of breathing may continue to increase throughout the period of work, although there may be a slight decrease in the tidal volume. It will be recalled that the adjustment of heart function during severe exercise follows a similar pattern, that is, a continuing rise in heart rate associated with a slight decrease in the stroke volume.

*Aftereffects of exercise on breathing.* The time required for breathing to return to the preexercise level is determined by the severity and duration of the exertion and by the physical condition of the subject. When work of moderate intensities is performed in a steady state, the minute volume of breathing falls off rapidly, more or less duplicating in reverse the time required for the attainment of maximal ventilation at the beginning of exercise (Fig. 38). The excess breathing during this period suffices to repay the small oxygen debt incurred at the beginning of exercise before the completion of the circulatory adjustments. Following very severe exertion the return of breathing to the preexercise level may be greatly delayed in proportion to the magnitude of the oxygen debt that must be repaid.* The respiratory rate usually returns to normal more slowly than does the depth of breathing.

For a given work load the larger oxygen debt incurred by a less physically fit person results in a greater delay in the postexercise return of breathing to the normal level.

## Regulation of breathing

The lungs must be ventilated at rhythmic intervals to replace the oxygen that has been absorbed into the blood and to remove the carbon dioxide that has been liberated from the blood. This is comparable to the operation of an air-conditioning system in a crowded room. The ventilation of the lungs is accomplished by alternation between *inspiration,* in which the chest is enlarged and air is drawn into the lungs, and *expiration,* in which the chest returns to its normal size and air is forced out of the lungs. The inspiratory enlargement of the chest results from the contraction of the respiratory muscles—the intercostal muscles, which elevate the ribs, and the diaphragm. These are skeletal muscles and are therefore controlled by the central nervous system. A group of nerve cells in the medulla, the *respiratory center,* controls the contractions of the respiratory muscles. When these nerve cells send impulses over motor nerves to the respiratory muscles, inspiration occurs. When the cells of the respiratory center cease to send impulses to the respiratory muscles, these muscles relax and expiration occurs.

If the discharge of nerve impulses from the respiratory center were con-

---

*The term *oxygen debt* is defined in the glossary and discussed at length in Chapter 18.

tinuous, the chest would be held in a position of inspiration, and no ventilation of the lungs would occur. It is obvious therefore that something must periodically inhibit the respiratory center to permit expiration to occur. Not only must breathing be rhythmic to be effective but its rate and depth must also be adjusted to the requirement of the body for absorbing oxygen and eliminating carbon dioxide. In strenuous muscular exercise, for example, the *minute volume of ventilation* (the amount of air breathed in and out per minute) may be increased to 10 times the resting level.

*Regulation of breathing at rest.* The respiratory center behaves as if it were sensitive to changes in the chemical composition of its blood supply. Respiration increases with a rise in the carbon dioxide tension or the acidity of the arterial blood and decreases with a fall in carbon dioxide tension or acidity. It was believed for many years that the neurons of the respiratory center are directly influenced by these chemical agents; however, recent work indicates that there are receptors in the medulla which respond to chemical changes in both the blood and the cerebrospinal fluid and that these receptors send nerve impulses to the respiratory neurons. Under normal conditions the carbon dioxide tension in the arterial blood is nicely adjusted to give exactly the right amount of stimulation to the respiratory control mechanism.

In order for expiration to alternate with inspiration it is necessary for the respiratory center to discharge rhythmic bursts or volleys of nerve impulses rather than a steady stream of impulses. It was taught for many years that expiration results from periodic inhibition of the respiratory center by nerve impulses from a higher center in the brain stem (pneumotaxic center) and from stretch receptors located in the lungs (the Hering-Breuer reflex). Recent work strongly suggests that the cells of the respiratory center are automatically rhythmic in their discharge and that the other influences just mentioned simply modify the inherent rhythm of the respiratory center. The neurons of the respiratory center may constitute part of an oscillatory system; electronic analogs have been built that produce bursts of discharges very similar to rhythmic discharge of impulses from the respiratory center.[7]

Under special conditions other factors may influence breathing. For example, if the oxygen tension of the blood falls, as at high altitudes, a small mass of tissue (called the carotid body because of its location near the bifurcation of the common carotid artery at the angle of the jaw on each side) is stimulated, and impulses are sent over nerve fibers to the respiratory center. The result is an increase in breathing which tends to compensate for the decreased oxygen content of the inspired air. Breathing may also be modified by nerve impulses reaching the respiratory center from the cerebral cortex (basis of the increased breathing that occurs during emotional excitement) and by way of sensory nerves from many parts of the body (especially the skin, muscles, and joints). Finally, breathing is increased by a rise in body temperature from any cause.

*Increased breathing during exercise.* Exercise increases the metabolism of the body and hence the requirement for oxygen. In response to this demand for more oxygen the rate and depth of breathing are promptly increased. The nature of the stimulus that causes increased breathing during exercise has been the subject of much speculation. The answer might seem obvious—the increased carbon dioxide produced by the working muscles might be thought to stimulate the respiratory center. That this is not the final answer is indicated by two lines of evidence:

1. Moderate exercise produces a greater increase in respiration than can be induced by breathing the highest concentration of carbon dioxide that can be tolerated.
2. Although the arterial blood carbon dioxide concentration often rises slightly during mild exercise, it may actually fall below normal during more strenuous exercise[8] because it is eliminated in the lungs at a faster rate than it is produced in the muscles.

It has been reported[9] that influences originating in exercising limbs result in a stimulation of breathing. The nature of this influence is not clear. Passive movements of the joints of the extremities result in increased breathing in anesthetized dogs, suggesting that stimulation of proprioceptors may contribute to the stimulation of respiration in exercise. It has been claimed that sensory nerve endings in the muscles, the joints, or perhaps in the veins leading from the working muscles are stimulated by the metabolic products released from the muscles. This problem has been analyzed critically by Gray[10] who was unable to arrive at a definite conclusion concerning either the mechanism or the importance of this peripheral mechanism for respiratory stimulation. Experiments[11, 12] indicate that there are no specific receptors sensitive to chemical changes involved in the respiratory stimulation resulting from contraction of the leg muscles but that the local chemical changes associated with exercise augment the proprioceptive impulses from the joints of the extremities.

There is evidence that respiration may be stimulated in exercise by a powerful reflex originating in chemoreceptors bathed by mixed venous blood. These receptors may be located in close relation to the first portion of the pulmonary artery.[13] If this is confirmed, it will constitute a mechanism that makes respiration directly responsive to the metabolic changes occurring in working muscles, something that has long been sought.

Severe muscular exercise causes the body temperature to rise, and elevation of the body temperature by means of hot baths may cause a considerable increase in the minute volume of respiration.[14]

Comroe[15] evaluates the contribution of the rise in body temperature to the hyperpnea of exercise as follows: "The temperature rise is certainly not responsible for the onset of the hyperventilation, for the onset of the former is too slow. The few continuous measurements of rectal temperature made during exercise show that temperature may rise within 1 to 2 minutes, certainly within 5 minutes. Since in steady state exercise, the hyperpnea reaches its maximum before the temperature reaches its peak, the temperature rise cannot be largely responsible for the hyperpnea. Furthermore, the temperature rise varies in different individuals performing the same amount of work. Yet it is difficult to escape the conclusion that fever must be of great importance in explaining the hyperventilation that occurs in very strenuous exertion when the body temperature rises dramatically. It is also very likely that the temperature increase can explain the long recovery period following muscular exercise for the body temperature and respiration return to normal at about the same time; except for the first three minutes after exercise (when the respiratory volume falls rapidly), the temperature and respiration curves are parallel."

The manner in which a rise in body temperature stimulates the respiratory center is uncertain; among the possibilities that have been suggested are (1) direct stimulation of the respiratory center, (2) stimulation of cortical centers or the carotid and aortic bodies, (3) other reflex pathways, and (4) the effect of increased temperature on the acidity and other physicochemical properties of the blood.

Among the other factors that have been suggested as contributing to the increased breathing during exercise are impulses from the cerebral cortex and the liberation of epinephrine into the blood.

The difficulty with past attempts to explain the cause of the increased breathing during exercise has been that none of the factors just discussed can increase breathing to the level observed in severe exercise. Gray[10] has analyzed these factors both separately and in combination and has proposed a multifactor theory of respiratory control in which the total effect of these factors is determined by an algebraic relation among the separate factors. Thus each factor makes its own contribution, and no one factor is solely responsible. This concept promises to furnish a more nearly adequate explanation of the regulation of breathing than has heretofore been available. Grodins[16] has analyzed the problem of the stimulus to breathing during exercise mathematically and suggests the operation of a specific exercise stimulus, originating in the working muscles and proportional to the metabolic rate. He believes this stimulus, the nature of which is uncertain (perhaps muscle temperature), is additive to the known chemical stimuli.

The problem of the factors responsible for the increased breathing in exercise has been considered in a number of recent reviews, including those by Dejours[17] and by Hornbein.[18] The mounting evidence in favor of a major role of neurogenic influences originating in the region of the exercising muscles is presented in a series of papers.[19, 20, 21]

## Nature of "second wind"

Although so-called "second wind" is not entirely or perhaps even primarily a respiratory adjustment, it is discussed at this point because its outstanding feature is a dramatic relief of the respiratory distress that exists prior to the adjustment.

An excellent description of the subjective aspects of the situation before and after the onset of second wind has been given by Schneider:[3]

"During violent exercise, such as running or rowing, there is frequently developed a feeling of distress with which is associated considerable breathlessness; but if the exercise be continued, this distress disappears and may be replaced by a sense of great relief. When this change occurs we say we have our 'second wind.'

"The symptoms that precede second wind are varied. There may be a look of distress on the face, often thought of as an anxious expression. The head may throb and swim. The breathing is rapid and comparatively shallow; the pulse is rapid and fluttering or irregular. The person may feel a sense of constriction around the chest, but outstanding among the symptoms is the feeling of breathlessness. Muscle pains sometimes occur.

"With the onset of second wind the breathlessness and discomfort sometimes disappear quite suddenly. The look of distress disappears from the face; the head becomes clearer; and the muscles seem to react with renewed vigor. The breathing becomes easier, the minute volume is usually reduced, the frequency retarded, and the depth increased. Even the heart action may change; its beat becomes slower and regular. Some find that a rise in body temperature and sweating also accompany second wind. The man can now continue his exertion with comparative comfort. There are individual differences in the way adjustments are made; in some persons the sensation of the relief coming with the second wind is very definite, while in others it may be so indefinite as to pass unrecognized."

The physiological basis of second wind is not entirely clear. It almost certainly represents the coordinated adjustment of a number of functions; it must not be confused with the steady state,* although the achievement of a steady state is doubtless one of the factors involved. A survey of the changes, both subjective and objective, that occur with the onset of second wind gives some indication of the possible basis as well as of the complexity of the phenomenon.

1. Respiration
   (a) Relief of dyspnea (feeling of breathlessness)
   (b) Reduction in rate and minute volume of breathing
   (c) Reduction in alveolar carbon dioxide pressure
   (d) Decrease in oxygen consumption and achievement of a steady state
2. Heart
   (a) Decrease in heart rate and more regular rhythm
3. Muscles
   (a) Relief of swelling that often occurs (this may be delayed)
   (b) Relief of muscle pain
4. Temperature regulation
   (a) Rise in temperature of active muscles
   (b) Appearance of sweating
5. Brain
   (a) Disappearance of sensations of dizziness, etc.

An analysis of these changes gives some insight into the nature of second wind. Since it ordinarily appears only in rather strenuous exercise and

---

*The steady state* is the condition in which oxygen intake is adequate to meet oxygen requirements, so that no further accumulation of lactic acid and oxygen debt takes place.

may fail to appear in exceptionally well-trained athletes, it apparently represents the achievement of a comprehensive equilibrium that was absent in the initial stages of exertion. The initial dyspnea is probably the result of an intense reflex drive to the respiratory center originating in the exercising limbs that are working under partially anaerobic conditions. The outpouring of lactic acid into the blood not only contributes to the dyspnea but by decomposing bicarbonate also causes a temporary increase in the output of carbon dioxide and in the alveolar carbon dioxide pressure. With the achievement of a steady state that often coincides with the onset of second wind, metabolic conditions in the working muscles become more nearly normal, resulting in a decrease in the production of lactic acid and in the reflex drive to the respiratory center. The reported *decrease* in oxygen consumption is difficult to explain; one might expect rather an increase resulting from more adequate oxygen supply to the working muscles. With the reduction in respiratory rate, the oxygen requirement of the respiratory muscles is reduced, and this may afford a partial explanation of the decrease in total oxygen consumption. Another possible factor is that the increased efficiency of the exercising muscles reduces their oxygen requirement.

The decreased heart rate is undoubtedly associated with the increase in stroke volume, although the suddenness of its onset indicates that additional factors, as yet unidentified, are involved.

The changes that occur in the exercising muscles may eventually be found to be the basic factor in second wind. Of particular significance are the experiments of Berner and associates[22] who made continuous recordings of rectal and axillary temperatures and of respiration during the performance of work on a stationary bicycle. They found that second wind developed earlier the warmer the room and the heavier the work done. If the room temperature was low or if the subject was cooled by fans, the onset of second wind was delayed or prevented entirely. Since there was no particular correlation between the occurrence of second wind and the rectal temperature or the appearance of sweating, the authors concluded that the temperature of the working muscles, not the temperature of the body as a whole, is the determining factor. Their explanation that the beneficial effect of the rise in muscle temperature is caused by the resulting improvement in the ability of the muscle to remove lactic acid is not convincing. In view of the sudden onset of second wind, it is more likely that the relief of respiratory distress is due to removal of or diminution in a reflex drive originating in the muscles. The complete explanation of the influence of muscle temperature on the development of second wind must await further study. It is of interest in this connection that in the experiments of Berner and associates just referred to second wind usually involved two factors—relief of respiratory distress and a feeling that the performance of work was easier. The relative emphasis placed on these two factors varied from subject to subject and even in different experiments on the same subject. Finally, although the relief of respiratory distress usually coincided with a fall in the minute volume of breathing, this was not invariably true, so that the view that the second wind is entirely a matter of relief of respiratory distress was not substantiated.[23]

It is obvious that second wind is a complex phenomenon involving physiological adjustments of many types and that much additional work is needed before a complete analysis will be possible.

### Advanced study topics

1. Why is predominantly costal breathing in exercise less efficient than predominantly diaphragmatic breathing?
2. Review the recent literature on pulmonary ventilation in current issues of *Respiration*.
3. Describe a respiration spirometer and its uses.
4. Work continuously until either second wind or a stitch in the side occurs and fully describe the episode.
5. Evaluate breathing exercises.

### References

1. McKerrow, C. B., and Otis, A. B.: Oxygen cost of hyperventilation, J. Appl. Physiol. 9:375, 1956.
2. Schneider, E. C., and Ring, G. C.: The influence of a moderate amount of physical training on the respiratory exchange and breathing during physical exercise, Am. J. Physiol. 91:103, 1929.
3. Schneider, E. C.: Physiology of muscular activity, ed. 2, Philadelphia, 1939, W. B. Saunders Co.
4. Gordon, B., Levine, S. A., and Wilmaers, A.: Observations on a group of marathon runners, Arch. Int. Med. 33:425, 1924.
5. Bresnahan, G. T., and Tuttle, W. W.: Track and field athletics, ed. 3, St. Louis, 1950, The C. V. Mosby Co.
6. Krogh, A., and Lindhard, J.: A comparison between voluntary and electrically induced muscular work in man, J. Physiol. 51:182, 1917.
7. Young, A. C.: Neural control of respiration. In Ruch, T. C., and Patton, H. D., editors: Physiology and Biophysics, ed. 19, Philadelphia, 1965, W. B. Saunders Co.
8. Barcroft, J., and Margaria R.: Some effects of carbonic acid on the character of human respiration, J. Physiol. 72:174, 1931.

9. Comroe, J. H., Jr., and Schmidt, C. F.: Reflexes from the limbs as a factor in the hyperpnea of muscular exercise, Am. J. Physiol. 138:536, 1943.
10. Gray, J. S.: Pulmonary ventilation and its physiological regulation, Springfield, Ill., 1950, Charles C Thomas, Publisher.
11. Dejours, P., Mithoefer, J. C., and Raynaud, J.: Evidence against the existence of specific ventilatory chemoreceptors in the legs, J. Appl. Physiol. 10:367, 1957.
12. Dejours, P., Mithoefer, J. C., and Labrousse, Y.: Influence of local chemical change on ventilatory stimulus from the legs during exercise, J. Appl. Physiol. 10:372, 1957.
13. Riley, R. L.: Pulmonary function in relation to exercise. In Johnson, W. R., editor: Science and medicine of exercise and sports, New York, 1960, Harper & Row, Publishers.
14. Landis, E. M., Long, W. L., Dunn, J. W. Jackson, C. L., and Meyer, U.: Studies on the effects of baths on man. III. Effects of hot baths on respiration, blood and urine, Am. J. Physiol. 76:35, 1926.
15. Comroe, J. H., Jr.: The hypernea of muscular exercise, Physiol. Rev. 24:319, 1944.
16. Grodins, F. S.: Analysis of factors concerned in regulation of breathing in exercise, Physiol. Rev. 30:220, 1956.
17. Dejours, P.: Control of respiration in muscular exercise. In Field, J., editor: Handbook of physiology. Section 3, Respiration, vol. 1, Washington, D. C., 1964, American Physiological Society, p. 631.
18. Hornbein, T. F.: The chemical regulation of ventilation. In Ruch, T. C., and Patton, H. D., editors: Physiology and biophysics, ed. 19, Philadelphia, 1965, W. B. Saunders Co.

19. Kao, F. F., Michel, C. C., and Mei, S. S.: Carbon dioxide and pulmonary ventilation in muscular exercise, J. Appl. Physiol. **19**:1075, 1964.

20. Asmussen, E., and Nielsen, M.: Experiments on nervous factors controlling respiration and circulation during exercise employing blocking of the blood flow, Acta Physiol. Scand. **60**:103, 1964.

21. Asmussen, E., Johansen, S. H., Jørgensen, M., and Nielsen, M.: On the nervous factors controlling respiration and circulation during exercise. Experiments with curarization, Acta Physiol. Scand. **63**:343, 1965.

22. Berner, G. E., Garret, C. C., Jones, D. C., and Noer, R. J.: The effect of external temperature on second wind, Am. J. Physiol. **76**:586, 1926.

23. MacKeith, N. W., Pembrey, M. S., Spurrall, W. R., Warner, E. C., and Westlake, H. J. W. J.: Observations on the adjustment of the human body to muscular work, Proc. Roy. Soc., London, sB. **95**:413, 1924.

# 16

# Gas exchange and transport

## Physiological applications of the gas laws

The exchange of gases in the lungs and in the tissue capillaries is due entirely to the physical force of diffusion. Accordingly some knowledge of the elementary laws that govern the behavior of gases is essential for an understanding of gas exchange in the body.

Gas molecules are characterized by random movement at high velocity. A consequence of the random molecular motion is that a gas tends to expand and fill any space that is available to it. If the concentration of gas molecules is greater at point A than at point B, the average number of molecules moving from A toward B will be greater than the number moving from B toward A. In more general terms gas molecules *diffuse* from a point of higher concentration to a point of lower concentration. When rapidly moving gas molecules strike the walls of a containing vessel or other type of restraining influence such as a membrane, they exert force against the wall. The force exerted per unit area is called the *pressure* of the gas. In general the magnitude of the pressure exerted by a gas will depend on two factors: (1) the number of impacts per unit time and (2) the velocity of each impact. The impact velocity depends on the temperature of the gas, while the frequency of impacts depends on the concentration of molecules as well as on their average velocity. Since gas pressure is the driving force that causes diffusion of gases from one point to another, it is customary in physiological discussions to consider the pressures rather than the concentrations of gases. Thus at sea level the barometric pressure is 760 mm. Hg. The pressures of oxygen, nitrogen, and carbon dioxide in atmospheric air may be calculated as follows:

(1) Oxygen concentration = 20.93%

$$\text{Oxygen pressure} = \frac{20.93}{100} \times 760 = 159.1 \text{ mm. Hg}$$

(2) Nitrogen concentration = 79%

$$\text{Nitrogen pressure} = \frac{79}{100} \times 760 = 600.4 \text{ mm. Hg}$$

(3) Carbon dioxide concentration = 0.03%

$$\text{Carbon dioxide pressure} = \frac{0.03}{100} \times 760 = 0.2 \text{ mm. Hg}$$

A further generalization may be drawn from these calculations. In a mixture of gases each gas exerts its pressure independently of the presence of other gases and in proportion to its concentration in the mixture. This is known as the law of partial pressures.

If a gas mixture is moist, the water vapor exerts a pressure proportional to its concentration and to the temperature of the gas. This influences the pressures exerted by the other gases in the mixture. For example, if the atmospheric air is completely saturated with moisture and its temperature is 20° C., the pressure of the water vapor is 17.4 mm. Hg. The combined pressure of the other gases is then 760 – 17.4 = 742.6 mm. Hg, and the partial pressure of each gas is reduced proportionately.

Alveolar air is normally almost completely saturated with moisture at body temperature (37° C.), and the water vapor pressure is about 45 mm. Hg. Accordingly the pressures of the other alveolar gases are as follows:

$$(1) \text{ Oxygen} = \frac{14.5}{100} \times (760 - 45) = 103.7 \text{ mm. Hg}$$

$$(2) \text{ Carbon dioxide} = \frac{5.5}{100} \times (760 - 45) = 39.3 \text{ mm. Hg}$$

$$(3) \text{ Nitrogen} = \frac{80}{100} \times (760 - 45) = 572 \text{ mm. Hg}$$

For convenience the alveolar pressures of oxygen and carbon dioxide are usually considered to be 100 and 40 mm. Hg, respectively.

If a gas is in contact with a liquid in which it is soluble, the gas molecules diffuse into the liquid. The dissolved molecules likewise move in all directions so that some of them escape from the liquid. When equilibrium between the gas and the liquid is reached, equal numbers of gas molecules are entering and leaving the liquid per unit of time. The liquid is said to be saturated with the gas at the existing pressure of the gas. If the gas pressure is increased, more gas molecules dissolve in the liquid until a new equilibrium is reached; and conversely, if the gas pressure is decreased, dissolved molecules leave the liquid. Thus the concentration of gas molecules dissolved in a liquid is proportional to the pressure of the gas to which the liquid is exposed (Henry's law). The gas concentration is also influenced by the solubility of the gas in the liquid and by the temperature.

The "pressure" of a gas dissolved in a liquid is actually a measure of the tendency of the gas to escape from the liquid and is usually referred to as the "tension" of the dissolved gas. Thus if water is exposed to oxygen at a pressure of 100 mm. Hg, the oxygen tension in the water at equilibrium is 100 mm. Hg. The actual *concentration* of dissolved oxygen molecules depends on the solubility of oxygen in water and on the temperature.

The tendency of a gas to diffuse from a point of higher pressure to one of lower pressure is given a quantitative significance by the use of the term "diffusion gradient," which is defined as the *difference* in gas pressure between two points (expressed in mm. Hg). It is this difference in pressure, not the absolute values of the pressure at the two points, that is the driving force in gas diffusion. For example, if the gas pressure at point A is 100 mm. Hg and the gas pressure at point B is 40 mm. Hg, the diffusion gradient between the two points is 100 – 40 = 60 mm. Hg. It is obvious that the diffusion gradient could be increased either by increasing the gas pressure at point A or by decreasing it at point B (or both).

It is now possible to consider the quantitative aspects of gas diffusion in the lungs and in the capillaries of tissues. The manner in which diffusion is modified by local factors will also be pointed out.

## Gas exchange in the lungs

The pressure of oxygen in the alveolar air is approximately 100 mm. Hg, and the oxygen tension in the mixed venous blood (the blood pumped into the pulmonary vessels from the right ventricle) averages about 40 mm. Hg. The oxygen diffusion gradient is 100 – 40 = 60 mm. Hg, and oxygen passes rapidly from the alveolar air into the pulmonary capillary blood. It was thought at one time that the blood leaves the pulmonary capillaries with an oxygen tension 5 to 15 mm. Hg below that of the alveolar air, and various explanations were offered for the apparent failure of the oxygen diffusion to reach an equilibrium. More recent data indicate that the oxygen tension of the blood leaving the lungs is probably between 95 and 100 mm. Hg.[1] It is thought that diffusion equilibrium between alveolar air and pulmonary capillary blood is virtually complete, the slightly lower oxygen tension in the arterial blood being due primarily to the admixture of small amounts of blood that escape aeration in the lungs.

The carbon dioxide pressure in the alveolar air is approximately 40 mm. Hg in the resting subject. The carbon dioxide tension of the mixed venous blood is variable but is usually 5 or 6 mm. Hg higher than that of the alveolar air. The carbon dioxide diffusion gradient is quite small in comparison with that of oxygen, but the blood leaving the lungs is in practically complete equilibrium with the alveolar air; that is, the carbon dioxide pressures of the alveolar and of the arterial blood are practically the same. This is best explained on the basis of the great solubility of carbon dioxide in the membrane, which gives it a very high diffusion rate.

## Gas exchange in the tissues

The arterial blood, with an oxygen tension of about 100 mm. Hg and a carbon dioxide tension of about 40 mm. Hg, is pumped by the left ventricle into the systemic arteries. In the capillaries of tissues oxygen diffuses from blood to tissues, and carbon dioxide diffuses from tissues to blood under the driving force of the respective diffusion gradients, just as in the lungs.

A quantitative analysis of gas exchange in the tissues is difficult because of the influence of local factors. If an organ becomes active, for example, its oxygen consumption increases and the average tissue oxygen tension is diminished. This increases the oxygen diffusion gradient from blood to tissues and hastens the diffusion of oxygen. The increased production of carbon dioxide associated with activity likewise accelerates the passage of this gas into the blood. The tissue diffusion gradients are also influenced by the volume flow of blood and the number of open capillaries. Under resting conditions in organs such as skeletal muscles many capillaries are closed. This means that some muscle fibers lie at relatively great distance from an open capillary, so that oxygen must diffuse over a considerable distance. The oxygen tension in these distant muscle fibers is likely to be low as a result. If additional capillaries open, as during exercise, the average distance between any muscle fiber and the nearest capillary is lessened, so that the tissue oxygen tension is raised. This partially offsets the fall in the oxygen tension of tissue that results from the greater rate of oxygen consumption in the active tissues. This point is illustrated by Fig. 39 and is amplified in subsequent discussions.

The oxygen tension in the tissue cells is influenced not only by the rate at which the cells are using oxygen and by their distance from the nearest capillary but also by their location relative to the arterial or the venous end of their nearest capillary. Assume for the sake of simplicity that a particular cell is supplied by one capillary only, that the length of the capillary is great in comparison to the diameter of the cell, and that the blood oxygen tension falls linearly as the blood flows through the capillary. It is clear

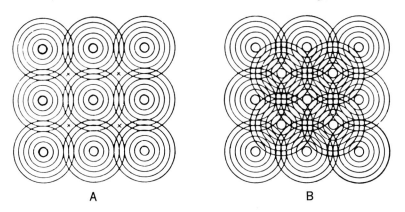

A            B

**Fig. 39. A,** Area with nine open capillaries. Each concentric circle represents a drop of 5 mm. Hg oxygen tension from that in the capillary, which is 30 mm. Hg. The X's represent areas of zero oxygen tension. **B,** Thirteen capillaries open in the same area. Most of the tissue is supplied from more than one capillary. There are no areas of zero pressure. (From Barcroft, J.: The respiratory function of the blood, Cambridge, 1925, Cambridge University Press.)

that the most favorable conditions are enjoyed by cells near the capillary and near the arterial rather than the venous end of the capillary, while cells far from the capillary and nearer the venous than the arterial end of the capillary are in the least favorable situation. The term "lethal corner" has been applied to the cells in the latter category; in many cases these cells obtain barely sufficient oxygen under normal conditions, and they would be the first to suffer when oxygen becomes less available to the organ.

It should be clear from this discussion that the concept of a "tissue oxygen tension" is a meaningless abstraction. Oxygen tension in a tissue varies from cell to cell and in the same cell from time to time.

The diffusion of carbon dioxide from the tissues into the blood is subject to the same influences. Because of the high diffusion rate of carbon dioxide, it is probable that its tension in the tissues seldom exceeds that in the venous blood very greatly. The value of the diffusion gradient is probably about 5 to 10 mm. Hg under most conditions.

## Transport of oxygen by the blood

*Reaction between oxygen and hemoglobin.* Each 100 ml. of arterial blood contains on the average about 20 ml. of oxygen. At the oxygen tension of arterial blood and at body temperature, only about 0.2 ml. of oxygen can dissolve in this volume of blood, so that 99% of the oxygen must exist in some form other than physical solution. This nondissolved oxygen exists in loose chemical combination with the pigment hemoglobin. Dissolved oxygen reacts reversibly with hemoglobin according to the equation $Hb + O_2 \rightleftharpoons HbO_2$, in which Hb is the symbol for a molecule of reduced hemoglobin (hemoglobin not combined with oxygen) and $HbO_2$ represents a molecule of oxyhemoglobin (hemoglobin combined with oxygen). Two points concerning this reaction are worthy of emphasis. First, the combination of oxygen with hemoglobin is not a true oxidation but a loose, easily reversible combination. Second, the reaction is of the mass action type; that is, its velocity is proportional to the product of the active masses of the reacting constituents. Since the amount of hemoglobin remains fairly constant, the direction of the reaction is actually determined by the concentration or rather the tension of oxygen. If the concentration of dissolved oxygen decreases (as in the capillaries of tissue due to diffusion of oxygen from the blood into the tissues), the oxygen tension falls, and the reaction $Hb + O_2 \rightleftharpoons HbO_2$ proceeds to the left, so that more oxygen goes into solution and is available for diffusion out into the tissues. In the capillaries of the lungs the diffusion of oxygen from the alveolar air raises the oxygen tension in the blood, and the reaction proceeds to the right, with the result that almost all Hb is converted to $HbO_2$.

*Oxygen dissociation curve.* The proportion of the hemoglobin that is combined with oxygen is expressed as percent saturation. If, for example, three fourths of the hemoglobin molecules are combined with oxygen in a sample of blood, the oxygen saturation is 75%. This is a more convenient characterization of the degree of oxygenation than is the oxygen *content* of the blood, since the content varies not only with the oxygen tension but also with the hemoglobin concentration. The oxygen saturation of different samples of blood having widely different hemoglobin concentrations is the same if all samples have the same oxygen tension. Suppose, for example, that a sample of blood from a normal subject has a hemoglobin concentration of 15 grams per 100 ml., whereas the blood of an anemic subject has only 7.5 grams per 100 ml. When saturated with oxygen at 100 mm. Hg, the blood of the normal subject will have approximately 20 vol.% oxygen and that of the anemic subject about 10 vol.% oxygen, yet the oxygen tension and the percentage saturation of the two samples are the same.

Although the oxygen saturation of blood is determined primarily by the oxygen tension, it is influenced by two other factors—temperature and acidity. An increase in temperature or acidity favors the reaction $HbO_2 \rightarrow$ $Hb + O_2$, so that the oxygen saturation at a given oxygen tension is decreased. A fall in temperature or acidity has the opposite effect.

If temperature and acidity are held constant, the relation between oxygen tension and oxygen saturation may be determined. Samples of blood having the same hemoglobin content are exposed to gas mixtures having different tensions of oxygen. When equilibrium has been reached, the oxygen content of each sample is determined. The oxygen content of a sample of blood completely saturated with oxygen is used as a reference; the saturation of this sample is 100%. A sample having one half the oxygen content of the reference sample is 50% saturated, and so on. If the percent saturation is plotted against the oxygen tension, a curve called the *oxygen dissociation curve* is obtained (Fig. 40). The use of this curve makes possible a quantitative analysis of the gas exchange in the lungs and in the capillaries of tissues during both rest and exercise.

Reference to the dissociation curve indicates that blood returning to the lungs with an average oxygen tension of 40 mm. Hg is approximately 60% saturated. As oxygen diffuses from the alveoli into the blood, the oxygen tension rises steadily, with the result that more and more of the reduced hemoglobin combines with oxygen to form oxyhemoglobin. The blood leaves the lungs with an oxygen tension of about 100 mm. Hg and an oxygen saturation of about 98%. No oxygen is lost from the blood until it reaches the capillaries of tissues. There the blood is separated by the very thin capillary membrane from tissue fluid having an oxygen tension of about 40 mm. Hg (resting conditions). The dissolved oxygen in the blood immediately begins to diffuse through the capillary membrane. Since the amount of dissolved oxygen in the blood is very small (about 1% of the total), the oxygen tension drops as oxygen diffuses into the tissues. The fall in blood oxygen tension initiates the reaction $HbO_2 \rightarrow Hb + O_2$, and the oxygen thus liberated goes into solution, raising the oxygen tension and increasing the rate of diffusion. This process of diffusion of the oxygen made available by the breakdown of oxyhemoglobin continues as the blood flows along the capillary, and the blood finally leaves the capillary with an oxygen tension

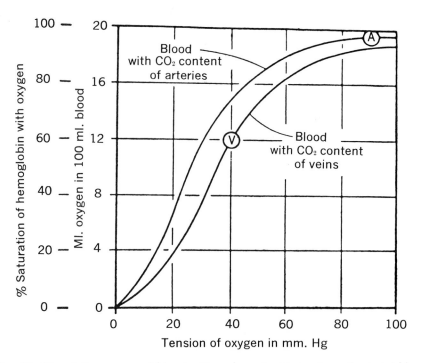

**Fig. 40.** Dissociation curves of blood with carbon dioxide tensions of arterial blood (upper curve) and of venous blood (lower curve). Point **A** represents arterial blood and point **V** the average venous blood in a resting subject. (From Carlson, A. J., and Johnson, V. E.: The machinery of the body, ed. 2, Chicago, 1941, University of Chicago Press.)

of about 40 mm. Hg and an oxygen saturation of about 60%. It is apparent that in passing through the capillary, the blood has lost 98 − 60 = 38% of its total oxygen; this fraction of the total oxygen that is delivered to the tissues is known as the *coefficient of oxygen utilization*. It is obvious that an increase in this coefficient would increase the volume of oxygen delivered to the tissues in unit time. It will be shown later that this occurs as one of the adaptive processes during exercise. Under conditions of strenuous exertion, up to 90% of the oxygen may be removed from blood flowing through the contracting muscles. The large amount of oxygen remaining in the venous blood under resting conditions thus constitutes a factor of safety that can be called on in times of increased need.

Reference to Fig. 40 indicates that the carbon dioxide tension influences the position of the dissociation curve. An increase in the carbon dioxide tension shifts the curve to the right, so that the oxygen saturation at any given oxygen tension is diminished—in other words, carbon dioxide "drives" oxygen out of the blood. The same is true for any acid (carbon dioxide acts as an acid since it combines with water to form carbonic acid). In the capillaries of tissues carbon dioxide enters the blood from the tissues and increases the breakdown of oxyhemoglobin. During exercise this effect is greatly increased because of the larger amounts of acid metabolites formed in the active muscles. In the lungs the diffusion of carbon dioxide into the alveoli lowers the acidity of the blood, which hastens the combination of oxygen with hemoglobin.

**Oxygen exchange during exercise.** Most of the physiological adjustments during exercise are directed toward the delivery of a greater volume of oxygen to the working muscles. The increase in blood flow through the muscles has been discussed in previous chapters. For this adjustment to be fully effective, there must be provision for maintaining a normal saturation of the blood with oxygen in spite of the more rapid blood flow through the lungs. Ideally this would mean that blood would leave the lungs about 98% saturated with oxygen, as under resting conditions. Actually very few determinations have been made of the saturation of the arterial blood during exercise, and these few reports are not in close agreement, perhaps because of differences in techniques. The problem may be stated as follows: The blood flowing through the lungs must remain in the pulmonary capillaries a minimal length of time to allow diffusion of oxygen into the blood from the alveolar air. If the cardiac output in exercise should be 4 times as great as during rest, the blood would, on the average, spend only one fourth as much time in the pulmonary capillaries, and oxygen exchange would no doubt be incomplete. This does not happen because one of the adjustments to exercise is the dilatation of the small vessels in the lungs and probably the opening of vessels that were closed during rest.[2] This permits an increase in the *volume* of blood flowing through the lungs each minute without a corresponding increase in the *velocity* of blood flow. It has been estimated that oxygen exchange in the lungs is probably adequate to bring about normal saturation of the blood with oxygen so long as the oxygen uptake does not exceed 4 liters per minute (about 12 to 16 times the consumption of oxygen during resting conditions).

This topic has recently been reinvestigated and the factors involved analyzed in a very clear manner.[3] In light and moderate exercise (400 and 700 kg.-m./min.) both the alveolar and the arterial oxygen tensions rose (1.3 and 5.0 mm. Hg, respectively) and the difference between alveolar and arterial oxygen tension fell from 14.7 mm. Hg at rest to 11.0 mm. Hg during exercise. Since the difference between alveolar oxygen tension and the end-capillary oxygen tension has been shown to be negligible, most of the alveolar-arterial oxygen tension difference is the result of (1) venous admixture (for example, from the bronchial veins)—about 10 to 15%—and (2) uneven distribution of alveolar ventilation to pulmonary capillary blood flow—about 85 to 90%. The authors attribute the increase in arterial oxygen tension in mild and moderate exercise to improvement in the latter.

The reported decrease in oxygen saturation of the arterial blood in very heavy exercise may be caused in part by inadequate oxygen exchange in the lungs, but a more important factor probably is the effect of the increased acidity and temperature of the blood on the oxyhemoglobin dissociation curve (both factors tend to decrease the affinity of hemoglobin for oxygen).

In the capillaries of the working muscles local metabolic conditions greatly facilitate the delivery of large amounts of oxygen. In the first place the lowered oxygen tension of tissues, which results from the increased rate of oxygen consumption in the active tissues, increases the oxygen diffusion gradient between blood and tissues. At the same time the large quantities of carbon dioxide and lactic acid produced in the contracting muscles diffuse into the capillaries where they facilitate the breakdown of oxyhemoglobin with the liberation of freely diffusible oxygen. The local rise in temperature resulting from the increased production of heat of active muscles has the same effect on the breakdown of oxyhemoglobin as does the increased acidity. The net result of these local factors is to increase the coefficient of oxygen utilization from the resting value of about 0.3 up to 0.7 to 0.9. For an excellent experimental analysis of the relation between the saturation of the venous blood leaving working muscles and the ratio of aerobic to anaerobic metabolism in the muscles see Pernow et al.[4]

The interplay of the various factors that influence the delivery of oxygen to the muscles during exercise may be illustrated by the following quantitative example: (1) The cardiac output may be increased 4 times. (2) Dilatation of muscle vessels with compensatory vasoconstriction elsewhere may increase the relative blood flow through the muscle as much as fivefold. Factors 1 and 2 together may increase the total blood flow through the active muscles to 20 times the resting value. (3) The coefficient of oxygen utilization may be increased to 3 times the resting value (which is usually low in skeletal muscles). Thus the combination of all three factors permits an oxygen delivery to the muscles that may be $4 \times 5 \times 3 = 60$ times as great as during rest. These are conservative figures. There is good evidence that the consumption of oxygen during maximal activity of muscles may be as much as 75 to 100 times that of the resting muscles.

## Factors limiting the supply of oxygen to exercising muscles

This important and complex problem has been analyzed mathematically by Riley[5] with some interesting results. Theoretically the limiting factor might be the capacity for ventilating the lungs or for pumping blood. Not only is there a limit to the increase in pulmonary ventilation and cardiac output that can be achieved in exercise but there is also a definite energy cost of breathing and of pumping blood that might become excessive in strenuous exercise.

There is good evidence that pulmonary ventilation is still capable of further increase when the maximal cardiac output has been reached, so that the supply of oxygen to exercising muscles is not ordinarily limited by ventilatory capacity. By implication, circulatory rather than respiratory function is the limiting factor, but this does not necessarily mean that cardiac activity is inadequate. Astrand[6] believes that the capacity of the heart to increase the cardiac output is greater than is the ability of the muscles to receive the blood, at least in exercise that involves only a portion of the musculature, as in running. The evidence for this view is that oxygen intake is lower during maximal work with the arms than during maximal work with the legs and lower during maximal work with the legs alone than during maximal work with the arms and legs combined. The explanation may be that the capacity of the muscles for receiving blood is dependent on their ability to return blood to the heart, and this in turn is dependent on the pumping action of the skeletal muscles discussed in an earlier chapter. The greater the mass of muscles involved in exercise, the greater the contribution of the "muscle pump" to the venous return, and hence the greater the capacity of the muscles to receive an increased cardiac output.

It is also conceivable that maximal dilatation of the muscle vessels might still fall short of accommodating all the blood flow that the cardiac output would support, especially when exercise involves only a small proportion of the total muscle mass.

An additional factor that may limit the blood flow to muscles is the necessity for diverting a portion of the cardiac output to increasing the blood flow in the skin vessels for purposes of heat dissipation. The importance of this factor would depend not only on the severity and duration of the exercise but also on the environmental temperature and humidity.

In an excellent study of the factors that determine the "maximal oxygen intake" (the greatest oxygen intake achieved by a subject in response to progressive increase in work load), Mitchell et al.[7] concluded that the increase in cardiac output and the ability of the tissues to extract oxygen from the blood perfusing them (that is, to increase the arteriovenous oxygen difference) are the only factors of importance. They believe that the ability of the vascular bed to accommodate the increased cardiac output is of minor importance and that pulmonary ventilation and gas exchange are never limiting in normal subjects.

Under abnormal circumstances the limiting factor in exercise may be pulmonary ventilation or cardiac output (for example, exercise at high altitude or the presence of respiratory or cardiac disease), and increased exercise tolerance depends on correction of these abnormalities. Under normal conditions, however, increased efficiency of the muscle pump may be as important a result of training as is increased maximal cardiac output.

## Administration of oxygen before, during, and after exercise   ✕

Athletic coaches and trainers frequently administer oxygen to athletes during time-out periods, with the objectives of increasing the rate of recovery from previous exercise and improving the subsequent performance. The rationale of this procedure is based more on testimonials than on experimental evidence.

In laboratory tests nearly all workers agree that the administration of oxygen following exercise has little influence on the rate of recovery. This would be expected since the decrease in cardiac output after the cessation of exercise makes it possible for the blood to remain in the pulmonary capillaries long enough to achieve equilibrium with the alveolar air. There is less agreement concerning the beneficial effects of breathing oxygen just before exercise. It is difficult to explain the occasional report[8] claiming such benefit in view of the fact that the arterial blood is virtually saturated with oxygen when room air is breathed during rest.

By contrast it is fairly generally agreed that the administration of oxygen *during* exercise is beneficial, although there is disagreement concerning the degree of benefit. Opposing viewpoints are presented in reports by Miller[9] and Bannister and Cunningham.[10] Since the administration of oxygen during exercise is not feasible in the usual types of athletic events, the question is of academic rather than practical importance. The psychological aspects of reported benefits from oxygen inhalation during sporting events should not be underestimated.

## Transport of carbon dioxide in the blood

We have seen that nearly all the oxygen present in blood is in a bound form, and the same is true of carbon dioxide. Most of the carbon dioxide in blood is in the form of bicarbonate. Of the remainder, a portion exists in direct combination with hemoglobin (to form a "carbamino" compound), and another portion is in physical solution. The mechanisms involved in the transport of carbon dioxide are best visualized by a description of the events occurring with the uptake of carbon dioxide in the tissue capillaries and its elimination in the lung capillaries.

Blood enters the tissue capillaries with a carbon dioxide tension of about 40 mm. Hg. Under resting conditions the average tissue carbon dioxide tension may be assumed to be perhaps 45 to 50 mm. Hg, and accordingly carbon dioxide diffuses from the tissues into the blood. This increases the carbon dioxide tension in the blood plasma, and some of it therefore diffuses from the plasma into the erythrocytes, where about 20% of the carbon dioxide combines directly with hemoglobin. Another 10% remains in solution, and about 70% combines with water to form carbonic acid. This reaction occurs to only a slight extent in the plasma because it is a very slow reaction unless catalyzed by an enzyme. This enzyme, known as carbonic anhydrase, is present exclusively within the erythrocytes (and in certain other cells such as the kidney tubule cells and the gastric glands cells that secrete hydrochloric acid); none is present in the plasma. The carbonic acid formed under the influence of carbonic anhydrase must be neutralized in order to prevent a dangerous rise in acidity. Some of the neutralization is effected by the buffer action of hemoglobin in the following manner. Hemoglobin is a weak acid, and it exists partly in the form of free acid and partly as the potassium salt of the acid. Since a weak acid and its salt constitute a buffer system, hemoglobin can act in the same manner as any other buffer system. Since hemoglobin is a weaker acid than carbonic acid, the following buffer reaction will take place:

$$KHb + H_2CO_3 \rightleftharpoons HHb + KHCO_3$$

This reaction proceeds from left to right in the tissue capillaries because of the increasing concentration of $H_2CO_3$. The result is the substitution of a weaker acid (HHb) for a stronger acid ($H_2CO_3$) that is the essence of any buffer reaction.

Hemoglobin contributes in a second way to the disposition of the extra carbonic acid by what is known as the isohydric reaction. Not only is hemoglobin an acid but oxyhemoglobin is a stronger acid than is reduced hemoglobin. Thus when oxyhemoglobin gives up its oxygen in the tissue capillaries, it becomes converted to a weaker acid (reduced hemoglobin) and must therefore give up some of the base with which it was combined; this base is then available for neutralizing carbonic acid.

$$K_2HbO_2 + H_2CO_3 \rightleftharpoons KHHb + KHCO_3 + O_2$$

In this reaction the liberation of 1 molecule of oxygen permits the neutralization of 1 molecule of carbon dioxide.

The end result of the reactions within the erythrocytes is the direct combination of about 20% of the extra carbon dioxide with hemoglobin and the conversion of about 70% to bicarbonate. Many of the newly formed bicarbonate ions diffuse out of the erythrocytes into the plasma (in exchange for an equal number of plasma anions—mostly chloride), so that although most of the bicarbonate is formed in the erythrocytes, much of it is transported in the plasma. A small amount of carbonic acid is formed from carbon dioxide in the plasma and is buffered there, mostly by the plasma proteins, to form a little additional bicarbonate. All the reactions just discussed are, of course, exactly reversed in the lung capillaries.

It is apparent that hemoglobin accounts in one way or another for the binding or neutralization of about 90% of the extra carbon dioxide that is taken up by the blood flowing through the tissue capillaries. It is thus almost as important in the transport of carbon dioxide as it is in the transport of oxygen.

A final statement should be made about the blood buffer systems because of a common misunderstanding. The most important blood buffer for carbon dioxide (as carbonic acid) is hemoglobin. The most important blood buffer for all other acids is the bicarbonate system (carbonic acid and its salt, sodium or potassium bicarbonate in the plasma and erythrocytes, respectively). The bicarbonate system obviously cannot buffer carbonic acid since it could not substitute a weaker acid for a stronger one.

The transport of larger amounts of carbon dioxide from the muscles in exercise presents no particular problem since all of the reactions discussed previously can be increased within rather wide limits. The extra lactic acid formed when the oxygen supply is not entirely adequate is buffered by all the blood buffers but chiefly by the bicarbonate system since it is present in the largest amount. This reaction is as follows:

$$HL \text{ (lactic acid)} + NaHCO_3 \rightleftharpoons NaL + H_2CO_3$$
$$H_2CO_3 \rightleftharpoons H_2O + CO_2$$

Since the $CO_2$ formed in the second reaction is "blown off" in the lungs, this is an extremely efficient buffer reaction.

### Advanced study topics

1. Describe the mechanism of hemoglobin function.
2. Review the recent literature on gas exchange and transport in current issues of the *Journal of Physiology.*
3. Describe a method of measuring blood oxygen and carbon dioxide tension.
4. Measure the effects that the breathing of pure oxygen has on various performances.
5. What type of exercise training best increases oxygen transport capacity.

### References

1. Lambertson, C. J., Bunce, P. L., Drabkin, D. L., and Schmidt, C. F.: Relationship of oxygen tension to hemoglobin oxygen saturation in the arterial blood of normal men, J. Appl. Physiol. 4:873, 1952.
2. Roughton, F. J. W.: The average time spent by the blood in the human capillary and its relation to the rates of CO-uptake and elimination in man, Am. J. Physiol. 143:621, 1945.
3. Hesser, C. M., and Matell, G.: Effect of light and moderate exercise on alveolar-arterial $O_2$ tension difference in man, Acta Physiol. Scand. 63:247, 1965.
4. Pernow, B., Wahren, J., and Zetter-quist, S.: Studies on the peripheral circulation and metabolism in man. IV. Oxygen utilization and lactate formation in the legs of healthy young men during strenuous exercise, Acta Physiol. Scand. 64:289, 1965.
5. Riley, R. L.: Pulmonary function in relation to exercise. In Johnson, W. R., editor: Science and medicine of exercise and sports, New York, 1960, Harper & Row, Publishers.
6. Astrand, P. O.: Human physical fitness with special reference to sex and age, Physiol. Rev. 36:307, 1956.
7. Mitchell, J. H., Sproule, B. J., and Chapman, C. B.: The physiological meaning of the maximal oxygen intake test, J. Clin. Invest. 37:538, 1958.
8. Hill, L., and Flack, M.: The influence of oxygen inhalations on muscular work, J. Physiol. 54:292, 1920.
9. Miller, A. T., Jr.: The influence of oxygen administration on the cardiovascular response to exercise, J. Appl. Physiol. 5:165, 1952.
10. Bannister, R. G., and Cunningham, D. J. C.: The effects on the respiration and performance during exercise of adding oxygen to the inspired air, J. Physiol. 125:118, 1954.

# 17

# Effects of exercise on other body functions

Muscular exercise is such a commonplace occurrence that the extent to which it alters the normal, routine activities of the body is seldom realized. Strenuous exercise requires a total mobilization of the body's resources to make possible the tremendous increase in metabolism in the working muscles, and as a result, other less immediately vital functions may suffer. This situation has its counterpart in the curtailment of normal peacetime activities that occurs when a nation engages in war. As simple illustrations one might cite the shunting of blood to the active muscles at the expense of the normal flow to the gastrointestinal tract (which alters the rate of digestion), to the kidneys (with a decrease in the secretion of urine), and to the skin (which interferes with the regulation of body temperature). It is the purpose of this chapter to examine some of these incidental but often important side effects of exercise.

## Blood changes during exercise

The full significance of blood changes during exercise can be appreciated only when they are considered against the background of the overall function of the blood.

The cells of the body can function normally only when they are provided with oxygen and food materials, when their waste products are removed promptly, and when their temperature and acidity are carefully regulated. The maintenance of these stable conditions is the principal function of the blood.

The tissue cells of higher animals are not in direct contact with the external environment. They live in a protected internal environment, the *interstitial fluid*, which surrounds each cell as a thin film. Materials passing in either direction between blood and tissue cells must diffuse through this fluid film. The stabilizing effect of the interstitial fluid is the direct result of its intimate relation to the blood in the capillaries of the tissues. As the cells use oxygen and food materials, more of these substances diffuse from the blood into the interstitial fluid and thence into the cells, and as the cells produce metabolic wastes, these diffuse in the reverse direction, from the cells to the blood. The composition of the blood itself is preserved by its ability to take in oxygen in the lungs and food materials in the liver and intestines and to eliminate carbon dioxide in the lungs and other waste products in the kidneys. The circulation of the blood is thus the basic factor in the maintenance of nearly constant conditions in the tissue cells. During exercise these functions of the blood are strained to the limits of their capacity, and changes may occur in the composition of the blood despite the admirable mechanisms that tend to prevent such changes. Much can be learned about the effects of exercise on the tissue cells by a study of the changes in the blood.

## Changes in the chemical constituents of the blood

The normal concentration of blood glucose (about 100 mg.%) represents a balance between the rates at which glucose is added to the blood (from the liver and the intestines) and removed from the blood by the tissues that use it. This balance is maintained during light and moderate work, so that there is little change in the level of the blood sugar. In more strenuous exertion adrenaline is secreted in large amounts, and this hormone stimulates the delivery of larger amounts of glucose from the liver, so that the concentration of the blood glucose may rise considerably. If the exercise is both strenuous and prolonged, the level of the blood glucose may finally fall below resting levels due to exhaustion of the stores of liver glycogen that give rise to the blood sugar.[1] In short bursts of anaerobic work such as sprints there is ordinarily little change in the concentration of blood glucose either during or after the exertion.

It will be recalled that contracting muscles produce lactic acid when their supply of oxygen is not adequate to meet the energy requirements. The rise in the concentration of blood lactic acid during exercise is, therefore, an indication of the amount of anaerobic metabolism involved. The normal resting concentration of blood lactate is about 5 to 10 mg.% (the reason for the presence of lactic acid in the blood during rest when the oxygen supply is presumably adequate is not clear). At the beginning of exercise the concentration of blood lactate rises because the delivery of oxygen to the muscles cannot be increased immediately. If a steady state is reached, the level of blood lactate ceases to rise and may actually fall as exercise continues. If a steady state is not achieved, blood lactate rises throughout the period of exercise and may reach levels as high as 200 mg.%. When the same subject performs different types of exercise, the extent of the rise in blood lactate is an index of the severity of the work.[2] When several subjects perform the same task, the rise in blood lactate is greater the less the cardiovascular fitness of the subject.[3, 4]

When acids such as carbon dioxide and lactic acid are poured into the blood in increased amounts during exercise, a dangerous rise in blood acidity is prevented by the action of *buffers*, which neutralize the acids. Carbon dioxide presents little difficulty because it is readily eliminated in the lungs. Lactic acid is buffered by the blood bicarbonate, which is accordingly reduced in amount. Very strenuous exercise, especially if it is prolonged, may produce so much lactic acid that the bicarbonate buffer is greatly reduced in amount, and the blood acidity begins to increase rapidly. Exhaustion ordinarily follows soon after. It has been claimed by some that one of the beneficial effects of training is an increase in the amount of buffer in the blood, but this is denied by other workers. There are also conflicting reports concerning improvement in the capacity for exercise as a result of the administration of alkali before exercise.

**Effects of exercise on the blood cells.** Changes in blood cell counts during exercise have been emphasized out of all proportion to their importance, perhaps because of the ease with which the studies can be carried out.

The red blood cell count is frequently increased in the early stages of exercise, probably because of simple hemoconcentration (transfer of fluid from the blood to the tissues). During more prolonged exercise, fluid passes into the blood, and the resulting dilution, of course, lowers the red blood cell count. Very strenuous exertion may also cause an increased rate of destruction of red blood cells due to compression of the capillaries by muscular contraction and to increased velocity of blood flow.[5] This is especially noticeable in persons of sedentary habits who sporadically indulge in exercise.

There is a rather general belief that the number of red blood cells per unit volume of blood is increased by training, but the actual experimental evidence in man is not very convincing.

**White blood cell changes during exercise.** Exercise of any type increases the leukocyte count; even random activity causes a significant rise above the basal level.[6] Following brief periods of strenuous exertion the increase in the white blood cell count is caused primarily by an increased number of lymphocytes, but if the exercise is more prolonged, the further rise in cell count is caused almost entirely by an increase in the neutrophils. The rise in the leukocyte count during exercise is remarkably rapid. Thus a count of 35,000 cells per cubic millimeter of blood (normal count, 5,000 to 8,000) has been recorded immediately following a quarter-mile race lasting less than 1 minute. The most reasonable explanation for the increases in the white blood cell count during exercise is that large numbers of the cells, which at rest are adherent to the walls of the blood vessels, are suddenly washed into the circulation by the increased volume and velocity of blood flow.[7]

The greater the degree of stress associated with exercise, the greater is the rise in the white blood cell count, so that less fit persons show a greater rise than do athletes when the same exercise is performed by both. The reason for this is not at all clear.

Stress of any sort (strenuous exertion, excitement, anxiety, etc.) results in an increased secretion of the hormones of the adrenal cortex, and one of the results produced by these hormones is a decrease in the number of eosinophils in the blood. The maximal effect is usually reached several hours after the stress and serves as a useful index of its severity. Associated with the decrease in eosinophils, there is also a decrease in the numbers of lymphocytes and an increase in the numbers of neutrophils. The mechanism of the production of these changes in leukocytes is not well understood.

## Body temperature during exercise

The body temperature is normally maintained within narrow limits by a balance between the rates of heat production and heat loss. The rate of heat production may be increased very greatly in strenuous exercise, and the rate of heat loss must increase proportionately if the body temperature is to be maintained constant. The two major physiological responses to increased heat production are increased blood flow to the skin (which brings heat to the surface where it can be dissipated) and increased sweating. It will be recalled, however, that the shunting of greater proportions of the cardiac output to the muscles involves compensatory vasoconstriction in other areas, of which the skin is one of the most important. It is apparent that a conflict of interests is involved, so that neither muscles nor skin may receive an optimal blood flow. It is then not surprising that body temperature should rise in exercise, and this was long believed to indicate an inadequate response by the temperature regulating mechanisms. It is now believed that in some way the hypothalamic thermostat may be "reset" to a higher level in exercise and that the body temperature rises to the new set point. The body tolerates the rise in temperature during exercise surprisingly well (possible explanations are given in Chapter 22), and a certain amount of elevation in temperature, especially in the active muscles, is probably beneficial.[8] On the other hand, strenuous exercise, especially when performed under conditions of high environmental temperature and by persons who are not heat acclimatized, may lead to "heat exhaustion" (a form of circulatory collapse resembling shock) or to "heat stroke" (a potentially fatal condition in which the body temperature rises to alarming levels).

The rise in body temperature for a given amount of exercise appears to be less in trained men than in untrained men. There is however considerable variability in individual cases; in one marathon race the runner who was least distressed at the end of the race had a temperature of 104° F.[9] The common belief that the rise in body temperature during exercise is greater in obese subjects because of the insulating effect of the subcutaneous fat is not supported by direct experimental studies.[10]

## Kidney function during exercise

The role of the kidneys in preserving homeostasis during and after the stress of exercise has been discussed in an earlier chapter. Our concern in this section is rather with the ways in which exercise may influence the functioning of the kidneys. The decrease in the rate of formation of urine during exercise caused both by decreased renal blood flow[11] and by increased reabsorption of water in the renal tubules[12] has been mentioned.

Exercise not only affects the volume of the urine formed but also its composition. The urine turns more acid, indicating that some of the excess acid produced in the contracting muscles is eliminated in this way. Glucose may also appear in the urine after exercise because the rise in the concentration of blood glucose results in the filtration of so much glucose that the tubules can no longer reabsorb all of it. Albumin commonly appears in the urine after strenuous exercise, although it is absent in the urine of normal resting subjects. It is believed by some that the appearance of albumin in the urine is caused by increased permeability of the glomerular capillaries, but other experiments[13] indicate that the cause is more complex, involving in addition the effect of the increased acidity of the kidney tissue on the function of the tubules. Aside from the protein just mentioned, there is little or no increase in the amount of protein breakdown products in the urine after exercise, indicating that the common belief that athletes require a higher dietary intake of protein is probably not true.

## Water and salt balance during exercise

A discussion of water and salt balance during exercise appears in Chapter 14.

## Effects of exercise on the digestive system

The traditional belief that exercise interferes with digestion has been investigated in studies on the influence of exercise on the secretion of gastric hydrochloric acid and on the peristaltic movements of the stomach.[14] The results may be briefly summarized as follows: Short, violent exercise and prolonged, exhausting exercise inhibited the secretion of acid and the peristaltic movements of the stomach during and for a short time after the exercise. This was followed by a period during which both the secretion of acid and the motility of the stomach were increased above normal. Mild exercise increased gastric motility and secretion of acid slightly. The authors concluded that exercise has little influence on the ultimate digestive task of the stomach. Depressed activity during and immediately following the period of activity is balanced by a subsequent period of increased activity, and in the end, exercise closely associated with mealtime does not seem detrimental as far as digestion is concerned. It was also observed that repetition of the exercise (that is, training) resulted in a gradual decrease in the effect on gastric secretion and motility. Although it has not been investigated, it is probable that similar changes occur in intestinal secretion and motility.

The ingestion of a full meal may, however, have important effects on the ease and efficiency of athletic performance. Distention of the stomach by raising the pressure in the abdominal cavity may interfere with the descent of the diaphragm in inspiration, thus diminishing the efficiency of the respiratory response to exercise. The influence of the subjective feeling of fullness and lethargy after a large meal on athletic performance has not been studied under controlled conditions. It has been reported, however, that distention of the stomach produced by drinking 1 to 1.5 liters of water just prior to exercise had no effect on cardiovascular response to running on a treadmill or on performance time in swimming and track events.[15]

## Advanced study topics

1. Describe the response of homeostatic mechanisms to exercise.
2. Review the recent literature on the regulation of body functions during exercise in current issues of the *Journal of Experimental Medicine*.
3. Describe a method of measuring blood lactic acid.
4. Observe the effects of a full meal before strenuous exercise on performance and well-being.
5. What recommendation should be made to athletes regarding the intake of extra salt?

## References

1. Dill, D. B., Edwards, H. T., and Mead, S.: Blood sugar regulation in exercise, Am. J. Physiol. **111**:21, 1935.
2. Wells, J. G., Balke, B., and van Fossan, D. D.: Lactic acid accumulation during work. A suggested standardization of work classification, J. Appl. Physiol. **10**: 51, 1957.
3. Bock, A. V., van Caulaert, C., Dill, D. B., Fölling, A., and Hurxthal, L. M.: Studies in muscular activity. III. Dynamical changes occurring in man at work, J. Physiol. **66**:136, 1928.
4. Dill, D. B., Talbott, J. H., and Edwards, H. T.: Studies in muscular activity. VI. Response of several individuals to a fixed task, J. Physiol. **69**:267, 1930.
5. Brown, G. O.: Blood destruction during exercise, J. Exper. Med. **36**:481, 1922; **37**:113, 187, 207, 1923.
6. Sturgis, C. C., and Bethell, F. H.: Quantitative and qualitative variations in normal leukocytes, Physiol. Rev. **23**: 279, 1943.
7. Leslie, C. J., and Zwemer, R. M.: The influence of muscular activity on physiologic leukocytosis, Am. J. M. Sc. **190**: 92, 1935.
8. Berner, G. E., Garrett, C. C., Jones, D. C., and Noer, R. J.: The effect of external temperature on second wind, Am. J. Physiol. **76**:586, 1926.
9. Savage, W. L.: Physiological and pathological effects of severe exercise (the marathon race), Am. Phys. Ed. Rev. **16**:1, 1911.
10. Miller, A. T., Jr., and Blyth, C. S.: Lack of insulating effect of body fat during exposure to internal and external heat loads, J. Appl. Physiol. **12**:17, 1958.
11. Barclay, J. A., Cooke, W. T., Kenney, R. A., and Nutt, M. E.: The effect of exercise on the renal blood flow in man, J. Physiol. **104**:14, 1945.
12. Klisiecki, A., Pickford, M., Rothschild, P., and Verney, E. B.: II. The absorption and excretion of water by the mammal,. Proc. Roy. Soc., London, sB **112**:521, 1933.
13. Javitt, N., and Miller, A. T., Jr.: Mechanism of exercise proteinuria, J. Appl. Physiol. **4**:834, 1952.
14. Hellebrandt, F. A., and associates: Studies in the influence of exercise on the digestive work of the stomach, Am. J. Physiol. **107**:348, 355, 364, 370, 1934.
15. Little, C. C., Strayhorn, H., and Miller, A. T., Jr.: Effect of water ingestion on capacity for exercise, Res. Quart. **20**: 398, 1949.

# Part three

# Metabolic and environmental aspects of exercise

# 18

# *Metabolism in exercise*

Muscular exercise requires an increase in the metabolic reactions that supply the energy for all the varied activities of living cells. The immediate source of energy is thought to be the breakdown of high-energy compounds such as adenosine triphosphate (ATP), but the ultimate source is the oxidation of foodstuffs that makes possible the restoration of the high-energy compounds. The increased requirement for the transport of oxygen to working muscles and for the transport of carbon dioxide and other metabolites from the muscles involves adjustments in respiration and circulation. The increased heat production in exercise necessitates adjustments in the temperature-regulating mechanisms. The diversion of blood to the working muscles and to the skin (for temperature regulation) results in alterations in the functions of the kidneys. In these and many other ways the entire body is affected by the increased metabolism that provides the energy for exercise. The central features of the metabolic changes are discussed in this chapter, and the changes in other physiological activities are discussed in succeeding chapters.

## *Resting metabolism*

The intensity of metabolism is ordinarily measured in terms of the amount of oxygen consumed or of the amount of heat produced per unit of time. Since the measurement of heat production requires very elaborate equipment, it is seldom used, but it can be calculated from measured values of oxygen consumption and is expressed as Calories (or kilocalories). The consumption of 1 liter of oxygen is associated with the production of about 5 Calories of heat. The amount of oxygen consumed per unit of time during rest depends on a number of factors, the most important of which is body weight. In order to compare the metabolism of large and small persons the metabolic rate is often expressed as the amount of oxygen consumed (or heat produced) per kilogram of body weight or per square meter of body surface. Since the amount of fat (which does not consume oxygen) is quite variable in different persons, metabolism is sometimes expressed in terms of the "fat-free body weight." Methods for estimating the fat content of the body are described in a later chapter. Other factors that influence resting metabolic rate are age, endocrine function, and environmental temperature. It should be apparent that the first requirement for estimating the energy cost of exercise is an accurate measurement of the metabolic rate at rest.

The rate of oxygen consumption may be measured either by the "open-circuit" or by the "closed-circuit" technique. In the open-circuit technique

**Fig. 41.** Open-circuit technique of measuring the rate of oxygen consumption. Subject, at the right, pedals a precision bicycle ergometer (Milhard). Chest electrodes lead to electrocardiograph (Sanborn). Observer, at the left, draws sample of exhaled air from Tissot gasometer (Collins). Percentage of oxygen in volume of air exhaled is compared with percentage in atmospheric air to calculate oxygen utilized.

(Fig. 41) the subject's expired air is collected for a definite period of time and the volume and oxygen concentration measured. Since the oxygen concentration in the inspired air is known (20.93% in the case of atmospheric air), the oxygen consumption is readily calculated. For example, if the volume of expired air collected in a 10-minute period is 70 liters and the oxygen concentration is 17%, the total oxygen consumption for the 10-minute period may be calculated as follows. Each 100 ml. of expired air contains 3.93 ml. less oxygen than 100 ml. of inspired air, or each liter of expired air contains 39.3 ml. less oxygen than does a liter of inspired air. Therefore 70 liters of expired air contain $70 \times 39.3 = 2,751$ ml. less oxygen

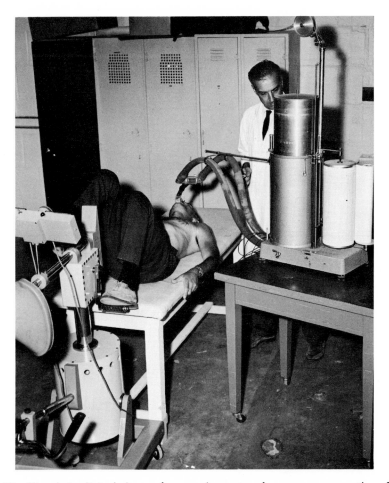

**Fig. 42.** Closed-circuit technique of measuring rate of oxygen consumption. Subject, at the left, pedals precision bicycle ergometer (Milhard) and breathes in and out of a 13.5-liter respirometer (Collins). Carbon dioxide is removed by soda lime granules within respirometer. Volume of oxygen removed from spirometer is recorded on chart at the right.

than the 70 liters of air inspired, or 2,751 ml. of oxygen have been consumed in the 10-minute period. The rate of oxygen consumption is then 275.1 ml. per minute.

In the closed-circuit method (Fig. 42) the subject breathes in and out from a spirometer containing air or oxygen. The carbon dioxide in the expired air is absorbed by a special chemical compound (soda lime), and the rate of oxygen consumption is calculated from the rate of fall of the spirometer bell as the oxygen in the bell is used up.

If both oxygen consumption and carbon dioxide production are measured, it is possible to estimate the proportions of the various foodstuffs being oxidized since the ratio of carbon dioxide produced to oxygen consumed (respiratory quotient, or R.Q.) is different for the various foodstuffs. The R.Q. for the combustion of carbohydrate is 1, for fat it is 0.7, and for protein, about 0.8. Textbooks of physiology should be consulted for further details.

## Energy cost of exercise

The expenditure of energy can be monitored by (1) direct measurement of work output, (2) direct measurement of heat output, (3) measurement of the net caloric intake, (4) measurement of the transformation of fuels in the body, (5) measurement of carbon dioxide production, an index of fuel oxidation, and (6) measurement of oxygen consumption.

The energy cost of various activities is best expressed in terms of the oxygen consumption required since oxygen consumption and not heat production is usually measured. In the older literature, however, the energy cost of different tasks is usually expressed in terms of Calories, and this remains a useful approach in the evaluation of the role of exercise in nutritional requirements, weight reduction, etc.

The oxygen requirement of a given activity may be expressed in two ways: (1) as the oxygen consumed during the activity and recovery (see discussion of oxygen debt later in this chapter) and (2) as a multiple of the resting oxygen consumption. The term METS, an abbreviation of metabolisms, is based on the latter expression.

The severity of different types of physical work can be assessed by measurement of oxygen requirements. Work is then categorized according to general levels of intensity as shown in Table 5.

*Table 5.* Classification of work intensity

|  | *METS* | $O_2(l./min.)$ | *Cal./min.* |
|---|---|---|---|
| Very light work | 1-2 | below 0.5 | below 2.5 |
| Light work | 2-3 | 0.5-1.0 | 2.5- 5.0 |
| Moderate work | 3-4 | 1.0-1.5 | 5.0- 7.5 |
| Heavy work | 4-6 | 1.5-2.0 | 7.5-10.0 |
| Very heavy work | 6-8 | 2.0-2.5 | 10.0-12.5 |
| Maximal work | over 8 | over 2.5 | over 12.5 |

## Measurement of oxygen consumption

The volume of oxygen consumed during moderate and strenuous exercise is determined using the open-circuit method illustrated in Fig. 41. The error of measurement is negligible in this system, but the expired air must be analyzed by chemical or electronic means.

If the work is very light and a high degree of accuracy is not required, a simpler closed-circuit method can be utilized. The closed-circuit technique measures the volume of oxygen removed from the spirometer (Fig. 42).

## Oxygen requirement and oxygen intake

The oxygen requirement of a given act is the volume of oxygen necessary for the performance of the act and for recovery. If the exercise is moderate, this requirement may be satisfied by the oxygen intake, and recovery keeps pace with activity. If the exertion is severe, this relation breaks down, and an oxygen debt is incurred. In this case the oxygen requirement of the exercise is the sum of the oxygen intake during exercise and the oxygen debt that is repaid during recovery.

The oxygen requirement of exercise is determined by a combination of factors. Some of the most important of these factors are the severity or intensity of work, the total size of the working muscles, the duration of work, the speed of work, the economy of muscular activity, the state of training, and certain environmental factors, notably temperature and humidity.

*Intensity of work.* It was pointed out in Chapter 3 that the tension exerted by a contracting muscle is dependent on two factors—the number of fibers contracting and the frequency of their contraction. Muscle tone, which is based on the low-frequency activation of a small proportion of the total number of muscle fibers, requires a very small oxygen intake. The same is true of a weak voluntary contraction. If a stronger contraction is needed, additional muscle fibers must be brought into activity, and the frequency with which each fiber contracts must be increased; both of these adjustments increase the oxygen requirement of the muscle.

*Duration of work.* Within certain limits the oxygen requirement of work is directly proportional to its duration. If, however, the intensity is great enough or the duration long enough to induce a state of fatigue, the oxygen requirement per unit of time usually begins to increase rapidly. This is easily explained by recalling the shape of the fatigue curve of an isolated muscle. As a muscle begins to tire, the tension developed by each fiber is reduced, and hence more fibers must be brought into activity if the same level of work is to be maintained. The oxygen requirement is increased in proportion to the increased number of active muscle fibers.

*Rate or speed of work.* The relation between the oxygen requirement of work and the speed of performance is complex. For many types of work there is an optimal speed at which the oxygen requirement is minimal. If the work is performed at a slower or a faster rate, the mechanical efficiency is diminished and the oxygen requirement increased. Fig. 43 illustrates this

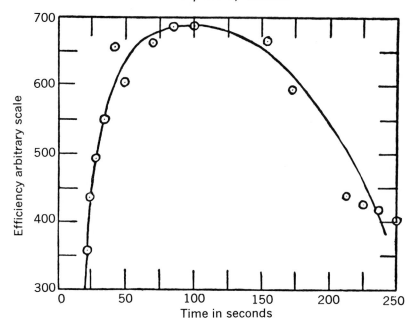

**Fig. 43.** Curve of the mechanical efficiency of the body during stair climbing at different speeds. (From Lupton, H.: Analysis of effects of speed on mechanical efficiency of human muscular movement, J. Physiol. **57:**337, 1923.)

relation for the act of climbing stairs in which the body weight is lifted at each step. The net result of two opposing factors determines the optimal speed of performance:

1. A rapidly contracting muscle has been shown to develop less tension than does a muscle contracting more slowly because of the limited rate at which the chemical changes underlying muscle contraction can occur.

2. A definite amount of energy is required to *maintain* tension in a muscle once it is developed, and the slower the contraction, the greater is the proportion of the total energy used for this purpose (that is, tension must be maintained over a longer period of time to accomplish a given amount of work at a slower rate of contraction).

The first factor tends to make work more economical (lower oxygen requirement) at low speeds, whereas the second factor results in a smaller oxygen requirement at high speeds. The worker, if left to his own devices, usually automatically adopts the optimal rate of working; this is, of course, impossible in assembly line work.

There is another important type of work in which there is *apparently* no optimal speed. This is exemplified by the act of running. Table 6 indicates that the oxygen requirement of a runner in a 120-yard dash increases in direct proportion to the speed. Actually the difference between these two types of activity is more apparent than real. In running, even at low speeds,

***Table 6.*** Oxygen requirements for running 120 yards at different speeds*

| Speed (yards per second) | Oxygen requirement | |
|---|---|---|
| | *Liters per 120 yards* | *Liters per minute* |
| 5.56 | 1.83 | 5.08 |
| 6.45 | 2.71 | 8.75 |
| 7.15 | 2.94 | 10.50 |
| 7.24 | 3.08 | 11.13 |
| 7.70 | 3.85 | 14.81 |
| 8.40 | 4.33 | 18.17 |
| 9.10 | 6.27 | 28.46 |
| 9.23 | 7.36 | 33.96 |

*From Sargent: Proc. Roy. Soc., London, sB **100:**10, 1926.

the subject is usually exceeding the optimal speed for horizontal locomotion. In walking, on the other hand, there is a definite optimal speed of about 100 yards (120 steps) per minute.[1]

*Economy of muscular activity.* In activities involving an element of motor skill, the same amount of work is usually performed with a smaller oxygen requirement by the trained athlete. This is due primarily to the fact that the acquisition of motor skill results in the suppression or elimination of extraneous muscular movements which, while contributing nothing to the performance of the task, require oxygen.[2, 3, 4]

*Environmental factors.* The mechanical efficiency of the body is apparently little altered by rather wide changes in external temperature and humidity. For example, in one study there was found to be little difference in the oxygen requirement of men working on a bicycle ergometer in a cold room (54° F.) and in a warm room (93° F.).[5] It is quite possible, however, that in activities requiring skill high temperatures might result in a lowered mechanical efficiency by diminishing the accuracy of neuromuscular coordination. There is no doubt that working capacity (output of work in a given time) is diminished by unfavorable environmental factors, especially by a combination of high temperature and high humidity.

Physiological criteria for setting the upper limits for men working in the heat have been proposed.[6] It is recommended that the upper safe limit of rectal temperature is 100.5 to 102.5° F. (38.1 to 39.4° C.).

## Aerobic and anaerobic metabolism

An appreciation of the complexities of the metabolic adjustments that must occur during exercise requires some knowledge of the basic reactions from which cells may derive energy. These are of two general types, *aerobic* (requiring oxygen) and *anaerobic* (not requiring oxygen). For reasons that will be apparent later, aerobic metabolism is far more efficient than is anaerobic metabolism (that is, more energy is derived from the utilization of a given amount of foodstuff when the reactions occur under aerobic than under anaerobic conditions). Anaerobic metabolism is, nevertheless, of great importance because it permits activity to continue, at least for limited periods of time, when the supply of oxygen is inadequate to provide all the energy needed by aerobic metabolism. This fact will be examined in detail in the discussion of oxygen debt.

The end result of aerobic metabolism is the oxidation of foodstuffs to carbon dioxide and water (in the case of protein, nitrogenous end products are also formed and are excreted in the urine). It is a common misconception that foodstuffs are "burned" by oxygen as coal is burned in a stove. Actually the oxidation of foodstuffs consists of the removal of hydrogen rather than the addition of oxygen; after a complex series of reactions the hydrogen combines with oxygen to form water. The carbon dioxide is produced not by the "burning" of carbon but by the splitting out of $CO_2$ from the —COOH groups in the foodstuff molecule. Under both aerobic and anaerobic conditions glucose (or glycogen) is converted by a series of enzymatic reactions to the 3-carbon compound, pyruvic acid. Under aerobic conditions the pyruvic acid is next converted to acetic acid (a 2-carbon acid), and this enters a complex cyclic reaction (the Krebs cycle), during which it is completely broken down to carbon dioxide and water. The complete oxidation of 1 molecule of glucose results in the formation of 38 molecules of ATP. In the absence of oxygen the glycolytic phase proceeds normally to the stage of pyruvic acid, but the pyruvic acid is then converted to lactic acid, the end product of anaerobic metabolism; the net energy yield is only 2 molecules of ATP per 1 molecule of glucose. In summary, the complete oxidation of 1 molecule of glucose to carbon dioxide and water results in the liberation of enough energy to form 38 molecules of ATP, whereas the anaerobic breakdown of 1 molecule of glucose to 2 molecules of lactic acid liberates enough energy for the formation of only 2 molecules of ATP. In addition, the resulting accumulation of lactic acid increases the acidity of the cells, and this interferes with the activity of many of the enzymes involved in various cellular activities. The formation of ATP (and similar high-energy phosphate compounds) made possible by the energy liberated during the oxidation of foodstuffs constitutes the process of oxidative phosphorylation and is the key reaction in the harnessing of the energy derived from the breakdown of foodstuff molecules. The breakdown of the high-energy phosphate compounds is the immediate source of energy for all the activities of the body, including the contraction of muscle.

*The steady state.* It was mentioned that for short periods of time it is possible to engage in exercise of such severity that the oxygen requirement far exceeds the oxygen intake. In continuous exercise lasting more than a few minutes, however, the oxygen intake must be adequate to meet the oxygen requirement. When this condition exists, the subject is said to be in a "steady state." He is in the state of approximate equilibrium between the processes of breakdown and recovery with respect to his muscle metabolism. When a subject is in genuine steady state, as, for example, at rest or during a long walk at constant speed, the oxygen consumption and carbon dioxide elimination are uniform, and the lactate concentration in the blood, the heart and respiratory rates, and the body temperature are all constant no matter how long (within reasonable limits) the exercise may last. When these "reasonable limits" have been exceeded, exercise may be terminated by accessory factors such as muscle soreness, formation of blisters, or exhaustion of the glycogen reserves.

When a resting subject begins to exercise, a new steady state is not achieved immediately. The circulatory and respiratory adjustments that make possible a greater oxygen intake come into play gradually, and in heavy work several minutes may be required for the oxygen intake to reach the level of the steady state. During this preliminary period a small oxygen debt is incurred that is repaid during the brief recovery period that follows the exercise. Fig. 44 illustrates this lag in reaching the steady state, as well as the constant rate of oxygen consumption during the maintenance of the steady state.

The rate of oxygen intake may rise from 250 ml. per minute at rest to a value of 2.5 to 4.5 liters per minute, during a steady state of exercise, depending on the size, strength, and other characteristics of the subject. Robinson, Edwards, and Dill[7] found that the American middle distance

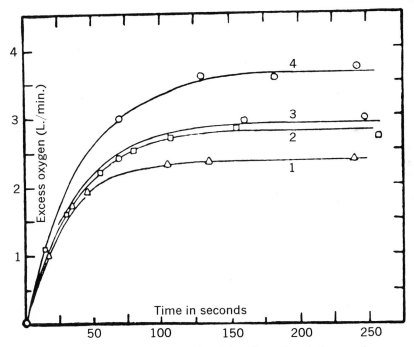

**Fig. 44.** The steady state in the rate of oxygen absorption during running at speeds of **1,** 193.5 yards per minute; **2** and **3,** 135 yards per minute; and **4,** 169 yards per minute. Note the lag of approximately 100 seconds in reaching the steady state; during this lag period an oxygen debt is being incurred. (From Hill, A. V., and Lupton, H.: Muscular exercise, lactic acid, and the supply and utilization of oxygen, Quart. J. Med. **16:**135, 1923.)

runner, Lash, was able to achieve an oxygen intake of 5.35 liters per minute during an exhausting run on a treadmill; this was 21.4 times his resting level. Astrand[8] reports that the Swedish cross-country skier, Jernberg, reached an oxygen intake of 5.9 liters per minute. The highest value recorded by Hill[9] in his study of athletes at Cornell University was 4.4 liters per minute in an oarsman rowing on a machine. He required 4.7 minutes to reach this level of oxygen intake. There is evidence[10] that in the steady state the upper limit for performing work under truly aerobic conditions corresponds to about 70% of the maximal oxygen consumption. It should be pointed out in this connection that a constant level of oxygen intake during exercise is not sufficient evidence in itself to establish the existence of a steady state. The oxygen consumption may be constant simply because the subject has reached his maximal level of oxygen intake and lactic acid may be accumulating. This can be checked by successive determinations of the concentration of lactic acid in the blood or more simply by noting whether or not the oxygen intake increases further with a slight increase in the intensity of the work.

*Oxygen debt during exercise.* The concept of the oxygen debt has played a prominent part in discussions of the oxygen requirements during exercise for many years, and yet its basis is still poorly understood. The term "oxygen debt" was coined by A. V. Hill as a convenient expression of the fact that the deficit in oxygen intake during strenuous activity represents a debt that is repaid during recovery. For example, if a man exercises at a rate that requires 4 liters of oxygen per minute (if all the energy is to be provided by oxidation of foodstuffs) but is able to take in only 3 liters of oxygen per minute, he incurs an oxygen debt of 1 liter for each minute of exercise. Then during the recovery period his oxygen intake will remain above the resting level until the debt has been repaid. During the period of exercise three fourths of the necessary energy was obtained by oxidative (aerobic) metabolism and one fourth by nonoxidative (anaerobic) metabolism.

Since the contraction of an oxygen debt is ordinarily associated with the accumulation of lactic acid that disappears in the recovery period, the earliest theory was that the extra oxygen consumption during recovery served to oxidize the lactic acid to carbon dioxide and water. This simple explanation had to be modified when it was found that the excess oxygen consumption during recovery was sufficient to permit the oxidation of only a portion of the lactic acid. The modified theory was that the oxidation of part of the lactic acid supplied the energy to reconvert the remainder to glucose or glycogen, largely in the liver. Even this explanation proved too simple when it was demonstrated that an appreciable oxygen debt may be associated with moderate exercise in which there is no accumulation of lactic acid. The theory that the accumulation of lactic acid is the cause of the increased oxygen consumption during recovery is made questionable by some recent experiments on anesthetized animals.[11] The muscles of the hind legs were stimulated electrically and measurements were made of the rates of disappearance of the excess lactic acid and of the decline in excess oxygen consumption during the recovery period. When the experiment was repeated after removal of the liver, the lactic acid level remained elevated after the period of muscle contraction, and yet the rate of oxygen consumption returned to normal at the usual rate. It is apparent that the accumulation of lactic acid does not cause the oxygen debt but that both are by-products of anaerobic metabolism. The relation between the rise in blood lactic acid concentration and the oxygen debt is very controversial.[12-17]

One theory[18] of the nature of the oxygen debt is based on the chemical changes in contracting muscle (Chapter 2). It will be recalled that the immediate source of energy for muscle contraction is the explosive breakdown of ATP (adenosine triphosphate) to ADP (adenosine diphosphate) and inorganic P (phosphate). The rebuilding of the high-energy compound ATP from ADP and P requires oxidative energy. When adequate oxygen is not available, ADP and P accumulate, and it has been found that increased concentrations of ADP and P actually stimulate the uptake of oxygen by cells. This appears at present to be a reasonable explanation of the basis of the oxygen debt—depletion of ATP and accumulation of ADP and inorganic P.

***Oxygen intake and oxygen debt as limiting factors during exercise.*** The maximum effort that can be exerted over a given period of time is limited by the maximum amount of oxygen that the subject can absorb per minute and by the maximum oxygen debt that he is able to contract. Since these are both measurable quantities, it should be possible to predict the limits of exertion for any person from the results of laboratory tests (omitting emotional factors). It has been established that when the maximum oxygen debt has been incurred the body becomes incapable of further effort. These facts permit one to estimate the duration of exertion that is possible when the oxygen requirement is greater than the maximal oxygen intake. Assume that an athlete is able to absorb 4 liters of oxygen per minute and to incur an oxygen debt of 15 liters. If he runs at a speed requiring 5 liters of oxygen per minute, he must go into debt for oxygen at the rate of 1 liter per minute, and this intensity of exertion could be sustained for 15 minutes. If the speed of running is increased until the oxygen requirement is doubled, the excess of oxygen requirement over oxygen intake is 10 – 4 = 6 liters per minute, and exhaustion would occur at the end of 15/6 = 2.5 minutes.

In running, the oxygen requirement increases as the square or cube of the speed. Therefore doubling the rate of running from an initial level requiring 4 liters of oxygen per minute increases the oxygen requirement per minute from 4 to 8 times. A man does not have time to incur his maximal oxygen debt in short sprints. It has been estimated that 50 to 55 seconds of running at top speed would be required before the maximal oxygen debt would be reached.

Since the maximum amount of exertion that is possible before exhaustion occurs is determined by the upper limits of the oxygen intake and the oxygen debt, the question naturally arises as to the factors that set these limits. The factors limiting oxygen intake have been discussed in earlier chapters. The factors that set the upper limit of the oxygen debt have not been definitely established. In an isolated muscle of a frog, stimulated electrically, contraction ceases when the concentration of lactic acid has risen to about 300 mg. per 100 grams of muscle. It is possible that the accumulation of lactic acid also determines the limit of muscular activity in a human being—at least an increase in the blood lactic acid concentration to about 200 mg. per 100 ml. of blood is usually associated with exhaustion. It is uncertain whether and to what extent depletion of ATP may contribute to the limitation of exertion. Only empirical answers will be possible until the factors responsible for the oxygen debt are more clearly defined. The interrelations of aerobic and anaerobic metabolism during strenuous exercise are analyzed in a paper by Margaria et al.,[19] which the student is urged to read.

## Influence of training on oxygen requirement, oxygen intake, and oxygen debt

The results of training may be summarized briefly as follows:
1. The oxygen requirement for a given task is diminished as a result of more efficient use of muscles and elimination of extraneous movements and of greater mechanical efficiency of the muscles themselves.
2. The maximal oxygen intake is increased through improved capacity of the heart to pump blood and through circulatory and respiratory adjustments.
3. It has been claimed that training increases the amount of oxygen debt that can be reached. If this is true, it may be due to an increase in the amount of buffer available for neutralizing lactic acid, to an increase in the amount of ATP, creatine phosphate, or myoglobin in the muscles, or perhaps to a greater ability to persist in exercise despite the discomfort of impending exhaustion.

A more complete discussion of the results of training will be found in Chapter 26.

## Mechanical efficiency of work

Efficiency is defined as the ratio of work performed to the energy cost of the work. The energy cost is easily calculated from the excess oxygen consumed, but the amount of work accomplished is often difficult to measure unless an ergometer of some type is used. The work performed during ordinary activities and many types of sport usually can be estimated only in terms of the vertical lift of the body; this neglects the work accomplished in forward movement of the body and results in low values for mechanical efficiency. Under favorable conditions the body can perform work with about the same mechanical efficiency as a gasoline engine, that is, about 20 to 30%. In activities such as underwater swimming the mechanical efficiency may be very low because of the frictional resistance of the water. Efficiency improves with training because of the elimination of unnecessary movements. It is diminished by excessive loads, excessive rate of work, and fatigue.

## *Fuel of muscular exercise*

Accurate information concerning the type of fuel used by working muscles is essential for the intelligent planning of diets to meet the nutritional requirements of people engaged in strenuous activity and for evaluating the role of exercise in weight-reduction programs. This information has been obtained by a variety of methods and is now reasonably complete. Since oxidative energy can be derived from the utilization of all three major foodstuffs (carbohydrate, fat, and protein), the problem is to determine the relative proportions of the total energy derived from each. Over reasonable periods of time the amount of protein that is oxidized can be calculated from measurements of the amount of nitrogen excreted in the urine, each gram of urinary nitrogen representing the combustion of 6.25 grams of protein. If the urinary nitrogen excretion during a 24-hour period is compared in resting subjects and again when they engage in heavy muscular work throughout the day, it is found that only about 2% of the extra energy expenditure is derived from the oxidation of protein. The remaining 98% must then be derived from carbohydrate and fat. There is thus no scientific basis for the belief that heavy work requires a greatly increased intake of protein.

When the respiratory quotient is corrected for the small amount of protein metabolism, the resulting "nonprotein R.Q." reflects the utilization of carbohydrate and fat and the relative proportions of each. Since the R.Q. of carbohydrate oxidation is 1 and that of fat is 0.7, intermediate values of the nonprotein R.Q. indicate the utilization of mixtures of the two.

A resting subject on an average diet has a nonprotein R.Q. of about 0.8, indicating that about two thirds of his energy requirement is derived from fat and one third from carbohydrate (neglecting the small contribution of protein). In light to moderate exercise the proportions of carbohydrate and fat utilized are about the same as during rest. In more strenuous exercise the R.Q. rises toward 1, indicating that more of the energy is derived from carbohydrate, but if hard work is continued for a period of hours, the R.Q. begins to fall and eventually approaches 0.7. It thus appears that carbohydrate is used preferentially by working muscles so long as it is available but that continued hard work may exhaust the reserve supply of carbohydrate (principally the glyocogen stores in the liver and muscles) and force the muscles to derive their energy from fat. In extreme cases, as in marathon races, depletion of the carbohydrate reserve may result in a serious lowering of the blood sugar level, and exhaustion and collapse may follow because of impairment in the function of the central nervous system, which requires an adequate supply of glucose at all times.

The prediction of the type of foodstuffs being utilized from measured values of R.Q. is open to criticism, since it can be influenced by many other factors. Studies in which the source of energy for muscle contraction is determined by analyzing the concentrations of glucose and of free fatty acids in the blood entering and leaving the muscle and by analyzing changes in the levels of these foodstuffs in the muscle during work have challenged the traditional concept that carbohydrate is necessarily the predominant fuel for working muscle.[20] The utilization of fatty acids as a source of energy requires the availability of oxygen, while glucose (or glycogen) can be metabolized to lactic acid when oxygen is limited. It is possible that glucose is the major fuel for muscular activity during very strenuous work of short duration (in which there is a predominance of anaerobic metabolism) and that fat (in the form of free fatty acids) is the major substrate during sustained work of moderate intensity when oxygen is available for the mitochondrial oxidation of fatty acids.

Recent studies[21] have suggested a mechanism for the mobilization of fat for use as an energy source during exercise. It was found that (1) the intravenous injection of pituitary growth hormone resulted in a rise in the plasma level of free fatty acids, (2) during a walk lasting several hours there was a rise in the plasma levels of growth hormone and of fatty acids, and (3) when glucose was ingested before and at 30-minute intervals during the walk, there was no rise in blood glucose concentration, but the usual rise in growth hormone and free fatty acid levels in the plasma was abolished. The next problem to be solved concerns the nature of the stimulus that controls the release of growth hormone from the pituitary gland in response to exercise.

### Advanced study topics

1. What metabolic changes provide the energy for aerobic work and anaerobic work?
2. Review the recent literature on metabolism in exercise in current issues of the *Journal of Sports Medicine and Physical Fitness.*
3. Describe an open-circuit method of measuring oxygen consumption during heavy exercise.
4. Classify several physical activities in terms of oxygen requirement.
5. What type of exercise training best improves anaerobic work capacity?

### References

1. Benedict, F. G., and Murschhauser, H.: Energy transformations during horizontal walking, Carnegie Institute of Washington, Publication no. 231, 1915.
2. Workman, J. M., and Armstrong, B. M.: Oxygen cost of treadmill walking, J. Appl. Physiol. 18:798, 1963.
3. Field, J., editor: Handbook of physiology. Section 4, Adaptation to the environment, Washington, D. C., 1964, American Physiological Society.
4. Dill, D. B.: Oxygen used in horizontal and grade walking and running on the treadmill, J. Appl. Physiol. 20:19, 1965.
5. Dill, D. B., Edwards, H. T., Bauer, P. S., and Levenson, E. J.: Physical performance in relation to external temperature, Arbeitsphysiol. 4:508, 1931.
6. Wyndham, C. H., Strydom, N. B., Morrison, J. F., Williams, C. G., Bredell, G. A. G., Maritz, J. S., and Munro, A.: Criteria for physiological limits for work in heat, J. Appl. Physiol. 20:37, 1965.
7. Robinson, S., Edwards, H. T., and Dill, D. B.: New records in human power, Science 85:409, 1937.
8. Astrand, P. O.: New records in human power, Nature 176:922, 1955.
9. Hill, A. V.: Muscular movement in man, New York, 1927, McGraw-Hill Book Company.

10. Hesser, C. M.: Energy cost of alternating positive and negative work, Acta Physiol. Scand. **63**:84, 1965.

11. Kayne, H. L., and Alpert, N. R.: Oxygen consumption following exercise in the anesthetized dog, Am. J. Physiol. **206**:51, 1964.

12. Huckabee, W. E.: Relationships of pyruvate and lactate during anaerobic metabolism. I. Effect of infusion of pyruvate or glucose and of hyperventilation, J. Clin. Invest. **37**:244, 1958.

13. Huckabee, W. E., and Judson, W. E.: The role of anaerobic metabolism in the performance of mild muscular work. I. Relationship to oxygen consumption and cardiac output, and the effect of congestive heart failure, J. Clin. Invest. **37**:1577, 1958.

14. Huckabee, W. E.: Relationship of pyruvate and lactate during anaerobic metabolism. IV. Local tissue component of total body $O_2$ debt. Am. J. Physiol. **196**:253, 1959.

15. Knuttgen, H. G.: Oxygen debt, lactate, pyruvate and excess lactate after muscular work, J. Appl. Physiol. **17**:639, 1962.

16. Margaria, R., Cerretelli, P., di Prampero, P. E., Massari, C., and Torelli, G.: Kinetics and mechanism of oxygen debt contraction in man, J. Appl. Physiol. **18**:371, 1963.

17. Wasserman, K., Burton, G. G., and Van Kessel, A. L.: Excess lactate concept and oxygen debt of exercise, J. Appl. Physiol. **20**:1299, 1965.

18. Pearl, D. C., Jr., Carlson, L. D., and Sherwood, W. W.: Mechanism of oxygen deficit, Proc. Soc. Exp. Biol. & Med. **92**:277, 1956.

19. Margaria, R., Cerritelli, P., and Mangili, F.: Balance and kinetics of anaerobic energy release during strenuous exercise in man, J. Appl. Physiol. **19**:623, 1964.

20. Fritz, I. B.: Factors influencing the rates of long-chain fatty acid oxidation and synthesis in mammalian systems, Physiol. Rev. **41**:52, 1961.

21. Hunter, W. B., Fonseka, C. C., and Passmore, R.: Growth hormone: Important role in muscular exercise in adults, Science **150**:1051, 1965.

# 19

# Energy requirement of physical activities

Estimates of the energy expenditure during various activities are useful for computing dietary requirements, for assessing the severity of activities, and for determining optimum means and rates of work. Considerations of human performance in work and sport usually involve some combination of the three applications.

## Computation of dietary requirement

The quantity of foodstuff required to sustain physical activity depends upon the intensity and the duration of the activity. A normal 150-pound man requires approximately 1,200 Calories daily to sustain his body processes in a resting condition. Vigorous physical labor continued throughout the day may raise the daily dietary requirement to 7,000 Calories. If the caloric intake does not balance the caloric expenditure, substances that compose body tissues will be consumed as energy fuels, and a loss in body weight will ensue. Conversely, an excessive dietary intake will cause substances to be stored in the body tissues, and the body weight will be increased. Lacking the apparatus to measure energy metabolism accurately, one can use a careful record of the body weight to provide an index of the caloric balance between the food intake and the energy requirement for a program of physical activities.

## Assessing severity of exercise

The severity of a calisthenic exercise, a sport, or an occupation must be determined before it can be used during convalescence or as a therapeutic measure. The amount of stress caused by the activity may be estimated by measuring the energy requirement. Such a cost list has been prepared,[1] but this must be used with caution because of wide fluctuations in values from patient to patient and in a given patient from one exercise period to the next. In addition the condition of the specific system that has been affected by the disease should be assessed by observing its adjustment to exercise. Some types of slow, heavy work such as weight lifting or wrestling cause a strain on the heart and circulation, especially if they are performed with the glottis closed. In these exercises the intrathoracic pressure may be increased to a level that reduces the flow of venous blood to the heart. This imposes a strain upon the heart by interfering with its oxygen supply. This type of stress is not assessed by energy determinations and should be considered separately.

## Work efficiency

The efficiency of performance of a piece of work may be evaluated by computing its energy requirement. A more efficient worker accomplishes a certain piece of work with less expenditure of energy. Evaluation of a task such as flying an airplane[2] can be accomplished by measurement of energy output. As a worker's duties increase in complexity, his muscular tension is increased, resulting in an increased metabolic rate. The level of skill of a performer may be assessed by observing his energy output during work. Generalized increases in skeletal muscular tension that elevate metabolism are characteristic of an inexperienced worker.

The energy requirement for a particular task may be reduced by (1) improving the skill elements of the task, (2) reducing extra movements, (3) improving the physical condition of the worker, and (4) adjusting the rate of work to an optimum rate. Observations on the energy requirements of various rates of work demonstrate that two factors are involved. There is an optimum rate at which a given piece of work is accomplished with the least expenditure of energy. There is also a maximum rate of work that can be sustained for a given period of time. In many instances when quantity of work is not a factor, the most rapid rate is the most economical, even though exhaustion may occur early, since the work period is so short that only a very small amount of the total energy is used for supporting the body processes. Work done at a rapid rate may be within the range at which skill is not limited, yet beyond the range of intensity at which a steady state can be established. At this rapid rate of work there is a progressive development of fatigue, and exhaustion becomes inevitable. Even though this rapid rate may require the least energy for the unit output of work, the work must soon be slowed considerably or stopped to allow a period of recovery during which time little or no work is accomplished. Thus it is evident that a definition of the optimum rate of work must involve a consideration of the steady state level as well as of the economy of energy.

***Table 7.*** Energy required by a 154-pound man for various physical activities*

| Activity | Total Calories per hour |
|---|---|
| Sleeping | 70 |
| Lying quietly | 80 |
| Sitting | 100 |
| Mental work seated | 105 |
| Standing | 110 |
| Seamstress, handwork | 115 |
| Singing | 120 |
| Driving a car | 140 |
| Office work | 145 |
| Housekeeping | 150 |
| Calisthenics | 160 |
| Walking, 2 m.p.h. | 170 |
| Piloting an airplane | 175 |
| Walking up stairs, 1 m.p.h. | 180 |
| Riding a bicycle, 5.5 m.p.h. | 190 |
| Walking down stairs, 2 m.p.h. | 200 |
| Bricklaying | 205 |
| House painting | 210 |
| Carpenter work | 230 |
| Billiards | 235 |
| Pitching horseshoes | 240 |
| Dancing, moderate | 250 |
| Swedish gymnastics | 260 |
| Laundress work | 270 |
| Baseball (except pitcher) | 280 |
| Horizontal walking, 3.5 m.p.h. | 290 |
| Rowing for pleasure | 300 |
| Wand drill | 310 |
| Dancing, vigorous | 340 |
| Table tennis | 345 |
| Horizontal walking, 3 m.p.h., carrying 43 lb. load | 350 |
| Walking up 3% grade, 3.5 m.p.h. | 370 |
| Baseball pitcher | 390 |
| Pick and shovel work | 400 |
| Shoveling sand | 405 |
| Swimming breaststroke, 1 m.p.h. | 410 |
| Bicycle riding, rapid | 415 |
| Swimming crawl stroke, 1 m.p.h. | 420 |
| Walking up 8.6% grade, 2.4 m.p.h. | 430 |
| Chopping wood | 450 |
| Skating, 9 m.p.h. | 470 |
| Sawing wood | 480 |
| Swimming breaststroke, 1.6 m.p.h. | 490 |
| Swimming backstroke, 1 m.p.h. | 500 |
| Snowshoeing (bearpaw), 2.5 m.p.h. | 520 |
| Skiing, 3 m.p.h. | 540 |
| Swimming sidestroke, 1 m.p.h. | 550 |

*The oxygen consumptions from which the caloric values in this table have been calculated are only approximations. Variables that must be considered in any interpretation of this table are size, body type and age of the subjects, differences between individuals of the same build, physical fitness and skill in the particular activity, nutritional condition, and environmental conditions (whether they help or hinder the individual).[4-8]

*Table 7.* Energy required by a 154-pound man for various physical activities—cont'd

| Activity | Total Calories per hour |
|---|---|
| Walking up 8.6% grade, 3.5 m.p.h. | 560 |
| Walking up 10% grade, 3.5. m.p.h. | 580 |
| Walking up stairs, 2 m.p.h. | 590 |
| Mountain climbing | 600 |
| Snowshoeing (trail snowshoes), 2.5 m.p.h. | 620 |
| Fencing | 630 |
| Skating, 11 m.p.h. | 640 |
| Rowing, 3.5. m.p.h. | 660 |
| Walking up 36% grade, 1 m.p.h. carrying 43 lb. load | 680 |
| Swimming crawl stroke, 1.6 m.p.h. | 700 |
| Parallel bar work | 710 |
| Horizontal running, 5.7 m.p.h. | 720 |
| Walking up 14.4% grade, 3.5 m.p.h. | 740 |
| Walking in 12-18 in. snow | 760 |
| Skating, 13 m.p.h. | 780 |
| Wrestling | 790 |
| Swimming backstroke, 1.6. m.p.h. | 800 |
| Horizontal running, 5 m.p.h. carrying 43 lb. load | 820 |
| Horizontal running, 7 m.p.h. | 870 |
| Walking up 36% grade, 1.5 m.p.h. carrying 43 lb. load | 890 |
| Running up 8.6% grade, 7 m.p.h. | 950 |
| Rowing, 11 m.p.h. | 970 |
| Football | 1,000 |
| Rowing, 11.3 m.p.h. | 1,130 |
| Swimming sidestroke, 1.6 m.p.h. | 1,200 |
| Horizontal running, 11.4 m.p.h. | 1,300 |
| Rowing, 12 m.p.h. | 1,500 |
| Swimming crawl stroke, 2.2 m.p.h. | 1,600 |
| Swimming breaststroke, 2.2. m.p.h. | 1,850 |
| Swimming backstroke, 2.2. m.p.h. | 2,000 |
| Horizontal running, 13.2 m.p.h. | 2,330 |
| Swimming breaststroke, 2.4. m.p.h. | 2,530 |
| Horizontal running, 14.8 m.p.h. | 2,880 |
| Swimming sidestroke, 2.2. m.p.h. | 3,000 |
| Swimming breaststroke, 2.7. m.p.h. | 3,690 |
| Horizontal running, 15.8 m.p.h. | 3,910 |
| Horizontal running, 17.2 m.p.h. | 4,740 |
| Horizontal running, 18.6 m.p.h. | 7,790 |
| Horizontal running, 18.9 m.p.h. | 9,480 |

## Maximum steady state work

The maximum rate of sustained work is a function of a person's ability to attain a steady state at high levels of exertion. In distance running, swimming, bicycling, skiing, or rowing the competitor must adjust his speed to a rate that is within his ability to maintain a steady state of physiological activity. An athlete raises his steady state level by three procedures.

1. He improves his *general physical condition* so that the organs may function to sustain a physiological equilibrium at higher levels of activity.
2. He improves his *skill* in the activity he is to perform so that there is an economy of expenditure of energy and so that the movements will be skillful even at very rapid rates.
3. He learns to recognize the maximum rate that can be maintained in a physiological steady state. This is accomplished through *pacing*. Pacing is usually the last to be perfected. A characteristic of an in-experienced athlete is his inability to maintain a steady pace. He tends to exhaust himself early in the race by surpassing his maximum physiological steady state.

The energy required for maintaining the body functions at rest and during work is derived ultimately from the oxidation of foodstuffs. In a steady state of rest or moderate work the rate of oxygen consumption is an expression of the rate of energy production. In hard work in which the oxidation of the foodstuffs cannot keep pace with the energy requirement, the energy is liberated by anaerobic processes and an oxygen debt is accu-mulated. This oxygen debt is paid off during recovery. In steady state work the oxygen consumption during work is a measure of the energy require-ment of the work. During exhausting work, however, the energy require-ment is the sum of the oxygen consumed during work and the amount of the oxygen debt.

The manner in which Table 7 can be used is illustrated in Table 8.

*Table 8.* Estimate of daily energy expenditure of 150-pound college athlete

| Time | Hours | Activity | Calories per hour | Total |
|---|---|---|---|---|
| 12:00- 7:00 | 7.0 | Sleeping | 70 | 490 |
| 7:00- 7:30 | 0.5 | Morning toilet | 110 | 55 |
| 7:30- 8:00 | 0.5 | Breakfast | 110 | 55 |
| 8:00- 8:15 | 0.25 | Walking | 290 | 73 |
| 8:15- 9:00 | 0.75 | Study and writing | 140 | 105 |
| 9:00-12:00 | 3.0 | Class work (150 min.), standing and walking between classes (30 min.) | 200 | 600 |
| 12:00- 1:00 | 1.0 | Lunch | 110 | 110 |
| 1:00- 3:00 | 2.0 | Laboratory | 130 | 260 |
| 3:00- 6:00 | 3.0 | Team practice | 600 | 1,800 |
| 6:00- 6:15 | 0.25 | Walking | 290 | 73 |
| 6:15- 7:00 | 0.75 | Rest | 80 | 60 |
| 7:00- 8:00 | 1.0 | Dinner | 110 | 110 |
| 8:00- 8:30 | 0.5 | Conversation | 110 | 55 |
| 8:30-10:30 | 2.5 | Study and writing | 140 | 350 |
| 10:30-12:00 | 1.5 | Sleeping | 70 | 105 |
| Total expenditure in 24 hours | | | | 4,301 |

## Inefficiency of anaerobic work

When work is first started, it is carried on in a partly anaerobic condition. During light and moderate work this lag in the increasing rate of oxygen consumption in initial stages of work is slightly less than the lag in the decreasing rate of oxygen consumption after the work has stopped. A consequence of this postexercise deficit plus "interest" is that the efficiency of short periods of work is lower than the efficiency of work of longer duration. During very brief and heavy exertion the anaerobic part of the work is greater than during moderate exertion, and the excess oxygen consumed after the exercise may be 20 times that consumed during the work. Hence very severe work, which is performed mainly anaerobically with a subsequent aerobic recovery, may be as little as 40% as efficient as aerobic work.[3]

## Method of measuring work metabolism

Energy expenditure is commonly determined by calculations from respiratory data. The subject is connected to a Douglas bag or Tissot gasometer through a face mask or mouthpiece and a suitable length of tubing (Fig. 41). A system of valves allows the subject to inspire atmospheric air and to expire into the container for about 5 minutes. At the end of the period the volume of the air collection is noted and corrected to the volume of dry gas at standard temperature and pressure.

Samples of the expired air are collected from the bag or gasometer before it is emptied and analyzed for oxygen and carbon dioxide by means of the Haldane apparatus. From these various data the oxygen consumption per minute is calculated. The caloric value of 1 liter of oxygen when the fuel is carbohydrate is 5 Calories. Each Calorie has the energetic equivalent value of 3,086 foot-pounds. Thus when the fuel is predominately carbohydrate, the energy requirement during muscular work may be calculated from the oxygen consumption.[4]

## Energy requirement of activities

Table 7 gives a tabulation of the energy requirements of various activities. The figures in the table show the total metabolism during each activity. Work at the rate of over 900 Calories per hour is followed by a large oxygen debt. This debt is included in the figure representing the total energy requirement in such cases. Treadmill experiments in the Harvard Fatigue Laboratory have shown that work which results in an expenditure greater than 700 Calories per hour cannot be continued for much longer than 1 hour by the average man. Champion marathon runners run over 2 hours at a rate slightly faster than 11 m.p.h. They possess such superior physical equipment and they are in such a fine state of training that they can attain a steady state of physiological activity while using energy at the rate of approximately 1,300 Calories per hour.

Trained and untrained woodcutters, working hard all day for several days, were observed to expend an average of about 300 Calories per hour.

Although the daily work (cutting and stacking cords of wood) accomplished by the trained woodcutters was over 4 times greater than that of the untrained workers, the Caloric output was nearly the same.[9]

## Advanced study topics

1. What variables must be taken into consideration in determining the severity of a physical activity for an individual?
2. Review the recent literature on the energy requirement of physical activities in current issues of the *Archives of Physical Medicine*.
3. Describe a bicycle ergometer or treadmill.
4. Compute the efficiency of a bout of work.
5. What factors affect the energy requirement for a physical performance?

## References

1. Weiss, R. A., and Karpovich, P. V.: Energy cost of exercise for convalescents, Arch. Phys. Med. 28:447, 1947.
2. Corey, E. L.: Pilot metabolism and respiratory activity during varied flight tasks, J. Appl. Physiol. 1:35, 1948.
3. Asmussen, E.: Aerobic recovery after anaerobiosis in rest and work, Acta Physiol. Scand. 11:197, 1946.
4. Consolazio, F. C., Johnson, R. E., and Marek, E.: Metabolic methods, St. Louis, 1963, The C. V. Mosby Co.
5. Harvard Fatigue Laboratory: Manual of field methods for biochemical assessment of metabolic and nutritional condition, Boston, 1945.
6. Morehouse, L. E., and Cherry, R. B.: Energy cost of progression, National Academy of Sciences, Washington, D. C., July, 1946, Government Printing Office.
7. Karpovich, P. V., and Millman, N.: Energy expenditure in swimming, Am. J. Physiol. 142:140, 1944.
8. Smith, H. M.: Gaseous exchange and physiological requirements for level and grade walking, Washington, 1922, The Carnegie Institution of Washington.
9. Morehouse, L. E.: Unpublished field study, Harvard Fatigue Laboratory, 1946.

# 20

# *Efficiency of muscular work*

Work is accomplished by the expenditure of energy. When more work is done with the same energy expenditure or when a given amount of work is accomplished at a smaller energy cost, the *efficiency* of the performance is higher. Other factors that must be considered in an appraisal of the overall efficiency of performance include (1) the *rate* of work, (2) the *load*, (3) the *duration* of the work, (4) the *quality* of the work, and (5) the *speed of recovery* following the work period. It is apparent that efficiency is a complex measurement involving many variables. If the influence on efficiency of a single variable is to be estimated, the other variables must be kept constant.

## *Estimation of work efficiency*

Efficiency is expressed by the formula:

$$\text{Efficiency (in percent)} = \frac{\text{Work done} \times 100}{\text{Energy used}}$$

"Work done" is usually expressed in terms of foot-pounds or Calories (1 Calorie = 3,086 foot-pounds). For example, if a man weighing 150 pounds climbs stairs to a height of 20 feet, he performs 20 × 150 = 3,000 foot-pounds of work. The "energy used" in performing muscular work is ordinarily expressed in terms of the liters of oxygen consumed or in terms of the equivalent value in Calories of heat energy (1 liter of oxygen is equivalent to 5 Calories). If the efficiency of work is to be calculated from the formula just given, the work done and the energy used must be expressed in terms of the same unit. For example, if the 150-pound man uses 8

*195*

Calories of energy for his 20-foot climb, his energy expenditure is $8 \times 3,086$ = 24,688 foot-pounds, and the efficiency of his performance is as follows:

$$\frac{3,000 \times 100}{24,688} = 12.1\%$$

## Efficiency of muscle work

The formula for the efficiency of total body work cannot be applied to the estimation of the mechanical efficiency of a single muscle contraction. This is because muscle not only produces heat at rest, during contraction, and during relaxation but it also absorbs heat from its environment when it is stretched during contraction. Upon release, heat will flow from the muscle back to the environment.[1] This implies that muscle is not a simple heat engine but a mechanochemical system in which the chemical events in contraction are reversible.[2]

## Efficiency of work along a horizontal plane

In many of the physical activities of man movement occurs along a horizontal plane. In this type of work the arms and legs are raised and lowered with each step while the trunk is propelled along a steady plane with only a slight rise and fall at each step. In horizontal movement the external work accomplished is rather small. Other factors that require the expenditure of energy, such as the overcoming of muscle viscosity, the inertia of the bony levers, and external wind resistance, are practically impossible to measure. As a result of these complications, the efficiency of work along a horizontal plane is not usually expressed by the ratio of work done to energy used but rather by a consideration of the energy requirement for the particular distance and at the particular speed. The lower the energy requirement, the higher will be the efficiency.

## Efficiency of grade climbing

In walking or running up a slight grade most of the energy expended is used in movements of the arms and legs and is dissipated as heat; very little is used in actually raising the body. As the grade becomes steeper, more of the total energy expenditure is applied to raising the body, and the work efficiency is accordingly increased.

Estimates of the work efficiency of movement up a slight grade are practically useless for assessing the mechanical efficiency of the entire body.[3] They are of some value when the efficiencies of two or more persons are to be compared. For this purpose, the energy expenditure of each subject performing the same run is measured; the lower the energy expenditure, the higher is the efficiency. Steeper grades or higher rates of climbing differentiate more clearly among different persons because of the greater stresses involved.

Balke and Ware,[10] measured the cost of grade walking of U. S. Air Force personnel and found an average of 1.8 ml. oxygen per Kg.-m. of work done and the corresponding *absolute efficiency* was 27%. The energy expenditure per unit weight was nearly constant.

## Energy cost of progression

The comparative efficiencies of walking, running, climbing, and performing other forms of progression at various speeds along a horizontal plane or up varying grades may be evaluated by comparing the energy expanded in traveling a fixed distance such as a mile. Very slow rates of progression that are performed with low expenditures of energy are not efficient. Moving slowly to "save energy" is false economy when a certain distance has to be traversed.

Table 9 demonstrates that fewer Calories are used in walking a mile at

*Table 9.* Energy expenditures at various speeds and grades of different types of progression*

| Type of progression | Speed (m.p.h.) | Grade (%) | Energy expenditure 154-pound man | |
| --- | --- | --- | --- | --- |
| | | | Calories per hour | Calories per mile |
| Horizontal walking | 2.3 | 0 | 210 | 90 |
| | 3.5 | 0 | 290 | 85 |
| | 4.6 | 0 | 470 | 100 |
| Grade walking | 2.0 | 5.0 | 250 | 125 |
| | 2.5 | 5.0 | 290 | 115 |
| | 2.3 | 5.5 | 350 | 150 |
| | 3.5 | 5.5 | 450 | 130 |
| | 2.4 | 8.6 | 430 | 180 |
| | 3.5 | 8.6 | 560 | 160 |
| Horizontal walking carrying 43 lb. load | 1.0 | 0 | 210 | 210 |
| | 2.0 | 0 | 270 | 135 |
| | 3.0 | 0 | 350 | 115 |
| | 4.0 | 0 | 540 | 135 |
| (Running) | 5.0 | 0 | 820 | 165 |
| Grade walking carrying 43 lb. load | 0.5 | 35.8 | 370 | 740 |
| | 1.0 | 35.8 | 680 | 680 |
| | 1.5 | 35.8 | 890 | 595 |
| Skiing along level | 3.0 | 0 | 540 | 180 |
| | 5.0 | 0 | 720 | 145 |
| | 7.5 | 0 | 950 | 125 |
| Swimming (breaststroke) | 1.0 | | 410 | 410 |
| | 1.6 | | 490 | 305 |
| | 1.9 | | 820 | 430 |

*Based on data from Harvard Fatigue Laboratory in Morehouse and Cherry: Energy cost of progession, National Academy of Science, Washington, D. C., July, 1946, Government Printing Office. The same precautions should be used in interpreting these data as are noted in Table 7.

3.5 m.p.h. than when the speed is slowed to 2.3 m.p.h. or increased to 4.6 m.p.h. Speeds of grade climbing below 2.5 m.p.h. require the expenditure of more Calories each mile than do speeds of 2.5 to 3.5 m.p.h. Less energy is expended when a 43-pound load is carried at 3 m.p.h. than at either slower or faster speeds. In carrying the load up a steep grade, the faster speed is more economical, but at the greater speed the rate of energy expenditure becomes so high that a steady state of physiological activity cannot be established, and exhaustion occurs within a short distance. In the case of walking up a grade carrying a 43-pound load, it would appear that 1 m.p.h. is the optimal speed if the load is to be carried more than a mile, but 1.5 m.p.h. is optimal if the load is to be carried less than a mile. The same principles apply to skiing along a level. The faster speed is more economical, but the high-energy requirement at speeds above 5 m.p.h. prevent these rates from being continued for more than 1 hour. The rapidly increasing energy requirement as swimming speed is increased necessitates a moderately slow rate of swimming if the distance to be covered requires more than 1 hour. Extremely slow rates of swimming are uneconomical.

## Low economy of slow work

The reason for the low economy of progression at a slow rate is that a large part of the energy used during the work is required for the maintenance of body functions (digestive, glandular, etc.) that do not contribute directly to the performance of the work. When the distance is traversed in a shorter time, the energy cost of maintenance of these supportive functions is correspondingly reduced.

The increase in energy cost when work is performed at slow rates is shown in Table 10. The 1-mile climb at 0.5 m.p.h. requires 2 hours. At 1.5 m.p.h. the climb can be completed in 40 minutes. At the slow rate of work the energy cost of maintaining the human machine must be met for 80 minutes longer than at the faster rate of work. This increased energy cost, amounting to 145 Calories, reduces the work efficiency from 24 to 6%.

A dominant factor in human efficiency is the time spent in performing the work. The longer the work period, the lower the efficiency. In order to achieve the highest efficiency work should be performed at the most rapid rate within the limits of skill and endurance.

## Influence of work load on efficiency

An additional factor in work efficiency, as shown in Table 10, is the work load. When the speed was increased from 0.5 to 1 m.p.h., the work load was increased by 145,548 foot-pounds per hour and the efficiency improved from 13 to 14%. At 1.5 m.p.h. the work load was 436,444 footpounds per hour and the efficiency was 16%.

The increase in efficiency as the load is increased demonstrates that the percentage of energy utilized for the work is greater when fairly heavy work is done than when light work is done.

Net efficiency, in which the energy cost of recovery is added to the energy cost during work, is lowered as the load of brief bouts of heavy work is increased. The lowered net efficiency is explained on the basis of the low metabolic efficiency of the lactic debt mechanism.[5]

## Maximum rate of work

Work that requires an energy expenditure greater than 700 Calories per hour cannot be continued for much longer than 1 hour by an untrained man. Unless the man carrying the 43-pound load up the 35.8% grade (Table 10) was well trained, he could not be expected to climb at 1.5 m.p.h. for more than 1 hour since the energy expenditure at this rate is 890 Calories per hour. If the speed is reduced to 1 m.p.h., the energy requirement is reduced to 680 Calories per hour, and the work can be sustained for a longer period. If the distance is great, the speed should be reduced so that the climber is not exhausted by the work. Efficiency must be sacrificed for endurance in order to accomplish work of long duration. If the distance is short, greater speed or heavier loads are necessary if the work is to be performed with the greatest efficiency. A well-trained person is able to carry on work at a higher level of energy expenditure; thus he is able to perform work at higher speeds for longer periods.

*Table 10.* Relation of efficiency to rate and load of work—154-pound man carrying 43-pound load up 35.8% grade*

| Speed (m.p.h.) | Climbing 1 hour | | Climbing 1 mile | |
|---|---|---|---|---|
| | *Calories per hour* | *Efficiency* | *Calories per mile* | *Efficiency* |
| 0.5 | 370 | 13% | 740 | 6% |
| 1.0 | 680 | 14% | 680 | 14% |
| 1.5 | 890 | 16% | 595 | 24% |

*Data from Table 9.

## Racing plan

The steadiness in the rate of work is also a factor in efficiency. Work is done more efficiently if it is carried on at a steady rate. As shown before, it costs energy to accelerate. In distance races, whether running, swimming, rowing, or bicycling, energy must be conserved and a steady state established at a dangerously high level of energy expenditure. Under these conditions the race will be finished in the shortest time if the athlete has maintained a speed at which a maximum steady state level has been established for the number of minutes required for the event. Then, at the proper distance before the end of the race, he increases the speed so that the maximum oxygen debt is reached at the finish. In this race plan the maximum energy is expended in the most economical manner. If the maximum energy has not been used in a race and the competitor has not finished in exhaustion, he has not turned in his greatest possible performance. Detailed racing plans for swimming and track events are presented in textbooks on these subjects.[6, 7]

Physiological factors are not the only ones that enter into the efficiency complex. Other important factors such as heredity, environment, and economics are discussed elsewhere.[8, 9]

## Advanced study topics

1. How is the physical work of walking along a horizontal plane calculated?
2. Review the recent literature on the efficiency of muscular work in current issues of *Ergonomics*.
3. Determine how best to carry a hiking pack.
4. Observe the various rates and loads of work in different manual tasks.
5. Can heart rate be substituted for oxygen consumption in determining the efficiency of muscular work?

## References

1. Hill, A. V.: Production and absorption of heat by muscle, Science **131**:897, 1960.
2. Zierler, K. L.: Mechanism of muscle contraction and its energetics. In Bard, P., editor: Medical physiology, St. Louis, 1961, The C. V. Mosby Co., chap. 55.
3. Starr, I.: Units for the expression of both static and dynamic work in similar terms, and their application to weight lifting experiments, J. Appl. Physiol. 4:21, 1951.
4. Morehouse, L. E., and Cherry, R. B.: Energy cost of progression, National Academy of Sciences, Washington, D. C., July, 1946, Government Printing Office.
5. Henry, F. M., and DeMoor, J.: Metabolic efficiency of exercise in relation to work load at constant speed, J. Appl. Physiol. 2:481, 1950.
6. Armbruster, D. A., and Morehouse, L. E.: Swimming and diving, St. Louis, 1950, The C. V. Mosby Co.
7. Bresnahan, G. T., Tuttle, W. W., and Cretzmeyer, F. X.: Track and field athletics, ed. 5, St. Louis, 1960, The C. V. Mosby Co.
8. Brody, S.: Bioenergetics and growth, New York, 1945, Reinhold Publishing Corp.
9. Morehouse, L. E., and Rasch, P. J.: Sports medicine for trainers, Philadelphia, 1963, W. B. Saunders Co.
10. Balke, B., and Ware, R. W.: An experimental study of physical fitness of Air Force personnel, U. S. Armed Forces Med. J. **10**:675-688, 1961.

# 21

# Nutritional aspects
# of exercise

Any diet that contains a wide variety of foods in sufficient quantity to maintain normal body weight and to support growth is adequate for individuals in all categories of exercise habits—from sedentary to athletic. This concept is generally true, but there are certain dietary modifications that affect body functions in vigorous exercise.

Also, exercise affects the nutritional state of an individual. It is with these phenomena that this chapter is principally concerned.

## Quantity of food

The increased energy metabolism during muscular exercise must be supported by an equivalent increase in energy supply. If the demand exceeds the supply, body tissues are consumed in the course of the activity. The depletion of body tissues impairs the functions of the organs of which these tissues are a part. Furthermore physical efficiency is lower when body tissues are used as fuels for activity than when the fuels are supplied by the foodstuffs in an adequate diet.

The quantity of food required by active men varies to such an extent among the individuals in a group and also in a single person from day to day that the establishment of a standard dietary requirement for a group or a person would be meaningless. The total daily energy requirement for an active man may range from 3,000 to 8,000 Calories, depending upon his size and physical condition and the severity of the work performed each day. An experiment on rats[1] demonstrates some of the variables that affect the daily energy requirement. Twelve female albino rats from 4 to 12 months old were observed while quantitative variations in activity, food intake, and environmental temperature were induced. When activity was increased, the weight decreased if food intake was constant. When the food intake was increased, there was an increase in body weight when activity was constant. When environmental temperature was increased, there was a decrease in body weight when activity was constant. The quantity of food required to support increased physical activity and environmental stress is soon indicated by alterations in body weight.

A similar demonstration has been obtained in man.[2] Light workers, clerks and mechanics, were observed to have the least caloric intake. The intake was greater among workers who performed heavier work. Of interest also was an elevated food intake among the extremely sedentary individuals, the stallholders and supervisors. Increased food intake accompanying increased physical activity may be in some way related to an increased carbohydrate utilization.

## Body fat

Various types of competitive athletics require different proportions of fat to muscle for maximum performance. A minimum amount of fat is desirable in a distance runner, a high jumper, and a gymnast. These athletes must move their own weight in a highly economical fashion, and any added weight taxes the strength and endurance. Distance swimmers need a certain amount of fat distributed near the skin surface to diminish the heat loss to the water. Football players, especially linemen, employ the fat portion of their mass in achieving momentum and also as a cushion to absorb the shocks of repeated contact.

During severe athletic training the normal amount of fat is reduced to a minimum because this tissue is considered an encumbrance. It is an extra load to be carried and impedes the violent contraction of muscles. In this highly trained state man is best fitted for running, jumping, climbing, and fighting.

During a season of athletic training a slight loss in body weight may be expected at first due to a loss of fat. The initial loss is followed by a slow gain attributable to increased muscular development. One evidence of *staleness* or *overtraining* is a gradual loss of weight; that is, the weight lost during exercise is not regained as it should be. Rest and feeding are indicated when weight continues to decline.

## "Making weight"

"Making weight" by wrestlers, boxers, weight lifters, and jockeys is accomplished by profuse sweating and by abstaining from food and liquids for a few hours before weighing in. Weight loss up to 10 pounds (representing 5% of the body weight) was accomplished without any measurable deleterious effects in six wrestlers.[3] Weight loss was induced by a procedure considered orthodox by wrestling coaches. Food and water were withheld. The wrestlers, wearing heavy sweat suits, worked on the mats and alternated this with sitting in a heated cabinet. This abnormal loss of weight is regained in part after weighing in by eating and drinking. More than 5 pounds may be regained in a few hours.

## Weight loss in athletics

Losses of weight exceeding 10 pounds in 1½ hours have been reported during football games at the beginning of training. During especially exciting games a substitute who has been "sweating out" the entire game on the bench has been observed to lose 5 pounds. This weight is entirely and rapidly regained after eating and drinking.

## Semistarvation

A diet that is inadequate to support the needs of the body will soon result in a deterioration in fitness for exercise. When the daily caloric intake is reduced, the day-to-day output of voluntary work is reduced proportionally. A substandard diet causes a reduction in the performance of the physiological systems, especially the mechanisms for the delivery of oxygen and the removal of metabolic waste.[4]

## Dietary notions among athletes

The problem of what constitutes the optimum diet for athletes in training for competitive contests is probably older than organized sports. Many of the dietary superstitions of primitive tribes are based on the idea that certain foods—in particular the meat of certain animals—endow the consumer with the qualities of strength, endurance, and courage with which his prey was identified. Trainers and coaches have inherited something of this theory and have applied it to the athletes under their tutelage.

One of the most widespread of such practices has been the advocacy of eating large quantities of meat to replenish "muscle substance" following the "losses" supposedly incurred during severe muscular work. This particular practice was first recorded in Greece during the fifth century B.C. and ascribed to two athletes who had deviated from the hitherto traditional (chiefly vegetarian) diet of the time to a regimen entailing the intake of large quantities of meat and leading to increased body bulk. The fifth century B.C. also saw a change in cultural outlooks on physical fitness. Instead of being considered essentially a broad prerequisite in the defense of the country, physical fitness became subordinate to training for specific sports, excellence in which was considered superior to almost all other values.[5]

There are many dietary notions among athletes, and athletes have turned in championship performances after training on diets that in the light of accepted dietary standards would be considered inadequate in many respects. Many champions are vegetarians, others eat large quantities of meat, some of it raw. Most athletes reduce the intake of fat in their training diets, but others make no changes whatsoever and eat what they please or what is served to them with no regard to the possible effect of nutrition upon performance. These experiences are in line with recent experimental evidence that the ratio of fat, carbohydrate, and protein in the diet may be altered considerably before changes in work performance appear.

Within wide limits there appear to be certain dietary principles that are associated with improved performance in work and sport. Positive evidence for these principles is accumulating, but a well-controlled experiment has yet to be performed.

## Dietary ratio of carbohydrate, fat, and protein

As a result of observations of changes in performance records of highly trained athletes on different diets containing various proportions of the food principles, the following generalization has been made: a diet of 150 grams of fat, 700 grams of carbohydrate, and 100 grams of protein plus adequate minerals and vitamins daily was recommended for *distance* events; and 100 to 130 grams of fat, 350 to 400 grams of carbohydrate, and 210 grams of protein, mostly meat, was recommended for *speed* events.[6] These figures must, at best, be considered to represent the order of magnitude only. Further evidence is needed as a basis for the construction of diets with a view toward providing the best nutrition for muscular activity. To this end, the various food principles will be discussed separately.

*Carbohydrates.* Carbohydrates are essential dietary constituents but are not the exclusive fuel for muscle. The amounts of carbohydrate used are related to the work level. The depletion of blood sugar levels below 70 mg.% results in exhaustion. A low blood sugar level may interfere with the metabolism of the central nervous system to such an extent that a mild degree of oxygen want brings on symptoms similar to those obtained under conditions of extreme hypoxia. This indicates that the fatigue of protracted, exhausting exercise has a cerebral component. Associated with the fatigue of prolonged work is a loss of mechanical efficiency because of faulty coordination. Theoretically a diet rich in carbohydrates should contribute to the maintenance of normal blood sugar concentration for longer periods during prolonged physical work. Even though this is not always actually the case and exhaustion often occurs with a high blood sugar concentration and at high R.Q.'s, the theory is supported by observations in which industrial workers are found to work more efficiently on a carbohydrate-rich than on a fat-rich diet.[7] Evidently the blood sugar level does not always reflect the nutritional condition of the muscles, and also conditions other than the type of fuel affect the R.Q. Although the mechanisms of carbohydrate utilization are not entirely clear, there is sufficient evidence to support the principle that the athlete in training should have extra carbohydrate in his diet.

An exception to the superiority of high carbohydrate meals is observed in workers performing strenuous visual tasks requiring the recognition of fine details moving on a conveyor belt. For this type of work either a balanced standard meal or a high-fat meal was preferable.[8]

*Protein.* Protein in the form of meat is consumed in large quantities by athletes and men doing hard physical work. The quantity of protein needed for bringing about the highest capacity for work is probably much less than the amounts ordinarily consumed by active men. A long-distance racing cyclist who was a vegetarian performed with higher gross efficiencies on a low-protein diet, but he had better endurance on a high-protein diet.[9] Another man lived for years on a diet that provided a daily intake of only about 30 grams of protein. His physical efficiency was high, and he could perform severe exercise without increasing the nitrogen excretion.[10]

A carefully controlled study of the effect of restricted protein on men working in the heat[11] revealed no essential change in fitness for work in either temperate or tropical environments when dietary protein was varied from 76 to 105 and 149 grams per day, although a 4% higher work metabolism was associated with the highest protein intake.

To summarize, the dietary protein intake of an athlete may vary widely (75 to 150 grams daily) without any noticeable effect upon performance of intermittent (speed) activities. When work is prolonged (endurance), higher intakes of dietary protein accompanying higher calorie diets may be beneficial.

*Fats.* Subjects maintained on a fat-rich diet showed a smaller net muscular efficiency than when they were on a carbohydrate-rich diet.[12] By plotting R.Q. against net efficiency, extrapolation to pure fat metabolism (R.Q. of 0.70) indicated 11% greater energy expenditure per unit of work than for pure carbohydrate metabolism (R.Q. of 1).

Even though fat-rich diets are associated with reduced endurance and muscular efficiency, the exclusion of all fat from the diet is not recommended. Aside from the important vitamins and certain essential fatty acids in fats, there appears to be a fat-contained factor that is necessary for the normal metabolism of carbohydrate. A disturbed carbohydrate metabolism has been observed in rats maintained more than year on a fat-deficient diet.[13] In the light of these considerations it would seem that the amount of fat in the diet that will maintain a good nutritional condition and yet not materially reduce endurance or muscular efficiency is about 100 grams daily. Normal intake of fat should not supply more than 45% of the total calories. The fat content of the diet during training for an athletic event in which particularly high levels of performance are desired may be reduced to 75 grams or 25% of the total calories per day. The protein and carbohydrate content in this training diet would be approximately 15 and 60%, respectively, of the total calories per day.

## Vitamins

Vitamins in the diet are essential for good performance in work and sport. Following the principle that if a little of something is good, then a large amount of the same thing should be better, the discovery and identification of vitamins led to the administration of large doses of these substances in the hope that such a superdiet would result in superperformance. Where vitamins were lacking in the diet, these superdiets did improve performance, but extra vitamins added to normal diets did not improve performance. Healthy young men expending an average of 3,700 to 4,200 Calories per day are not benefited by a daily dietary supply in excess of 1.7 mg. thiamine chloride, 2.4 mg. riboflavin, and 70 mg. ascorbic acid.[14] Fortification of normal diets with vitamins does not improve fitness for work and exercise. This has been shown in static and dynamic work tests,[15] muscular endurance tests,[16] work in heavy industry,[17] and treadmill-running tests.[14] In neither brief, exhausting exercise nor in prolonged, severe exercise are there any indications of benefit due to dietary supplements of thiamine chloride, cocarboxylase, riboflavin, nicotinic acid, pyridoxine, pantothenic acid, and ascorbic acid or to vitamin B complex given intravenously.

Vitamins are stored in varying amounts in the body. When diets are deficient in vitamins, the stores are depleted, and the consequent deterioration in physical condition results in a reduction in the capacity for muscular work. The effects of deficiencies of the various vitamins are discussed separately because of the specific nature of the results in each case.

*Vitamin A deficiency.* In men maintained for 6 months on less than 100 international units of vitamin A daily after a preliminary massive dose period of 30 days, there was no change in plasma vitamin A levels, visual thresholds, or scores in moderate and exhausting work tests.[18] The fact that vitamin A did not disappear from the plasma in these subjects indicates that their reserves were not exhausted. The depletion of vitamin A stores in the body takes a very long time so that there is a substantial margin of safety in most cases.

Performance may be restricted by lack of vitamin A because of the effects on vision. People subsisting for long periods on diets very low in vitamin A develop night blindness.[19] Vitamin A intake may affect color vision. The daily administration of carotene to factory workers was followed by a 75% reduction in the number of rejections for off-color parts of stoves assembled by them.[20] Among normal persons subsisting on diets not markedly deficient in vitamin A, there is little relation between vitamin A intake, blood vitamin A concentration, and dark adaptation.[21]

*Vitamin B deficiency.* Diets containing about one third of the recommended optimum intake of vitamin B complex do not lead to deterioration in physical capacity within 2 weeks if the physical and environmental stresses are not great. Subjects put on a vitamin-deficient diet containing 0.16 mg. thiamine, 0.15 mg. riboflavin, and 1.8 mg. niacin per 1,000 Calories displayed no change in work capacity, psychomotor test scores, or clinical condition during the 2 weeks' deficiency period.[22] A similar lack of effect was observed when riboflavin only was limited to 0.31 mg. per 1,000 Calories.[23]

Thiamine is concerned in carbohydrate metabolism. When thiamine is deficient, lactic and pyruvic acids accumulate in abnormal amounts and muscular activity is depressed. Ten healthy men placed on a more severe thiamine restriction, doing harder physical labor and in a colder environmental temperature, showed a clear diminution in scores in physical tests in 1 week.[24] A trained subject who was fed a diet deficient in thiamine and riboflavin during a hot summer showed a significant decrease in performance on a bicycle ergometer.[25]

Vitamin B deficiency over a long period produces a deterioration in fitness for exercise even in the absence of hard physical labor or environmental stress. Subjects on a reduced thiamine, riboflavin, and ascorbic acid intake during a 12-week period experienced a reduction in work performance.[26]

The requirements for thiamine, riboflavin, and niacin are probably proportional to the intensity of the metabolism. It is justifiable to advise an increased intake of B vitamins when work is increased and when the stress of the environment is great. With a reasonably good diet this is guaranteed by simply increasing the total food intake.

*Vitamin C deficiency.* Low levels of vitamin C intake do not measurably reduce work performance. Men receiving only 40 mg. of ascorbic acid daily did not differ significantly in fitness for exercise nor in susceptibility to heat exhaustion from men receiving 540 mg. daily.[27]

*Vitamin E deficiency.* Rats on diets deficient in vitamin E show degenerative changes in muscles[28, 29] and diminished capacity for treadmill running.[30] Whether man shows similar responses to vitamin E deficiency has not yet been determined.

## Alkalinization

The fact that severe muscular work produces fixed acids that lower both pH and alkali reserve indicates that increasing the alkali reserve might benefit the performance of exercise. The maximal accumulation of lactate in the blood is greater when the alkali reserve is high.[31] The extra alkali reserve allows more prompt and complete neutralization of lactic acid as it is formed, and hence the higher level of blood lactate may indicate a better neutralization. Changes in the alkali reserve as a result of dietary alterations probably are not large enough to affect the ability of normal persons to perform muscular work.

## Distribution of meals

The effect of various distributions of meals throughout the day upon work performance indicates that frequent feeding is desirable. Three meals a day are superior to two meals a day with respect to physical efficiency.[32] Production in industry increases when midforenoon and midafternoon snacks are provided.[33] From the point of view of industrial efficiency, workers should be allowed a reasonable freedom of choice of what they eat and drink during the rest periods.[34]

A breakfast of coffee alone is insufficient to support a full morning of activity. A light breakfast consisting of fruit, one slice of buttered toast, milk, and coffee, if desired, will increase the level of performance in maximum work output and choice reaction time and also will decrease the magnitude of tremor during the latter part of the morning. A heavy breakfast, consisting of fruit, cereal and cream, egg, bacon, toast and jam, milk, and coffee, if desired, is also better than coffee alone. It is doubtful that the physiological responses after a heavy breakfast are better than after a light breakfast, especially if the morning's work is not strenuous.[35]

## Preexercise meal

The preexercise meal should be eaten at least 2 hours before performance begins so that the major portion of the food has been emptied from the stomach. When vigorous exercise is performed while the stomach is distended by food, the inspiratory descent of the diaphragm may be impaired. This perhaps explains why a heavy meal seems to "cut the wind." It is conceivable also that a stomach distended by food may encroach upon the action of the heart during heavy exercise, especially restricting filling. The consequent restriction of blood flow through the heart would ultimately affect endurance. Exercise probably does not affect the rate of digestion unless the activity is associated with psychic stress.[36] For a detailed discussion of the role of nutrition in the training regimen of an athlete, consult a recent textbook on scientific training of an athlete.[37]

### Advanced study topics

1. How can exercise be used in a program to control body weight?
2. Review the recent literature on the nutritional aspects of exercise in current issues of the *Journal of Nutrition*.
3. Describe a method of obtaining and analyzing dietary histories.
4. Observe the kinds and quantities of foods eaten by athletes before and during competition.
5. How can diet either hasten or delay the onset of fatigue in physical work?

### References

1. Brobeck, J. R.: Effects of variations in activity, food intake and environmental temperature on weight gain in the albino rat, Am. J. Physiol. **143**:1, 1945.
2. Mayer, J., and Bullen, B.: Nutrition and athletic performance, Physiol. Rev. **40**:369, 1960.
3. Tuttle, W. W.: The effect of weight loss by dehydration and the withholding of food on the physiologic responses of wrestlers, Res. Quart. Am. A. Health Phys. Ed. & Rec. **14**:158, 1943.
4. Schultz, F. W., Morse, M., and Hastings, A. B.: Acidosis as a factor of fatigue in dogs, Am. J. Physiol. **113**:595, 1935.
5. Mayer, J., and Bullen, B.: Nutrition and athletic performance, Physiol. Rev. **40**:369-397, 1960.
6. Dupain, G. Z.: Specific diets and athletic fitness; a preliminary investigation, Res. Quart. Am. A. Health Phys. Ed. & Rec. **10**:33, 1939.
7. Henschel, A.: Diet and muscular fatigue, Res. Quart. **13**:280, 1942.
8. Simonson, E., Brozek, J., and Keys, A.: Effect of meals on visual performance and fatigue, J. Appl. Physiol. **1**:270, 1948.
9. Wishart, G. M.: Efficiency and performance of a vegetarian racing cyclist under different dietary conditions, J. Physiol. **82**:189, 1934.
10. Strieck, F.: Metabolic studies in a man who lived for years on a minimum protein diet, Ann. Int. Med. **11**:643, 1937.
11. Pitts, G. C., Consolazio, F. C., and Johnson, R. E.: Dietary protein and physical fitness in temperate and hot environments, J. Nutrition **27**:497, 1944.
12. Christensen, E. H., and Hansen, O.: Arbeitsfähigkeit und Ernährung, Skand. Arch. Physiol. **81**:160, 1939.
13. Wesson, L. G.: Disturbed carbohydrate metabolism in rats maintained more than a year on a fat-deficient diet, Endocrinology **29**:900, 1941.
14. Keys, A., and Henschel, A.: Vitamin supplementation of U. S. Army rations in relation to fatigue and ability to do muscular work, J. Nutrition **23**:259, 1942.
15. Simonson, E., Baer, A., and Enzer, N.: The influence of vitamin B (complex) surplus on the capacity for muscular and mental work, Fed. Proc. **1**:81, 1942.
16. Karpovich, P. V., and Millman, N.: Vitamin B₁ and endurance, New England J. Med. **226**:881, 1942.

17. Bransby, E. R., Magee, H. E., Hunter, J. W., Milligan, E. H. M., and Rogers, T. S.: Influence of supplements of vitamins A, B₁, B₂, C, and D on growth, health, and physical fitness, Brit. M. J. 1:77, 1944.

18. Wald, G., Brouha, L., and Johnson, R. E.: Experimental human vitamin A deficiency and ability to perform muscular exercise, Am. J. Physiol. 137:551, 1942.

19. Dann, W. J., and Yarborough, M. E.: Dark adaptometer readings of subjects on diet deficient in vitamin A, Arch. Ophthal. 25:833, 1941.

20. Wise, R. C., and Schettler, O. H.: Report on the use of biophotometer and vitamin A therapy in industry, Ohio State M. J. 34:666, 1938.

21. Haig, C., and Patek, A. J.: The relation between dark adaptation and the level of vitamin A in the blood, J. Clin. Invest. 21:377, 1942.

22. Keys, A., Henschel, A., Taylor, H. L., Mickelsen, O., and Brozek, J.: Absence of rapid deterioration in men doing hard physical work on restricted intake of vitamins of B complex, J. Nutrition 27:485, 1944.

23. Keys, A., Henschel, A., Mickelsen, O., Brozek, J. M., and Crawford, J. H.: Physiological and biochemical functions in normal young men on a diet restricted in riboflavin, J. Nutrition 27:165, 1944.

24. Johnson, R. E., Darling, R. C., Forbes, W. H., Brouha, L., Egana, E., and Graybiel, A.: The effects of a diet deficient in part of the vitamin B complex upon men doing manual labor, J. Nutrition 24:585, 1942.

25. Foltz, E. E., Barborka, C. J., and Ivy, A. C.: Influence of diet deficient in vitamin B complex on work output of trained subjects, J.A.M.A. 121:1411, 1943.

26. Barborka, C. J., Foltz, E. E., and Ivy,

A. C.: Relationship between vitamin B complex intake and work output in trained subjects, J.A.M.A. 122:717, 1943.

27. Henschel, A., Taylor, H. L., Brozek, J., Mickelsen, O., and Keys, A.: Vitamin C and ability to work in hot environments, Am. J. Trop. Med. 24:259, 1944.

28. Knowlton, G. C., and Hines, H. M.: Effect of vitamin E deficient diet upon skeletal muscles, Proc. Soc. Exper. Biol. & Med. 38:665, 1938.

29. Tilford, I. R., Emerson, G. A., and Evans, H. M.: Histological changes in skeletal musculature of paralyzed suckling young of E-low rats, Proc. Soc. Exper. Biol. & Med. 41:291, 1939.

30. Kokas, E., and Borka, B. V.: Über Wirkung von E-Avitaminose auf das Arbeitsvermögen weisser Ratten, Pflügers Arch. ges. Physiol. 246:158, 1942.

31. Dennig, H., Talbott, J. H., Edwards, H. T., and Dill, D. B.: Effects of acidosis and alkalosis on capacity for work, J. Clin. Invest. 9:601, 1931.

32. Clarke, D., De Jongh, T. W., and Jokl, E.: Effect of mid-day meal upon physical efficiency of school children, Manpower (South Africa) 1:30, 1943.

33. Haggard, H. W., and Greenberg, L. A.: Diet and physical efficiency, New Haven, 1933, Yale University Press.

34. Haldi, J., and Wynn, W.: Industrial efficiency as affected by food intake during mid-morning and mid-afternoon rest periods, J. Appl. Physiol. 2:268, 1949.

35. Tuttle, W. W., Wilson, M., and Daum, K.: Effect of altered breakfast habits on physiologic response, J. Appl. Physiol. 1:545, 1949.

36. Hellebrandt, F. A., and Karpovich, P. V.: Fitness, fatigue and recuperation, War Med. 1:745, 1941.

37. Morehouse, L. E., and Rasch, P. J.: Sports medicine for trainers, Philadelphia, 1963, W. B. Saunders Co.

# 22

# *Exercise, heat, and body temperature*

## Concept of "body temperature"

The statement is often made that the normal body temperature is 98.6° F. and that deviations from this value indicate an abnormal temperature. Careful consideration of this statement raises two questions: What is the normal *range* of body temperature? Are all parts of the body at the same temperature?

If the oral or rectal temperatures of a group of resting subjects are measured at the same time, a range of values is obtained. For example, the oral temperatures of a group of 276 medical students measured between 8 and 9 A.M., ranged from 96.5° to 99.3° F.[1] There is also a diurnal variation of several degrees in the oral or rectal temperatures in the same individual, being highest in the late afternoon and lowest during the early morning hours. Finally, the rectal temperature is usually about 1° F. higher than the oral temperature, and even in the rectum there are variations of from 0.1° to 1.5° F., depending on the depth of insertion of the thermometer or other measuring device.[2] The need for careful standardization of procedures in experiments involving measurement of "body temperature" is obvious.

A rectal temperature of 99.6° F. does not mean that all parts of the body are at this temperature; for example, the skin temperature may be 10° to 15° F. lower than the rectal temperature, and if a needle thermistor is inserted into the subcutaneous tissue, temperatures intermediate between those of the skin and the rectum are recorded. From the standpoint of temperature regulation, it is convenient to consider that the body is composed of two compartments, a central core and a peripheral shell. The core consists of the contents of the cranial, thoracic, abdominal, and pelvic cavities and the deeper portions of the muscle masses of the extremities. The shell includes the skin, subcutaneous tissues, and the superficial portions of the muscle masses. It is of variable thickness, depending on the environmental temperature; it increases in thickness during exposure to cold and decreases in thickness in response to environmental heat or to exercise. The shell may be thought of as a layer of insulation surrounding the core and helping to maintain a constant core temperature. The temperature of the shell is not only lower than that of the core under nearly all conditions, but there is a gradient of temperature of the shell, from core temperature in its deepest portion to skin temperature at the periphery. In general, the temperature-regulating mechanisms operate in such a way that the temperature of the core is protected, whereas the temperature of the shell may vary considerably. Oral and rectal temperatures, if carefully measured, reflect the temperature of the core. Skin temperature may be measured by thermocouples or thermistors mounted in contact with the skin and shell temperature by needle thermistors inserted to various depths beneath the skin.

## Nature of the regulation of body temperature

The core temperature represents a balance between the rates at which heat is added to the body and lost from the body. When these two rates are equal, the temperature remains constant. Ordinarily the major source of heat gain is from metabolism, but under certain conditions the body may also gain heat from the environment. Heat is lost from the body by the physical processes of radiation, conduction, convection, and the vaporization of water. These are aided by two physiological factors—variations in the blood flow through the skin (which determine the amount of heat transported from the core to the surface) and the secretion of sweat (which provides water for cooling the skin by vaporization). Ordinarily the regulation of body temperature is achieved by adjustments in the rate of heat loss; the capacity for altering heat production is limited to such activities as shivering and voluntary muscular activity during exposure to cold. Variations in the rates of heat production and of heat loss that are necessary for the maintenance of a constant core temperature are controlled by temperature-regulating centers in the hypothalamus.

## Channels of heat loss

Heat loss by *conduction* occurs when the body is in direct contact with something that is colder than the skin. The rate at which heat is lost by conduction depends both on the difference in temperature between the skin and the medium in contact with the skin and on the heat conductivity of the medium. For example, water is a much better conductor of heat than is air, and for this reason the body loses heat much more rapidly in cold water than in air at the same temperature. Conductive heat loss is ordinarily of minor importance.

Heat loss by *convection* involves movement of the medium (air or water) in contact with the body surface. Cooler air or water is brought into contact with the skin, where it is warmed by conduction and then moves on, carrying with it the heat gained from the body. This is the principle of the cooling effect of fans.

Heat loss by *radiation* is the result of the fact that all warm bodies emit electromagnetic heat waves; this is the way in which the earth is warmed by the sun. The human body is constantly gaining and losing heat by radiation, but under normal environmental conditions the loss exceeds the gain, and this constitutes the most important channel of heat loss in resting men in moderate climates. When men are directly exposed to the sun in hot deserts, there may be a net gain of heat by radiation.

Heat loss by *vaporization* is due to the fact that the evaporation of water, that is, conversion from liquid to gas state, requires the absorption of 0.58 kilocalorie per gram of water vaporized. The vaporization of sweat on the skin cools the skin by abstracting from it the necessary heat to vaporize the water of the sweat (the abstraction of heat from the surrounding air is negligible because of the low heat content of the air). It should be emphasized that sweating cools the skin only if the sweat is vaporized. Under conditions of high relative humidity the sweat may simply drip from the skin without cooling it.

## Sources of heat gain

In a resting subject exposed to a comfortable environmental temperature, the heat gain is due entirely to metabolism. Metabolic heat production is increased in exercise; in very strenuous exercise it may increase as much as thirtyfold. Metabolic heat production is also increased during exposure to cold by the type of muscle contractions known as shivering. Finally, if the body is exposed to intense, direct sunlight or to warming devices such as stoves, it may gain heat by radiation, and if it is exposed to a medium having a high temperature (for example, very hot water), it may gain heat by conduction. The physiological adjustments of heat production are quantitatively much less important than are those of heat loss, and the regulation of body temperature is largely a matter of appropriate adjustments of heat loss.

## Physiological adjustments that determine heat loss

Although the actual loss of heat from the body is the result of the physical processes of conduction, convection, radiation, and vaporization of water, the operation of these physical processes is conditioned by physiological mechanisms that determine the amount of heat brought to the skin and the amount of sweat available for vaporization.

Heat is transported from the core to the skin primarily by the blood; only a small amount reaches the skin by conduction through the shell. Thus an increase in the blood flow to the skin increases the heat loss by conduction, convection, and radiation. The amount of skin blood flow is determined by the degree of constriction of the skin blood vessels, and this is regulated by the vasoconstrictor nerve fibers that supply these vessels. When vasoconstriction is increased, the blood flow through the skin and the heat loss from the skin are diminished; this occurs when the body is exposed to a cold environment, preventing excessive loss of heat. When vasoconstriction of the skin blood vessels is diminished, the increased flow of blood through the skin increases the heat loss; this occurs in response to greater heat production, as in exercise, or to an elevation of the environmental temperature.

The second physiological factor that determines heat loss from the skin is variation in the activity of the sweat glands. When heat load is increased, more sweat is secreted and evaporative heat loss is greater; this occurs in response to increased heat production (exercise) or to elevated environmental temperature. Exposure to cold, on the other hand, results in the cessation of sweating.

The adjustment of the amount of skin blood flow and of the amount of sweat secreted to meet changing requirements for heat loss or heat conservation is under the control of the temperature-regulating centers in the hypothalamus. These centers are stimulated both by changes in the temperature of the blood, which reflects core temperature, and by afferent impulses from the temperature receptors in the skin. The relative importance of these two sources of stimulation is uncertain, and it may vary according to whether the heat stress is of metabolic or environmental origin.

The regulation of sweating in exercise has been studied intensively in recent years, and conflicting points of view are not yet completely reconciled. It appears that when work intensity is varied while environmental temperature is maintained constant, the rate of sweating is determined by the deep body temperature. When, on the other hand, work of constant intensity is performed at different environmental temperatures, the sweat rate varies with the skin temperature.[3, 4] Furthermore, since for comparable values of rectal and skin temperatures both sweat secretion and skin circulation are much higher during work than during rest, Robinson[5] has suggested that neuromuscular reflexes take part in temperature regulation as they do in the regulation of respiration. He believes that the reflexes probably originate in thermoreceptors in the working muscles or in contact with veins draining the working muscles. In a recent study[6] from Robinson's laboratory direct evidence was obtained for a neurogenic stimulation of sweating in exercise. Isometric contractions of the arm muscles performed in a warm environment while the circulation to and from the working muscles was arrested by an inflated arm cuff resulted in a prompt increase in sweating (within 1.5 to 2.0 seconds after beginning the exercise). In these experiments warmed blood from the exercising muscles could not have reached the heat-regulating centers in the hypothalamus.

The operation of the temperature-regulating system may be illustrated by a description of the response to changing from a thermally neutral environment to a hot or a cold environment. On changing to a hot environment, the skin temperature rises and heat receptors in the skin are stimulated. Afferent impulses from these receptors are transmitted to the heat-loss center in the hypothalamus, which responds by decreasing the discharge of vasoconstrictor nerve impulses to the skin blood vessels and by sending impulses along the secretory nerve fibers to the sweat glands. The result is an increased capacity for dissipating heat from the skin, which balances hindrance to heat loss due to the increased environmental temperature, and body temperature is prevented from rising. Exposure to cold, on the other hand, stimulates cold receptors in the skin, and impulses are transmitted to the heat-conservation center in the hypothalamus, which responds by increasing the constriction of the skin blood vessels and by inhibiting the activity of the sweat glands. The result is a diminished rate of heat loss from the skin and a conservation of body heat.

## *Temperature regulation in exercise (See also Chapter 17)*

When exercise is performed under comfortable environmental conditions, the only problem is the elimination of the excess heat of metabolism. The additional problems that result from the performance of exercise in the heat will be discussed later.

The amount of excess heat produced in most types of exercise is known only approximately because of the difficulty of making the necessary measurements. Laboratory studies indicate that the rate of heat production may easily rise to 10 to 20 times that of the resting subject, and it may be as high as 30 times the resting level in extreme cases. This obviously imposes a severe burden on the temperature-regulating mechanisms, and the failure to prevent an excessive rise in core temperature may contribute to the earlier onset of exhaustion.

As the body temperature rises during exercise, there occurs an increase in the rate of sweating and in the amount of skin blood flow, the stimulus to the hypothalamic centers being an increase in blood temperature. In the case of the circulatory adjustment, however, there is a conflict of interests since there is a requirement for increased blood flow both to the skin and to the active muscles. The result is a compromise in which each requirement suffers, especially in very strenuous exercise performed in the heat. It has long been known that the deep body temperature rises during exercise and that the amount of rise is proportional to the severity of the exercise. This does not indicate that temperature regulation is inadequate, however, since for any level of exercise the temperature rises to a plateau that is then maintained without further increase. When a plateau is not achieved, the situation is abnormal; this will be discussed later.

It appears that the rise in body temperature in exercise is the result of a "resetting" of the hypothalamic "thermostat" at a higher level (just as is the case in clinical fever), so that heat loss balances heat production at a higher body temperature. Furthermore, since most of the excess heat is produced in the active muscles, their temperature rise is certainly greater than that of the whole body, as reflected in the oral and rectal temperatures. A rise in body temperature that is well tolerated by an exercising man may cause great distress in a resting man, and in fact, athletic performance is actually improved by a moderate rise in body temperature. Buskirk and Bass[7] offer the following explanation. The increased tolerance to hyperthermia in exercising persons is due to the fact that increased cardiac output permits the maintenance of an adequate cerebral blood flow, whereas exposure to heat without exercise is associated with a decreased cerebral blood flow (because of decreased cardiac output and cerebral vasoconstriction resulting from respiratory alkalosis). The beneficial effects of an elevated muscle temperature during exercise may perhaps be attributed to the resulting increase in the breakdown of oxyhemoglobin and delivery of oxygen to the muscle fibers and to the decreased internal viscosity of the muscle protoplasm. If the structural rearrangements that take place during contraction and relaxation of muscle fibers are facilitated by the elevated temperature, greater tension might be developed before the state of excitation of the fiber is over (Chapter 2).

## Exercise in the heat

When exercise is performed in a hot environment, especially by a person who is not heat acclimatized, the increased requirement for blood flow to the active muscles and to the skin for thermal regulation may exceed the capacity of the heart to increase the cardiac output. The situation then resembles the incipient circulatory shock of a person who has lost blood by hemorrhage, and fainting may occur, terminating a potentially dangerous activity. The circulatory inadequacy also results in impaired temperature regulation, and if the warning signs of dizziness and faintness are ignored, the extremely serious condition of heat stroke may result. The high rectal temperatures and pulse rates and the dizziness and nausea associated with exercise in the heat may be dramatically reduced by heat acclimatization, which is achieved by daily periods of work in the heat.

## Acclimatization to heat

The heat-acclimatized person is able to work in the heat with a lower rectal temperature and heart rate, a better regulation of body temperature, and fewer unpleasant symptoms than can a nonacclimatized person. The physiological basis of these improvements is obscure, but the end result appears to be an improvement in the capacity for maintaining adequate circulatory function. The process of acclimatization is rapid, being completed in a period of 4 to 7 days, and can be achieved by short intermittent periods (2 to 4 hours daily) of work in the heat; exposure to heat without exercise results in only slight acclimatization. Heat acclimatization is retained for several weeks after the cessation of exposure and then disappears slowly during a period of several months.

It is important to remember that well-conditioned athletes who have trained in a cool environment are not heat acclimatized, and their performance on a hot day may be disappointing. Of greater importance is the clear understanding of the potential danger of exhausting work in the heat by men who are not heat acclimatized; the results may be serious or even fatal.

although usually exhaustion terminates the activity before this point is reached.

A final practical point concerns the proper clothing for work in the heat. Uniforms and equipment that retard the loss of heat from the skin add to the dangers of the situation. There is need for a more scientific approach to the designing of such equipment, based on the requirement for adequate protection without undue hindrance to heat loss.

## Disturbances of heat regulation

When the total heat load of the body exceeds the capacity of the compensatory mechanisms, various incapacities occur. In the order of increasing severity, they are heat cramps, heat exhaustion, and heat stroke. The first two are not dangerous if they are recognized and if the activity is terminated; heat stroke, on the other hand, is an acute medical emergency and may be fatal if treatment is not rapid and vigorous. The pertinent facts about these three conditions may be summarized as follows.

*Heat cramp* is an indirect effect of exposure to heat, and the body temperature is usually normal. The muscle pain and spasms are the result of excessive loss of salt in the sweat, and the condition is relieved by rest and the administration of salt and water. *Heat exhaustion* characteristically occurs during heat waves, especially those occurring early in the summer, or when athletes who are not heat acclimatized engage in strenuous sports on a hot day. It is a form of circulatory inadequacy caused by pooling of blood in the dilated skin vessels or to marked dehydration. The symptoms include headache, dizziness, and vomiting. The body temperature is usually only slightly elevated, the skin is moist and cool, and the pulse is weak and rapid. Treatment consists of rest in the shade in a recumbent position and replacement of fluids if sweating has been copious. *Heat stroke* is a serious condition that can result in death; it requires the care of a physician. There is prostration and sometimes delirium, the skin is hot, dry, and flushed, and sweating is absent. Body temperature may rise to very high levels, approaching 110° F. in extreme cases. The cause is apparently a derangement of the temperature-controlling centers in the brain similar to that seen in fevers of infectious diseases. It is readily distinguished from heat exhaustion by the hot, dry skin and more profound prostration. Immediate steps should be taken to lower the body temperature (immersion in cold water, ice packs, alcohol spray) while awaiting the arrival of a physician.

### Advanced study topics

1. Describe the function of temperature-regulating centers in the hypothalamus.
2. Review the recent literature on exercise, heat, and body temperature in current issues of the *Journal of Tropical Medicine and Hygiene.*
3. Describe the use of the thermistor thermometer in measuring human body temperature.
4. Compare the clothing requirements of active and inactive individuals in the same cold environment.
5. How can body temperature become a limiting factor in sports performances?

### References

1. Ivy, A. C.: What is normal or normality? Quart. Bull., Northwestern Univ. Med. School 18:22, 1944.

2. Mead, J., and Bonmarito, C. L.: Reliability of rectal temperatures as an index of internal body temperature, J. Appl. Physiol. **2**:97, 1949.

3. Nielsen, B., and Nielsen, M.: On the regulation of sweat secretion in exercise, Acta Physiol. Scand. **64**:314, 1965.

4. Nielsen, B., and Nielsen, M.: Influence of passive and active heating on the temperature regulation of man, Acta Physiol. Scand. **64**:323, 1965.

5. Robinson, S.: The regulation of sweating in exercise. Advances in Biology of Skin (Pergamon) **3**:152, 1962.

6. Van Beaumont, W., and Bullard, R. W.: Sweating exercise stimulation during circulatory arrest, Science **152**:1521, 1966.

7. Buskirk, E. R., and Bass, D. E.: Climate and exercise. In Johnson, W. R., editor: Science and medicine of exercise and sports, New York, 1960, Harper & Row, Publishers.

# 23

# Environmental factors and exercise

## Heat

*Heat regulation.* Heat regulation in a trained subject under working conditions is remarkably effective. In temperatures ranging from 52° to 86° F. with moderate humidities the body maintains an average skin temperature during moderate work that is lower than that of a resting subject in the same environment. During work at a lower temperature a skin temperature is comfortable that would be intolerable in a resting subject. Evaporative cooling with increasing sweat secretion balances the extra heat resulting from increased work. Only at the upper range of work levels (400 Calories per hour and above) is there an increase in the skin temperature.[1, 2] The rectal temperature rises to the same level during constant moderate work in spite of changes in room temperature ranging from 41° to 97° F.[3]

*Work in dry heat.* During rest in the sun, the heat absorbed by the body from the surrounding air may exceed the amount produced by metabolism. During exercise in the sun, radiation and convection may add so much heat to that produced by the exercise that the heat loss by evaporation alone may exceed the production of chemical heat. There are individual differences in the effectiveness of temperature regulation. These differences depend in part on variable rates of sweat production. Acclimatization occurs after continued exposure to work in a hot climate. With acclimatization the sweat output is greater, and the salt content of the sweat is diminished as much as 50%. The susceptibility of some persons to heat cramps depends in part on the inability of their sweat glands to reduce salt losses to a low level. The maximum observed rate of evaporation obtained during work experiments in the desert was 1.7 liters per hour. The minimal rate of urine formation was 10 ml. per hour. The voluntary intake of water lagged behind the water loss in exercise.[4-7]

*Temperature and exhausting work.* High temperature and high humidity may have the same effects as a "warm-up" in aiding the performance of a brief bout of exhausting (anaerobic) work.[8]

**Work in wet heat.** Humidity has a marked effect upon the ability to perform prolonged moderate work in the heat. Men were able to tolerate a 60-minute exposure to 145° F. when humidity was 10%, but they could tolerate only 104° F. at 90% humidity.[9] This and further experiments support the common observation that "It's not the heat, it's the humidity." The wet-bulb temperature reading, which indicates the humidity, is a reliable index of the limits of man's ability to work. Dry-bulb temperature exerts a lesser influence. Marching for 4 hours at the rate of 3 miles per hour while carrying a 20-pound pack was observed to be easy at a wet-bulb temperature below 91° F., difficult at 91° to 94° F., and all but impossible above 94° F. Very high rates of sweating were observed under conditions of work in the hot, wet environment. The highest values were 4.2 liters per hour (9 pounds in 1 hour) and 3.5 liters per hour (23 pounds in 4 hours). An unusual syndrome was observed in which men lost more water in sweat than they could absorb from the gastrointestinal tract, no matter how fast they drank. They became sick; bloating, nausea, and cramps occurred, and vomiting produced complete disability.[10] The performance of acclimatized men in humid heat is seriously impaired by lack of adequate water intake and lack of physical fitness. Performance is also impaired to a lesser extent by lack of rest and sleep, by added clothing and equipment, by drinking alcoholic beverages, and by long periods of work. Sweating in humid heat is profuse and grossly inefficient; it wastes water and salt and is about as excessive whether water is drunk or not.[11] Replacement of water and salt is essential for efficient performance in humid heat. Thirst is a lagging guide to these needs.

**Protection from heat.** Heart rate and body temperature are the most significant and reliable indices of the effect of environmental temperature. An increase in body temperature of 1.5° F. should be the limit for work in industry. Workers may be protected against a rise in body temperature and an excessive increase in the heart rate by a blast of cool air or by ventilating the clothing with cool air by connecting a rubber hose to the back of a worker's coverall suit. A third means of protection against high environmental temperatures is the wearing of wet clothing. The use of wet clothing is especially effective during rest and work when the relative humidity is low and when there is a slight breeze.

**Fitness for work in the heat.** Resting and work heart rates and rectal temperatures obtained in a temperate environment do not indicate the fitness for performance of work in the heat. Although men in good physical condition suffer less than those in poor condition on first exposure to heat, work capacity is limited. Heart rate and body temperature rise to excessive levels, and heat prostration may ensue. These effects are chiefly circulatory, occasioned by the greatly augmented cutaneous blood flow (which increases heat elimination) and the consequent failure of the venous return to the heart.

*Acclimatization.* Acclimatization to heat begins with the first exposure, progresses rapidly, and is well developed by the third or fourth day. A striking observation during the initial exposure period is a marked flushing of the face and head that moderates with acclimatization. Work is performed with a lower body temperature and heart rate, and the blood pressure becomes more stable during acclimatization. Resting for 3 or 4 days in the heat, with activity limited to that required for subsistence, results in definite but only partial acclimatization. Some work in the heat is necessary for complete acclimatization. The ability to perform a maximum amount of strenuous work in the heat is attained most quickly by progressively increased work in the heat. Strenuous work on first exposure to heat is not well tolerated and often results in disability. If such work is maintained for several days, many men become incapacitated, and those who continue to work do so inefficiently. Inadequate rest at night results in less work or less efficient work on the following day, even by a well-acclimatized man. Acclimatization is well retained for 2 weeks. Men in good physical condition retain their acclimatization longer.[10] It is recommended by an authority on tropical medicine that white men in the tropics should take regular vigorous exercise.[12] Acclimatization can be produced about as readily by intermittent exposures to work in the heat as by continuous living and working in the heat.[13] Acclimatization developed by work in dry heat is carried over to performance in humid heat. The rate of loss of acclimatization, as measured by a decline in performance of work in the heat, although not great in 1 week is marked in 3 to 4 weeks.[10]

The mechanism of acclimatization has not yet been fully established. An hypothesis that fits most of the known facts has been advanced by Johnson,[14] who has said, "On first exposure to heat there is inefficient capillary circulation in the skin, with inefficient cooling of the blood and inefficient venous return from the skin. This might account for the great discomfort, increased rectal temperature, inefficient cooling power of a given volume of sweat, high skin temperature, malar flush, orthostatic hypotension, high pulse rate, and dependent edema. After the thalamic centers secure control over the skin capillary bed as a result of subsequent exposures to heat, the above extreme displacements of homeostasis are minimized."

*Sweating.* The rate of sweat excretion by different areas of the body has been measured by Weiner,[15] who used a simple technique. The area selected was dried for 10 seconds, and then a brass ring 7 cm. in diameter and 2 cm. deep was lightly pressed down on the area. The ring carried a well-fitting lid to minimize evaporation. The ring prevented sweat trickling away from the area or reaching it from adjacent areas. After 2 minutes the lid was removed, and during the next ½ minute the sweat within the ring was mopped up by means of a previously dried and weighed cotton pledget. The increase in weight of the pledget was then determined. Using this technique and studying subjects sweating profusely as the result of work in a hot, humid environment, Weiner observed that about 50% of the total secretion of sweat occurred on the trunk, 25% on the lower extremities, and 25% on the head and upper limbs. The palms and soles sweat little, illustrating the fact that there is a rather considerable difference in the intensity of sweating in different regions of the body.

The strain of work in hot environments can be relieved by sweating only when sufficient sweat can be secreted over the body surface.[16] This acclimatization to work in hot environments results, in part, from the increase in number of potentially active sweat glands over the skin surface so that sweating can be done more efficiently and with less dripping.

*Sweat chloride.* The concentration of chloride in the sweat (1) increases as work is prolonged, (2) varies in different persons, (3) varies inversely with the supply of drinking water, (4) increases as the rate of sweating increases, (5) decreases more after ingestion of saline solution than after an equal volume of water, and (6) within wide limits is independent of plasma chloride, plasma protein, and physical fitness. These variations in sweat chloride were found to exist in young men who marched for some hours in temperatures ranging between 100° and 120° F. with a relative humidity of 30% and in temperatures between 80° and 95° F. with a humidity of 85%.[17] Acclimatization involved a progressive decrease in skin and body temperature followed by a decreased excretion of sweat chloride during rest and steady state work. Acclimatization had no effect on sweat chloride during hard work. The lowering of body temperature during acclimatization is responsible for the variation in sweat chloride. If rectal and skin temperatures remain the same, the chloride content of the sweat does not differ before and after acclimatization.

*Blood sugar and sweating.* The ability to sweat is in inverse relation to blood sugar level. Sweat production is retarded after the ingestion of glucose. Hyperglycemia has a slight inhibiting effect upon the rate of sweating.[18]

*Sex differences.* The skin temperature of the female is higher in warm atmospheres and lower in cold atmospheres than that of the male. Women do not begin to sweat until the environmental temperature rises 2 degrees above the threshold for sweating in men, and the amount of sweating is less.[19]

*Water intake.* The ability to work in hot dry or hot humid environments depends largely upon a water intake that is sufficient to replace the water lost in sweat. The necessity of maintaining a water balance has been demonstrated under experimental conditions[21] (Fig. 45). Subjects acclimatized to intermittent exposure to heat walked at a fixed rate up a constant slope in an environmental temperature of 100° F. and a relative humidity of 35 to 45%. When water was not taken, their body temperature rose steadily to 102° F., and they tired easily and worked inefficiently. When they were allowed to drink as much water as they wished, their temperature did not rise as high, and they finished the walk in much better condition. When

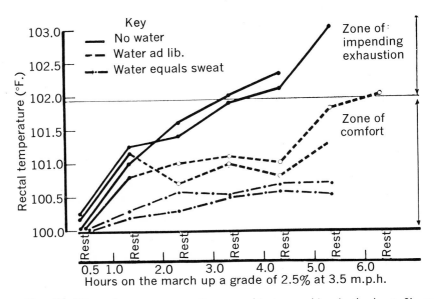

**Fig. 45.** Effect of water consumption on subjects marching in the heat. Six experiments on subject J. S. at temperature 100° F. and relative humidity 35 to 45%. (From Pitts, G. C., Johnson, R. E., and Consolazio, F. C.: Work in the heat as affected by the intake of water, salt, and glucose, Am. J. Physiol. **142**:254, 1944.)

they were required to drink enough water to replace their sweat loss, performance improved still further, and the body temperature rose either very little or not at all.

The body will not retain water unless there is salt to go with it. If a salt deficit is accumulated, forcing water results eventually in an equal output of urine. Drinking water temporarily relieves dehydration but lowers the concentration of salt in extracellular fluid, giving rise eventually to heat cramps.

*Thirst.* The normal thirst response does not guarantee that a working subject will ingest enough water to give him maximal protection against dehydration during work. Even when unlimited water is available, an average subject voluntarily incurs a substantial water deficit during work (Fig. 46). Men who are fully acclimatized sweat less and drink more but rarely voluntarily drink during work more than two thirds of the amount of water lost in sweat. The water deficit is replaced in the period after work is over. Water balance is to be encouraged during work in the heat. If by forcing fluids a water balance is maintained, maximal comfort is achieved, and the work is carried on with a minimal displacement of the total homeostasis.

*Dehydration.* Water should not be withheld on the grounds that it is bad for the worker or that dehydration toughens a man. Dehydration lowers physical efficiency by reducing the blood volume, cardiac output, and velocity of blood flow. Adequate hydration is indispensable for maximal

**Fig. 46.** Fluid in flask represents 8 liters of sweat, a common daily average loss during hard work in the heat.

efficiency. The best performance of work and sport in hot environments is obtained when the water lost in the sweat is replaced hourly by plain drinking water.

Water should be given in more frequent and smaller amounts in hot, dry climates. A hot, dry atmosphere is not tolerated as well as a hot, wet atmosphere when water losses are not replaced. When ample water is given, the same effect is obtained in a hot, dry (109° F., 38% humidity) atmosphere as in a hot, wet atmosphere at the same effective temperature (87.5° F., 87% humidity).[22]

*Salt.* A daily intake of 20 grams of salt appears to be sufficient for most men in most environments. A sodium chloride intake of about 15 grams per day was adequate for 49 men working in dry heat (120° F.). When the salt intake was reduced to 6 grams daily, they lost more than twice as much body weight (water), drank less water, and sweated less. They had higher pulse rates and rectal temperatures and poorer cardiovascular adjustments.

Dehydration, nausea, vomiting, tachycardia, hypotension, vertigo, and collapse occurred in 25% of the men on the low sodium chloride intake and in only 2.5% of those on the 15 grams daily intake. The subjects on the 6 grams daily salt intake suffered an average net deficit of 13 grams of salt for 3 days in the heat (8.39 grams on the first day). The volume of sweat lost varied between 5 and 8 liters (11 and 17.6 pounds) daily. There was no advantage when the daily salt intake was raised to 30 grams.[23]

Salt given without water produces gastrointestinal discomfort without improvement in heat tolerance. The same results are obtained with glucose. Given with water, both bring improved performance.[21] Extra salt or glucose added to the hourly supply of water in hot environments is not indicated in persons receiving meals containing adequate salt and carbohydrate.

The final stages of acclimatization to heat are marked by increased sweat loss and reduced salt concentration in the sweat. A more rapid onset of sweating promotes evaporative loss before body temperatures rise markedly. In this condition of adaptation men are able to remain in sodium chloride balance and retain their physical fitness on a salt intake as low as 5 grams per day while performing heavy work in a hot, wet climate and producing 4 to 9 liters of sweat in 24 hours.[24] This adjustment is due to a sharp fall in the urinary excretion of sodium chloride and to the ability of the sweat glands to produce a fluid containing lower concentrations of salt when the supply is diminished.

**Vitamin C.** Vitamin C (ascorbic acid) is present in sweat to the extent of 0.55 to 0.64 mg. per 100 ml. Because of this loss coal miners who sweat heavily develop scurvy on what would otherwise be an adequate diet.[25] The diet of men working in the heat should include larger amounts of foods containing vitamin C than are included in ordinary diets.

**Protein.** Alteration in the dietary ratio of fat, carbohydrate, and protein has little influence upon the ability to work in the heat. Theoretically, the specific dynamic action of a high-protein diet in hot weather places undue stress on the heat-dissipating mechanisms. Experimentally, altering the protein content of the diet from 76 to 105 to 149 grams per day had no demonstrable effect upon the feelings or work performance of human subjects under temperate, hot dry, or hot humid conditions.[26] The 4% higher work metabolism associated with the high protein intake was a negligible factor under the conditions of the experiments where the heat exposure was intermittent. In any event, if an active person is able to maintain heat balance at all, any extra heat load due to protein is physiologically insignificant in comparison with his caloric expenditure.

**Clothing.** No matter how lightweight it is, clothing definitely hinders the regulation of temperature in hot, humid environments because it limits the vaporization of water. As a result of this limitation, a clothed subject cannot tolerate work at as high a temperature as can a nude subject. A coverall of herringbone twill reduced by 2 degrees the temperature at which a standard work load could be performed.[27] In hot, dry environments, evaporation of sweat is, in the daytime, the sole avenue of heat loss because the gradients for radiation, conduction, and convection are small or actually reversed. Loose, lightweight clothing allows evaporation to proceed effectively and yet protects against heat absorption by radiation.[14]

*Body size.* Body size is a factor affecting the performance of work in the heat. A big man is at a disadvantage. Two men of similar degrees of physical fitness but who weighed 218 pounds and 97 pounds, respectively, ran or walked on a motor-driven treadmill at rates that raised the metabolism to 7 to 11 times the basal level. The larger man, in whom the ratio of weight to surface area was 20% greater, was forced to terminate the strenuous work test after 75 minutes and had an excessive heart rate and markedly elevated skin and rectal temperatures. The smaller man, under the same conditions, achieved a steady state of temperature regulation and heart rate.[28]

*Summary.* The conditions for the best performance of young men working in both moist and dry heat have been summarized by Johnson[14] as follows:

1. General
   (a) No chronic or acute debilitating diseases
   (b) Good general physical condition
2. Heat balance
   (a) Complete acclimatization for the particular environment and work encountered
   (b) Avoidance of unfavorable environmental conditions and excessive rates of work
   (c) As little clothing as consistent with protection against radiation and trauma
3. Nutrition
   (a) Maintenance of complete hydration hour by hour
   (b) Maintenance of adequate salt intake day by day
   (c) Maintenance of adequate intake of carbohydrate, total calories, and water-soluble vitamins

# Cold

Heat conservation involves hemodynamic and insulative phenomena. Vasoconstriction and adipose tissue are the major factors.

The body protects itself from exposure to cold by peripheral vasoconstriction, which conserves body heat by reducing blood circulation through cool areas of the body. Under the direction of the hypothalamus the temperature of the skin is permitted to fall, thus decreasing heat loss by reducing radiation and conduction.[29] Cooling of deeper tissues is resisted by increasing heat production through increases in metabolic rate by means of voluntary exercise or shivering. Humidity and air movement increase the rate of loss of body heat during exposure to cold. When fatigue from work or shivering has been reached, heat production will fall and heat loss will progress, resulting in a drop in body temperature.

*Diet.* Subjects exposed to cold maintain heat balance best when the proportion of fat in the diet is high[30] and least well when the proportion of protein is high.[14] In addition they are better off with many small meals than with a few large ones.

*Clothing.* Clothing can become a handicap in the temperature regulation of men working in the cold. Excessive sweating occurs when men fully clothed in standard Arctic uniforms work hard at 0° F. The sweat is condensed in the clothing and does not achieve skin cooling. During rest periods the moisture gradually evaporates and robs the body of heat that it can ill afford to lose at that time. When men working hard at 0° F. wore light clothing, their sweating was reduced from between 350 and 400 to 50 grams per hour.[31] Men working in the cold should be provided with sufficient layers of easily removable, loose clothing so that the amount of clothing can be adjusted to the rate of work and so that the moisture-laden air can be circulated away from the body in order to keep the clothing dry.

The hands and feet are first to cool when the entire body is cooled. Until the body is warmed, it is very difficult to rewarm the extremities. If the body is heated while the hands and feet are exposed to cold, constricted blood vessels will be reopened and temperatures in the hands and feet will rise. These observations indicate the importance of keeping the whole body warm.[32]

***Drying effect of respiration on oral mucosa.*** The drying effect of respiration on the oral mucosa is a function of the absolute vapor pressure of the inspired air. Marked drying of the mucosa occurs at air temperatures below 53° F. with any moisture content, at a temperature of 60° F. with less than 77% relative humidity, and at a temperature of 70° F. with less than 39% relative humidity. The drying effect is particularly marked during ice skating, skiing, snowshoeing, and tobogganing in the outdoor winter air. If the drying effect is to be controlled under normal conditions (70° F.), over 50% relative humidity must be maintained.[20]

***Influence of cold on efficiency.*** Data on performance as affected by extreme cold are not clear-cut because of difficulties in controlling shivering and because of water vapor and air currents between layers of clothing and outside the clothing. Reported deterioration of finger dexterity and hand strength[33] probably results from a lack of adequate local insulation, together with the greater susceptibility of the hands to extremes of temperature.

## Aquatic environments

The warmth of swimming-pool water is a critical factor in the function of the swimmer's temperature-regulating mechanisms. Bathers and other nonswimmers who perform only light exercise seem to be most comfortable in water warmed to 85° to 90° F. Learning to swim may take place faster in warm water than in cold because shivering and discomfort interfere with coordination and concentration.

Competitive sprint swimmers whose exposure to water lasts only a few seconds, as in the 50-yard dash, perform best in water between 84° and 94° F. Prolonged races are best performed in water between 74° and

79° F.[34] Since it is usually not feasible to change swimming-pool temperature for each race or to use separate pools for different events, a cool temperature (about 75° F.) is selected to accommodate the distance swimmers whose exposure is longer. Even at this temperature heat exchange is a problem, and acclimatization of distance swimmers is an important training objective. Shifting the blood to peripheral vessels for conductive and convective cooling during vigorous exercise in water may deprive the working muscles of the extra blood supply they need to support the heavy metabolic load.

Should survivors of shipwrecks in cold waters exercise in the water or remain quiet to preserve their body temperature? Exercise produces body heat but also causes peripheral dilatation, which brings the blood to the surface where the heat would be more quickly dissipated. Resting quietly in cold water would conserve energy fuels and may also permit the body to warm the water immediately next to the skin, providing a protective envelope. If the water is in motion, this advantage would be lost.

Marathon swimmers who are exposed to cold water for prolonged periods accumulate fat subcutaneously, rather than in the deep fat deposits.[35] The effectiveness of body fat in protecting channel swimmers from cold exposure is subject to question. As long as the fat tissue is warm it delays heat loss. When the fat becomes cold, however, it may be compared to an ice pack. The continued fall in deep temperature of the body following removal from cold environments may, at least in part, be explained on the basis of the continued loss of heat to the chilled inactive fat.

## Altitude

Residence at high altitudes results in adaptive processes that better enable the cells of the body to utilize the oxygen that is transported at low tension in the blood.

Investigations of the physiology of exercise at high altitude (15,000 feet above sea level) revealed a high degree of physical efficiency among the residents.[36] This capacity is the result both of training that is brought about by constant physical activity and of adaptive mechanisms at the tissue level such as an increased capillary bed, higher myoglobin content in the muscles, and increased enzymatic activity. Muscular exercise at high altitudes is carried out with lower lactate production in natives than in sojourners. This is a protective process, preventing a severe degree of acidosis that otherwise might occur, since the buffer concentration of the blood of men acclimatized to high altitudes is lower than that of sea-level residents.

Studies of muscular exercise carried out during mountain climbing expeditions showed that the aerobic capacity declined from sea level upward.[37] At about 26,000 feet above sea level the oxygen requirement for the slowest steady progress exceeded the climbers' aerobic capacity, and they were forced to work intermittently. The respiratory rate increased to 60 respirations per minute and climbers described taking 10 breaths for each step forward and upward. They had to rest every 1 to 2 minutes. The great increase in ventilation causes fatigue of the respiratory muscles and limits work at great altitudes.

## Work at high altitudes

Men at work at high altitudes readily develop mild states of hypoxia. Oxygen in the blood is diminished, an oxygen debt is quickly accumulated, and the recovery rate is retarded. Oxygen deprivation at high altitudes reduces exercise tolerance[38] and performance of tests of sensory and motor efficiency.[39]

## Exercise in space

Short exposure to the hypogravity environment of space is without physiological consequence. As long as pressure, temperature, and other life-support systems in the astronaut's capsule provide an earthlike environment, man is able to adapt readily to the gravity-free environment of space by adjusting to the lessened kinesthetic cues. His movements soon become precise, and the reduction of effort required to change posture is pleasant. No disorientation or disturbance of balance mechanisms is experienced. Physiologically he reacts as though suspended in water,[40] reclining in a hospital bed,[41] or immobilized.[42]

Prolonged immersion in water and prolonged bed rest or chair rest effectively simulate hypodynamics of prolonged space flight for physiological considerations. Unless the astronaut regularly performs exercises or other tasks requiring the application of tension against resistance, physical movement, and elevated expenditure of energy, he will experience loss of body tissue, function, and performance. The effects include decreases in red cell mass, plasma and total blood volume, decalcification of bone, loss of vasomotor tone, decrease in muscle tone and strength, loss of orthostatic tolerance, incoordination and loss of exercise tolerance.[43, 44] The astronaut counters these impairments by preflight conditioning which provides him with reserves of strength and cardiovascular endurance, by inflight physical exercise as prophylaxis to physiological deterioration, and by postflight rehabilitation programs of exercise to aid him in the recovery from the sedentary and hypogravity effects of prolonged space flight so that he can again assume the upright posture in earth's gravity and move about and work in it.

### Advanced study topics

1. Why is thirst a poor guide to water needs during work in humid heat?
2. Review the recent literature on environmental factors and exercise in current issues of the *American Journal of Physiology.*
3. Describe the operation of scuba (self-contained underwater breathing apparatus).
4. Outline the best ways for a person to acclimatize himself to unusual environments.

### References

1. Winslow, C.-E. A., Gagge, A. P., and Herrington, L. P.: Heat exchange and regulation in radiant environments

above and below air temperature, Am. J. Physiol. **131**:79, 1940.

2. Winslow, C.-E. A., and Gagge, A. P.: Influence of physical work on physiological reactions to the thermal environment, Am. J. Physiol. **134**:664, 1941.

3. Nielsen, M.: Die Regulation der Körper-temperatur bei Muskelarbeit, Skand. Arch. Physiol. **79**:193, 1938.

4. Dill, D. B., Hall, F. G., and Edwards, H. T.: Changes in composition of sweat during acclimatization to heat, Am. J. Physiol. **123**:412, 1938.

5. Adolph, E. F.: Heat exchanges of man in the desert, Am. J. Physiol. **123**:486, 1938.

6. Adolph, E. F., and Dill, D. B.: Observations on water metabolism in the desert, Am. J. Physiol. **131**:369, 1938.

7. Dill, D. B.: Applied physiology, Ann. Rev. Physiol. **1**:551, 1939.

8. Robinson, S., Dill, D. B., Harmon, P. M., Hall, F. G., and Wilson, G. W.: Adaptations to exercise of Negro and white sharecroppers in comparison with northern whites, Human Biol. **13**:139, 1941.

9. Taylor, C. L.: Heat tolerance for short exposures, Fed. Proc. **4**:70, 1945.

10. Bean, W. B., and Eichna, L. W.: Performance in relation to environmental temperature, Fed. Proc. **2**:144, 1943.

11. Eichna, L. W., Bean, W. B., Ashe, W. F., and Nelson, N.: Performance in relation to environmental temperature; reactions of normal young men to hot, humid (simulated jungle) environment, Bull. Johns Hopkins Hosp. **76**:25, 1945.

12. Manson-Bahr, P. H.: Manson's tropical diseases, ed. 11, Baltimore, 1941, The Williams & Wilkins Co.

13. Robinson, S., Turrell, E. S., Belding, H. S., and Horvath, S. M.: Rapid acclimatization to work in hot climates, Am. J. Physiol. **140**:168, 1943.

14. Johnson, R. E.: Applied physiology, Ann. Rev. Physiol. **8**:535, 1946.

15. Weiner, J. S.: Regional distribution of sweating, J. Physiol. **104**:32, 1945.

16. Park, C. R., and Palmes, E. D.: Thermal regulation during early acclimatization to work in a hot dry environment, Med. Dept. Field Research Lab., Proj. No. 2-17-1 (Ft. Knox, Ky., June, 1947).

17. Johnson, R. E., Pitts, G. C., and Consolazio, F. C.: Factors influencing chloride concentration in human sweat, Am. J. Physiol. **141**:575, 1944.

18. Ito, S.: Significance of blood sugar during sweat secretion in man, J. Orient. Med. (abstr.) **28**:61, 1938.

19. Hardy, J. D., and Milhorat, A. T.: Basal heat loss and production in women at temperatures from 23° C. to 36° C., Proc. Soc. Exper. Biol. & Med. **41**:94, 1939.

20. Winslow, C.-E. A., Herrington, L. P., and Nelbach, J. H.: The influence of atmospheric temperature and humidity upon the dryness of the oral mucosa, Am. J. Hygiene **35**:27, 1941.

21. Pitts, G. C., Johnson, R. E., and Consolazio, F. C.: Work in the heat as affected by the intake of water, salt and glucose, Am. J. Physiol. **142**:253, 1944.

22. Lee, D. H. K., and Boissard, G. P. B.: The effects of exercise in hot atmospheres upon the pulse rate, Australian M. J. **2**:664, 1940.

23. Taylor, H. L., Henschel, A., Mickelsen, O., and Keys, A.: The effect of sodium chloride intake on the work performance of man during exposure to dry heat and experimental heat exhaustion, Am. J. Physiol. **140**:439, 1943.

24. Adolph, E. F.: Physiological fitness for the desert, Fed. Proc. **2**:158, 1943.

25. Bernstein, R.: Excretion of vitamin C in sweat, Nature **140**:684, 1937.

26. Pitts, G. C., Consolazio, F. C., and Johnson, R. E.: Dietary protein and physical fitness in temperature and hot environments, J. Nutrition **27**:497, 1944.

27. Shelly, W. B., Eichna, L. W., and Horvath, S. M.: Effect of clothing upon the ability of acclimatized men to work at the upper limits of environmental heat, Fed. Proc. **4**:64, 1945.

28. Robinson, S.: Effect of body size upon energy exchange in work, Am. J. Physiol. **136**:363, 1942.

29. Smith, R. E.: Cold acclimation—an altered steady state, J.A.M.A. **179**:948, 1963.

30. Masoro, E. J.: Effect of cold on metabolic use of lipids, Physiol. Rev. **46**(1): 67, 1966.

31. Belding, H. S., Folk, G. E., Forbes, W. H., and Darling, R. C.: Secretion and evaporation of sweat in cold weather, Fed. Proc. **4**:7, 1945.

32. Rapaport, S. I., Fetcher, E. S., Shaub, H. G., and Hall, J. F.: Control of blood flow to the extremities at low ambient temperatures, J. Appl. Physiol. **2**:61, 1949.

33. Horvath, S. M., and Freedman, A.: The influence of cold upon the efficiency of man, J. Aviation Med. **18**:158, 1947.

34. Addee, D.: The effect of environmental temperature on heart rate, deep body temperature, and performance in swimming, Unpublished doctoral dissertation, University of Minnesota, 1953.

35. Pugh, L. G. C., and Edholm, O. G.: Physiology of channel swimmers, Lancet **2**:761, 1955.

36. Hurtado, A.: Animals in high altitudes: resident man. In Field, J.: Handbook of physiology. Section 4, Dill, D. B., editor: Adaptation to the environment, Washington, D. C., 1964, American Physiological Society.

37. Pugh, L. G. C.: Animals in high altitudes: man above 5,000 meters—mountain exploration. In Field, J.: Handbook of physiology. Section 4, Dill, D.

B., editor: Adaptation to the environment, Washington, D. C., 1964, American Physiological Society.

38. Houston, C. S., and Riley, R. L.: Respiratory and circulatory changes during acclimatization to high altitude, Am. J. Physiol. **149**:565, 1947.

39. Green, D. M.: Variations in the effect of anoxia on performance, Am. J. Physiol. **151**:588, 1947.

40. Graveline, D. E., and Jackson, M. M.: Diuresis associated with prolonged water immersion, J. Appl. Physiol. **17**:519, 1962.

41. Irvin, C. W., Jr., and Burgess, A. M., Jr.: The abuse of bed rest and the treatment of myocardial infarction, New England, J. Med. **243**:486, 1950.

42. Deitrick, J. E., Whedon, G. D., and Shorr, E.: Effects of immobilization upon various metabolic and physiological functions of normal men, Am. J. Med. **4**:3, 1948.

43. Keys, A.: Deconditioning and reconditioning in convalescence, Surg. Clin. North America **25**:442, 1945.

44. Lamb, L. E., Stevens, P. M., and Johnson, R. L.: Hypokinesia secondary to chair rest from 4 to 10 days, Aerospace Med. **36**:755, 1965.

# Part four

# Fatigue and training

# 24

# *Endurance*

## *Types*

Endurance may be considered to be the ability of the body to withstand the stresses set up by prolonged activity. Factoral techniques of analysis have resulted in the isolation of four factors in endurance: circulorespiratory, velocity, muscular structure, and body build.[1] Endurance for *exhausting* work depends mainly on the ability of the body to supply and use oxygen and to dispose of the rapidly mounting concentrations of lactic acid and carbon dioxide. Training for endurance results in an increased capillarization of the muscle, thus providing more channels for the delivery of oxygen and food and the removal of wastes. Distance runners and other participants in endurance-type athletics do not possess the hypertrophied muscles typical of those engaged in activities requiring great strength. Hypertrophy involves reduction of the diffusion surface area per unit volume of muscle fiber and thus a reduction in the oxygen supply to the fibers.[2] In addition, compared with a muscle containing an optimum amount of contractile tissue, there is a loss in efficiency because of the necessary passive deformation of inactive parts of the muscle mass; this in turn causes a relative increase in the metabolism in proportion to the work performed and therefore a reduction in efficiency.[3]

Endurance for *moderate* (steady state) activity depends upon the supply and utilization of phosphocreatine and fuels such as sugar. The fuel factor is recognized to be so critical in prolonged moderate work that it has been suggested[4] that it should be preceded by 2 days of rest from strenuous work in order to permit filling of the glycogen stores in the body. During prolonged work without food, as in running or swimming distances requiring more than 2½ hours to complete, the depletion of these stores is indicated by a marked fall in the blood sugar (hypoglycemia) and the appearance of fatigue. In such events an athlete benefits by light feeding at frequent intervals during the race. Other factors that influence endurance will be discussed.

## Strength

The strength of the working muscles is a limiting factor in endurance. A load easily carried by strong muscles may quickly exhaust weak ones. When a strong muscle lifts a comparatively light load, relatively few fibers need to be brought into play. As these become fatigued, their threshold of irritability is raised, and they fail to respond to the stimuli. The stimuli then arouse fresh fibers, and they take over the work while the fatigued fibers recuperate and resume the burden later on if necessary.

## Fat

Since fat increases the load the worker must move with each motion, it becomes a limiting factor in endurance. Athletes trained for endurance contests usually reduce the fat content of the body to a minimum. An exception to this is distance swimmers, in whom the increased buoyancy and decreased heat loss due to a layer of subcutaneous fat more than offset the disadvantage of the greater weight to be moved. A certain amount of fat is also desirable under conditions of prolonged restricted food intake.

## Maximal oxygen consumption

Maximal oxygen consumption is reached when the oxygen intake per unit time has attained "its maximum and remains constant . . . owing to the limitation of the circulatory and respiratory systems."[5] In normal subjects the maximal oxygen consumption achievable is usually taken as an index to maximal cardiovascular function. Descriptions of the methodology of measuring maximal oxygen consumption are found in many papers.[6, 7, 8]

## Oxygen debt

Short bouts of maximum activity, in which the event is completed within 30 seconds, are performed using only the immediate fuels of contraction and are concluded before the oxidative recovery processes are fully in action. Endurance for activities requiring violent exertion from 1 to 3 minutes is limited by the amount of oxygen debt that can be contracted and the concentration of lactic acid that can be tolerated. A lactate concentration exceeding 100 mg. per 100 ml. of blood is a common finding after maximal exercise involving large muscles.[9]

In more prolonged events of maximum exertion requiring more than 4 minutes to complete, the limiting factor appears to be the ability of the circulorespiratory system to supply the oxygen needed by the muscles. Trained individuals have a greater "aerobic capacity" than do others.[10] In prolonged events requiring 2½ or more hours to complete, the work rate is reduced so that a steady state is reached in which oxygen needs are easily met. Men who completed the Boston marathon had only average vital capacities for their size, and there was no significant relationship between the size of the vital capacity and the order in which the runners finished the race.[11]

## Respiration

Although lung capacity and other features of ventilation are not likely to become limiting factors in endurance, there may be other respiratory factors that impinge upon the nicety of physiological adjustments necessary to support continued physical activity. The phenomenon of hyperventilation in untrained persons, which undoubtedly restricts their ability to continue work, is little understood. The complexity of the stimuli controlling respiration, as outlined by Gray[12] and discussed in Chapter 15, may be further complicated by substances, yet unidentified, that are produced during exercise and that stimulate chemoreceptors. Asmussen and Nielsen[13] note that when oxygen is breathed during moderate exercise, ventilation is controlled by the effects of the rise in carbon dioxide tension and the rise in body temperature. As the work becomes more severe, other stimuli to respiration become active. One of these may be a substance produced by ischemic muscle that stimulates the chemoreceptors but itself is destroyed in the presence of oxygen. An alternative hypothesis offered by Bannister[14] is based on the theory that there is a chemoreceptor mechanism activated by arterial hypoxia that is inhibited by oxygen. The control bodies assume importance as chemoreceptors in regulating respiration only in emergencies and probably are not sufficiently stimulated to function in the slight oxygen deficits experienced during exercise. A further elucidation of these phenomena will have to be accomplished before their effects on endurance can be evaluated.

## Circulation

Adequate respiration requires not only that oxygen be available in the lungs but also that it be taken up by the blood and transported to the muscles. Present evidence suggests that when the blood flow is maximal, as during heavy exercise, oxygen uptake may be inadequate, and the blood may have a suboptimal oxygen tension when it passes from the lung.

The rate at which the oxygen is supplied to the muscles depends upon the rate of the circulation of the blood. Richards[15] and Asmussen and Nielsen[13] have postulated that the increased stroke volume during muscular work is produced by a more complete emptying of the ventricles during systole. Nervous and hormonal effects are suggested as reasons for the increase in the power of the systolic contraction.

## Motivation

Possibly the most important factor in endurance is the willingness to endure the discomfort that accompanies the onset of fatigue. Studies of participants in sports with severe endurance demands, such as rowing, have served to emphasize that many participants are motivated by a need to resolve personal problems. It may be possible that measures of endurance are quite largely measures of the compulsive drives that motivate a person. Step tests, treadmill running, and similar measurements very seldom give a true estimate of the endurance of the subject being tested since he is seldom motivated to put forth his best efforts. Laboratory findings indicate that significant cardiorespiratory changes occur when motivational stress factors are evident and that a greater work output is elicited.[16]

## Alkaline reserve

Studies in which blood alkalinity was increased experimentally showed that greater oxygen debts could be accumulated.[17, 18] However, college students who trained by running failed to show any increase in the alkaline reserve as a result of training.[19]

## Skill

A trained man benefits from a reduction in unnecessary movements. He achieves a greater net mechanical efficiency by using fewer muscles and by employing those used to better advantage. In addition, a physiological improvement from moderate training results from better coordination of the nervous control of respiration and circulation.[20] Utilizing oxygen consumption as a "skill index" in a study of running,[18] investigators found that the least skillful subject used half again as much oxygen as the most skillful person.

## Distribution of energy

*Adjustment of speed.* Records of running events given in Table 11 illustrate the adjustment of speed necessitated by an increase in the length of a race. The 100-yard and 220-yard dashes are run at full speed. The 220 is run at a faster average rate than the 100-yard dash because maximum speed is not attained until the runner is at least 50 yards from the start. During the first 50 yards the runner must accelerate from zero speed at the start to the maximum speed. Thus at least half of the 100-yard dash is completed before maximum speed is attained. When the race is continued to 220 yards, the sprinter can maintain maximum speed for the last 150 yards. Sprinters probably run faster than 24 m.p.h. during the latter portion of the dashes.

The maximum distance that trained sprinters are able to sprint at full speed is about 300 yards. In races beyond this distance the runner

*Table 11.* Adjustment of speed in running to length of race

| Event | Speed (m.p.h.) |
|-------|----------------|
| 220 yd. | 22.5 |
| 100 yd. | 22.0 |
| 440 yd. | 19.5 |
| 880 yd. | 16.6 |
| 1 mi. | 15.2 |
| 2 mi. | 14.0 |
| 3 mi. | 13.3 |
| 6 mi. | 12.9 |
| 10 mi. | 12.45 |
| Marathon (26 mi. 385 yd.) | 11.0 |

must conserve his energy by reducing speed in order to run the distance in the fastest possible time. If he attempts to run beyond 300 yards at full speed, he will soon collapse. Thus running events beyond the 300-yard distance must be considered endurance contests.

Since the 440-yard dash cannot be run at full speed all of the way, the speed must be adjusted slightly. If the runner should sprint the first 300 yards, he would have to reduce his speed the remainder of the distance to such an extent that his time for the race would be slow. He would also run the risk of collapsing during the latter portion of the race. Running the first 150 yards at an easy speed and then running the remainder of the race at full speed would be equally ineffective and hazardous. Acceleration during a race is exceedingly costly in energy; a steady pace is the most efficient. During the latter portion of a 440-yard or 880-yard run, the stride is somewhat shortened due to the poorer rate of muscular relaxation and the accumulation of contractures in the working fibers. For this reason, in this range runners are able to achieve their best times by running the early part of the race somewhat faster than the latter.[14]

The 440-yard dash cannot be run at full speed all of the way. The speed must be lowered about 3 m.p.h. (14%) below maximum, or the runner will exhaust himself before the 440 yards have been run. In order to run 880 yards a runner must reduce his speed about 5.5 m.p.h. (25%) below the maximum.

In order to complete the mile distance a runner must reduce his speed nearly one third (33%) below the maximum rate. In races of this distance a steady state of physiological activity must be established. High concentrations of lactic acid must be endured, and large quantities of oxygen must be utilized.

In races 2 miles and longer the rate of physiological activity attained is well below the maximum level at which the trained athlete can maintain physiological equilibrium. The lactic acid concentration and the oxygen debt are small, and the runner finishes the race in a condition that would permit him to run farther. Races of 15 miles and longer are run at approximately the same rate, which is about one half the maximum speed. This rate is well tolerated by a trained athlete. He finishes with the heart rate and blood pressure only mildly elevated, and his breathing is fairly easy. The limiting factors in long-distance races appear to be the nutritional status and the condition of the feet and legs.

The relationship between the homeostatic mechanism and the rate of energy liberation is sufficiently constant to permit a mathematical prediction of speed as a function of time.[21]

***Pace.*** The most economical distribution of effort in running over a distance of 0.5 mile or more or in swimming, cycling, or rowing equivalent distances is obtained by performing at a constant rate over the entire distance. The racing distance is covered in the shortest time when the total available energy is distributed evenly over the distance. Acceleration is so costly that changes in speed are too expensive to employ as deceptive tactics.

The achievement of proper pace requires extensive training. Pace training may be facilitated by the use of a pacing machine[22] which enables the athlete to follow a marker that is traveling at a fixed rate.

*Cheering.* Environmental stimuli, such as a competitive situation, the encouragement of the coach and teammates, and the cheering of the spectators, strengthen the movements of trained athletes and extend their endurance by raising the threshold of sensitivity to fatigue and by reinforcing nerve impulses to working muscles. These phenomena account for the fact that trained athletes usually perform better during competition than during practice. In laboratory studies using an arm ergograph subjects performed 1½ times as much work when they were observed as when they worked alone. When they were cheered by the observers at the first sign of fatigue, work output increased to 2½ times that of solitary work.

The same factors that improve the performance of a trained athlete may diminish the performance of a novice. Instead of distributing his energy evenly over the distance of the race, a novice responds to cheering by increasing his speed to such an extent that he approaches exhaustion early in the race. A novice often runs better in practice than he does in competition.

*Hypnosis.* Hypnosis has been observed to improve physical performance of strength and endurance events. An explanation for the increased performance during the hypnotic state is offered on the basis of the removal of inhibitory influences.[23]

*Training for endurance events.* In addition to pace training endurance may be improved by bettering general physical condition, increasing muscular strength, achieving greater neuromuscular coordination, and making physiochemical adjustments. In order to improve endurance the activities may be either speeded up or prolonged and preferably should include the same movements that will be used in competition. Through exposure the athlete increases his resistance to feelings of fatigue until physiological limits are reached. The ability to endure fatigue is probably the greatest factor in endurance for prolonged muscular work.

Through practice of endurance events the circulatory and respiratory systems become more efficient in supplying oxygen and in removing the waste products of metabolism. The temperature-regulating system enables the body to adjust effectively to the heat of muscular work. The skeletal and cardiac muscles become stronger and more efficient. Through training of the nervous system the movements become better coordinated, waste motions are eliminated, and the action between synergic and antagonistic muscles is refined. Through diet and exercise the oxygen-carrying capacity of the blood is improved, and the body is better able to mobilize and transport foodstuffs necessary for the support of physical activity.

## Measures of endurance

At rest the physiological differences between an athlete with a high level of endurance and a person with poor endurance are negligible. When they both start working, however, the differences quickly appear. They are most striking during the most vigorous work. An athlete with great endurance is characterized by the ability to withstand higher levels of lactic acid and to use larger volumes of oxygen and by a lower heart rate during prolonged work. The return of the heart rate and lactic acid concentration to normal is faster in a trained athlete.

To summarize, an athlete with great endurance can carry on exhausting work for a longer period and can establish a physiological steady state at higher levels of work. He can recover from work more quickly and is thereby enabled to start a second piece of hard work sooner than can a person with poor endurance.

## Advanced study topics

1. Are the cardiorespiratory responses to excitement in any way contributory to work endurance?
2. Review the recent literature on endurance in current issues of *Acta Physiologica Scandinavica*.
3. Describe a method of measuring blood sugar.
4. Observe daily practice schedules of endurance athletes in various sports.
5. Evaluate the bradycardia of training as an index of endurance.

## References

1. McCloy, C. H.: A factor analysis of tests of endurance, Res. Quart. **27**:213, 1956.
2. Maison, G. L., and Broeker, A. G.: Training in human muscles working with and without blood supply, Am. J. Physiol. **132**:390, 1941.
3. Buchthal, F., and Kaiser, F.: Optimum mechanical conditions for the work of skeletal muscles, Acta Psychiat. **24**:333, 1949.
4. Christensen, E. H., Krogh, A., and Lindhard, J.: Investigations on heavy muscular work, Quart. Bull. Health Organ. League of Nations **111**:388, 1934.
5. Hill, A. V.: Muscular activity, Baltimore, 1926, The Williams & Wilkins Co.
6. Taylor, H. L., Buskirk, E., and Henschel, A.: Maximal oxygen intake as an objective measure of cardio-respiratory performance, J. Appl. Physiol. **8**:73, 1955.
7. Mitchell, J. K., Sproule, B. J., and Chapman, C. B.: The physiological

8. Astrand, P. O., and Saltin, B.: Methods for determination of maximal oxygen uptake, Acta Physiol. Scand. **50**:175, 1960.
9. Astrand, P. O., Hallback, I., Hedman, R., and Saltin, B.: Blood lactates after prolonged severe exercise, J. Appl. Physiol. **18**:619, 1963.
10. Astrand, P. O.: Human physical fitness with special reference to sex and age, Physiol. Rev. **36** (3):307, 1956.
11. Gordon, B., Levine, S. A., and Wilmaers, A.: Observations on a group of marathon runners, Arch. Int. Med. **33**:425, 1924.
12. Gray, J. S.: The multiple factor theory of the control of respiratory ventilation, Science **103**:739, 1946.
13. Asmussen, E., and Nielsen, M.: Cardiac output during muscular work, Physiol. Rev. **35**:778, 1955.
14. Bannister, R. G.: Muscular effort, Brit. M. J. **12**:222, 1956.
15. Richards, D. W.: Discussion of Starling's law of the heart, Physiol. Rev. **35**:156, 1955.
16. Ulrich, C., and Burke, R. K.: Effect of motivational stress on physical performance, Res. Quart. **24**:403, 1957.
17. Dennig, H., Talbott, J. H., Edwards, H. T., and Dill, D. B.: Effect of acidosis and alkalosis upon capacity for work, J. Clin. Invest. **9**:601, 1931.
18. Dill, D. B., Talbott, J. H., and Edwards, H. T.: Studies in muscular activity. VI. Response of several individuals to a fixed task, J. Physiol. **69**:267, 1930.

meaning of the maximal oxygen intake test, J. Clin. Invest. **37**:538, 1958.

19. Robinson, S., and Harmon, P. M.: The lactic acid mechanism and certain properties of the blood in relation to training, Am. J. Physiol. 132:757, 1941.

20. Gemmill, C., Booth, W., and Pocock, B.: Muscular training. I. The physiological effect of daily repetition of the same amount of light muscular work, Am. J. Physiol. 92:253, 1930.

21. Henry, F. M.: Prediction of world records in running sixty yards to twenty six miles, Res. Quart. 26:147, 1955.

22. Morehouse, L. E.: Race efficiency, official N.C.A.A. swimming guide, 1942, p. 12.

23. Roush, E. S.: Strength and endurance in the waking and hypnotic states, J. Appl. Physiol. 3:404, 1951.

# 25

# *Fatigue and recovery*

Severe muscular exercise diminishes the capacity of muscles for further activity. This depressant action of strenuous activity is called *muscular fatigue*. It must be distinguished from the subjective sensations of tiredness, sleepiness, and muscular soreness which frequently accompany it. Continued stimulation of sensory organs, such as those of vision and hearing, may result in a diminished response, a process known as *adaptation*. It is not the same as fatigue, however, since changing the strength of the sensory stimulus slightly usually restores the full vigor of the sensory response. The synapses between neurons in the central nervous system and the junction between nerve fibers and muscle fibers (motor end plate) are readily fatigued by continued activity, and it is probable that so-called muscular fatigue in an exercising subject is largely a matter of loss of the capacity for transmission of nerve impulses to the muscle as well as exhaustion of the muscle itself.

The development of fatigue in a single organ that is subjected to repeated stimulation can be followed, and the extent of the reduction in its functional capacity can be predicted with a high degree of accuracy. This is not so easy in the case of so-called *general fatigue*. The fatigue resulting from the tedious repetition of dull, easy work is akin to boredom and it eludes measurement. General fatigue results from the stress of performing activities lacking in personal satisfactions. It may carry over into other types of activity, so that life itself seems to lack any satisfaction. If the attitude is persisted in, the outcome may be a flight into mental illness.

## General fatigue

**Symptoms.** The onset of fatigue in a person doing light work is seldom noticed by the subject. He is unaware that his standards of performance are deteriorating, and he may even believe that his efficiency is steadily increasing. His sense of timing is the first to fail, and errors and accidents begin to appear. As fatigue advances, the worker's grasp of the overall plan of the operation begins to fade so that eventually only the most prominent features of the task are performed and the rest are ignored. Attention is finally shifted from the performance of the task to the discomfort of the body. Deterioration in skill now proceeds rapidly.

Physiological fatigue is not the only factor that influences work performance. The importance of psychological, social, and socioeconomic factors is gradually being realized by industrial physicians and management officials. Under certain favorable conditions industrial output may actually increase toward the end of the working day in spite of fatigue. Music, for example, facilitates the social contacts among workers and relieves their boredom. It is most appreciated by those doing repetitive manual tasks but may hinder those whose work demands a high degree of mental effort. To be most effective music should be presented on two or three occasions during the working day but for comparatively short periods of time. Music time should be adjusted to industrial output curves in order to offset decrements ascribable to ennui or fatigue.[1]

*Chronic fatigue (staleness).* Fatigue is chronic when it is not relieved by a good night's sleep. Some of the prominent symptoms of this very common condition are subjective feeling of tiredness, loss of interest in work and other daily activities, increase in the effort that is necessary to perform the usual work, increased irritability and general emotional instability, loss of weight, poor appetite, increase in resting pulse rate and lowered blood pressure, a tendency to sigh frequently, tremor of the outstretched hands, pallor, and increased consumption of coffee, tobacco, and alcohol.

In chronic fatigue a vicious cycle may be set up. A person who is unable to sleep because he is worried may become worried because he is unable to sleep. Eventually he may resort to barbiturates or other drugs in order to sleep or to Benzedrine or other stimulants in order to stay awake and do his work. Anxiety in such states produces tension in the muscles, and these constant submuscular contractions have been suggested as a cause of fatigue.[2]

The energy costs of physical work seldom lead to chronic fatigue. The problems involved in chronic fatigue are emotional and situational, not physiological.[3] Under normal conditions overwork is itself a symptom of maladjustment.[4]

The most frequent causes of chronic fatigue are long hours of work, lack of sleep, maladjustment, and worry. The symptoms usually disappear after a period of rest away from work.

*Anxiety state.* The effect of severe fright, such as might occur in battle or in a tragic accident, is occasionally a disorganization of a person's motor nervous system that renders him incapable of skillful movement. This motor disorganization frequently persists, and the victim behaves continually as if the original traumatic situation were still in existence. Tremor of the hand may be so intense that he is incapable of buttoning a coat. There is a reduction of muscular strength, and in severe anxiety states there is often a loss of kinesthetic sense resulting in an incapacity to stand and walk. Recovery does not occur until improvement in the mental state is made.

*Effort syndrome.* A person with subnormal tolerance for exercise experiences breathlessness, rapid beating of the heart, sweating, and dizziness on even such mild exertion as climbing a short flight of stairs. Such effort intolerance may be caused by a constitutional inferiority present since infancy or it may have developed from emotional disturbance.

The effort syndrome may not be recognized if a person avoids heavy physical work. Possessing a frail physique and a conviction that he has always had a "weak heart" or "lung trouble," he has always dreaded the supposed ill effects of vigorous physical exercise. The response of the heart and respiration to exercise is usually as poor as if he possessed the supposed heart and lung disorders.

The effort syndrome is seen under pressure of a job requiring occasional physical exertion. Under such a condition of pressure the feelings of insufficiency may be exaggerated until the person is out of harmony with his surroundings. Recovery commences when he is restored to an environment that is within his effort capacity and when no further intense pressures are anticipated. The effect upon this person of a program of physical education that did not consider individual differences in response to exercise would probably be to increase emotional conflict and would result in further motor disorganization.

## Muscular fatigue

The term muscular fatigue refers to an impairment of the muscles' ability to respond to stimuli. This sort of fatigue may be measured by means of a strength decrement index,[5] which has been used for such practical purposes as studying the effects of various types of Army packs.[6] Muscular fatigue is a normal phenomenon and should be viewed as a normal response to a normal stress. Rest and sleep allow an opportunity for the reestablishment of homeostasis.[7]

The physiological causes of muscular fatigue, however, are not well understood. The laborer does not accumulate lactic acid or any other product of metabolic breakdown, and anaerobic reserves are not drawn on except during strenuous work or sport.[2]

*Site of fatigue.* Changes in the functional properties of nerve cells, the myoneural junction, and the muscle itself have been suggested as the basis of muscular fatigue. One theory is that the general fatigue that reduces the range and power of voluntary muscular activity is largely an affair of the central nervous system. Merton[8] objects to this theory on the basis of his observation that if the circulation to a fatigued muscle is occluded, there is no recovery of strength. Recovery occurs only after blood flow is restored. He contends that if fatigue were a phenomenon of the central nervous system, it is unlikely that recovery would be delayed by occluding the blood flow. The nerves themselves are believed to be indefatigable, but there is evidence that after repeated stimulation a spinal reflex may diminish and its pattern may alter.[9] Skilled activity is the first thing to suffer as an individual becomes fatigued.

If an isolated muscle is repeatedly stimulated by way of its motor nerve, the contractions become progressively weaker and finally cease. If the stimulating electrodes are then placed directly on the muscle, nearly normal contractions are elicited. From this demonstration it is logical to conclude that since the nerve fiber is practically indefatigable, the site of fatigue must be at the neuromuscular junction. However, Merton[8] disputes this theory and claims to have demonstrated that it is never possible to make a muscle contract by electrical stimulation after it has been fatigued by voluntary effort. He also has demonstrated that the failure of the muscle to respond cannot be caused by blockage of impulses at the neuromuscular junction since there is no falling off in the voltage of the muscle action potentials. According to his findings fatigue must be peripheral and result from the failure of the muscle to contract after the motor impulse reaches it.

The search for a specific chemical factor is continuing along the lines suggested by Torda and Wolff[10] who pointed out that muscle impairment may be partly attributed to the decrease of the local synthesis of an acetylcholine-like substance during prolonged muscular exertion. It is not known whether a depressor substance is released from the muscles or whether this results from utilization of some potentiator substances ordinarily present in the blood and used by the muscle to perform work.

Constant adjustments to fatigue are occurring in an exercised muscle. Associated with muscular fatigue are alterations in oxygen utilization and in cell permeability and in the transfer of ions across altered membranes. A loss of glycogen from the muscle results in a simultaneous release of sufficient potassium to maintain a constant ratio of potassium to nonfat solids inside the muscle.[11] The resultant imbalance between potassium and sodium in fatigued muscle is associated with a higher oxygen consumption than that which exists in normal muscle. If the adjustments to fatigue are effective, there is no damage to the muscle's contractile mechanism and no detectable exhaustion of its store of energy-yielding chemical substances. If the adjustments to fatigue are not effective, muscular fatigue can be carried to such a point that there is a reduction in the power of the muscle to do work which outlasts the immediate recovery from fatigue and may amount to permanent damage to the muscle.

***Cortical motor and sensory centers.*** The fatigue that influences performance in muscular work and sport is more directly related to the motor centers of the brain. Fatigue of the sensory centers is more significant in certain types of work involving small, accurate movements or requiring continual visual or auditory attention. There is little or no correlation between fatigue of motor centers and fatigue of sensory centers in different types of work.[12]

Fatigue of the motor and sensory centers may be measured by several techniques. In the *tapping test* the maximal frequency with which a telegraphic key can be tapped gives an index of the functional condition of the motor centers. The results of this test are not influenced by peripheral factors such as circulation, metabolism, etc.[13] Fatigue of the retinocortical (visual) center is indicated by a decrease in the *fusion frequency of flicker* (the rate at which alternating periods of light and dark produced by an electronic tube can be discriminated before "flicker" disappears, being replaced by a visual impression of uniform grayness[14]). In truck driving, which has a considerable manual component, the results of the tapping test and other tests of motor function such as simple reaction time, reaction coordination ability, and manual steadiness bear a closer relation to the number of hours of driving time than do tests of sensory function. The same is true of laundry workers.[12]

The relation between fatigue resulting from muscular activity and changes in the motor centers is further established by a rise in scalp potential over the area of the motor cortex at the height of physical exercise. This is followed by a drop in potential with fatigue and a change in polarity at exhaustion.[15]

Fatigue occurs within the reflex arcs during both mental and physical work. The threshold stimulus of the Achilles tendon reflex and of the knee jerk gradually rises during the working period. The rise in threshold accelerates slightly during mental work and markedly during physical work. Determination of the threshold stimulus for the Achilles tendon reflex before work is resumed indicates whether or not the fatigue of the previous work period has been relieved by rest.[16]

## Effect of exercise on mental work

Although fatigue of motor centers is important in the performance of muscular work and sport, fatigue of the sensory centers appears to be more important in the general sensation of fatigue. Although fatigue of motor and sensory centers are not related to one another, there is some spreading of fatigue from one type of center to the other. Flicker-fusion frequency is depressed after exhausting muscular work (700-yard run) and increased after 30 genuflections or static work.[17] This indicates that hard muscular work produces a certain degree of central nervous system fatigue, whereas light or moderate exercise, performed during pauses in sedentary occupations, improves the functional state of the central nervous system. Physical training in the schools should be administered in such a way as to avoid interference with the educational program. The activities during the school period should be short and moderate in order to have a stimulating effect on the capacity for mental work. Severe muscular work should be performed after school in order to avoid the depressing effect on the capacity for classroom work.

## Effect of sensory fatigue on muscular work

Systematic studies of sensory fatigue induced by a lack or curtailment of sleep show that there are no significant physiological changes with up to 200 hours of sleeplessness.[18] Reaction time[18] and body steadiness[19] are impaired by lack of sleep, but hand steadiness and handgrip strength[19] are not affected. Subjective estimation of well-being also bears little relation to work performance.[20] The lack of correlation between fatigue of sensory centers and fatigue of motor centers may explain the confusing experiences of athletes who have performed exceedingly well on days when they have complained of feeling too ill to enter competition, whereas their performance was unsatisfactory on other days when they had such a feeling of well-being that they felt capable of breaking records.

## Visual fatigue

Visual fatigue may be observed by the use of several different procedures. The fusion frequency of flicker, as stated previously, indicates the excitability of the retinocortical system. In office, laboratory, and dispensary work the fusion frequency of flicker was lower in the late afternoon than it was in the morning, but the decrement was much more pronounced in laboratory work including 3 hours' work with the microscope than in laboratory work without the use of the microscope.[21] Reversible visual "illusions" differ before and after vigorous exercise.[22] After 2 hours of hard inspection work at a very inadequate illumination, the fixation time and the corrective movements increased, whereas the rate of movements decreased. One manifestation of oculomotor fatigue is a blocking of eye movements for a fraction of a second, which enforces involuntary rests. Performance between these blocks is little affected. In very severe stress, such as requiring the eyes to move at the maximum attainable rate for 2 or more minutes, watering of the eyes may make reading impossible. The secretion of tears is interpreted as a spread of innervation to other effectors.[23]

## Auditory fatigue

Exposure to noise results in a hearing loss that is proportional to the duration of exposure. The cumulative effect of noise may finally result in permanent hearing loss. The recovery of acoustical threshold in riveters after a full day's work may take 15 hours.[24] The recovery is considerably accelerated when the lunch pause of 1 hour is spent in noiseless surroundings; also the increase of the acoustical threshold at the end of the working day is much less under these conditions. Cotton plugs saturated with mineral oil, to be introduced into the ear canal, are recommended for protection.

Typists working under office conditions of high noise level from a busy street had a greater expenditure of energy than when the noise level of the same office had been reduced by acoustical methods.[25] Reduction of the noise level increases the work output and diminishes errors, absenteeism, and employee turnover.

A varying noise causes a greater drop in work output than a steady noise. Pure tones of uniform loudness reduce output less seriously than does complex noise of equivalent loudness. Tones of frequencies above 512

CPS (cycles per second) reduce production more than lower frequencies of the same loudness, and above 512 CPS each increase in frequency was followed by further loss in production.[26]

## Cardiac fatigue

The contractile power of the heart is reduced by fatigue, particularly if it has been weakened by disease. This reduction in contractile power results in a diminished stroke volume and a less complete systolic emptying of the ventricles. The necessary cardiac output is maintained only at the expense of a dilatation of the ventricles and a further increase in the heart rate, both of which increase the likelihood of termination of the exercise through failure of the coronary blood flow to meet the increased metabolic requirements of the heart muscle (Chapter 10).

## Foot fatigue

Standing not only increases fatigue by cerebral anemia and reduction in cardiac output but also produces local fatigue of the feet, which frequently interferes with production in jobs that require prolonged standing. Change in posture from the upright to varying degrees of the recumbent position and periodic elevation of the feet serve as practical measures to reduce cardiovascular strain and fatigue, especially in hot environments.[27]

## Fatigue and infections

Extreme fatigue lowers the general resistance of the body to pathogenic microorganisms and appears especially to predispose the subject to respiratory infections such as the common cold.[28] The basis of this relation is not clear.

## Exhaustion

At the outset of physical exhaustion there is a significant lymphocytosis suggestive of an "irritation phenomenon" such as is frequently seen in infections or other depleting conditions.[29] After a short but exhausting performance athletes frequently exhibit a syndrome consisting of pronounced weakness, profuse perspiration, blurred vision, a throbbing headache, nausea, and vomiting. This has been termed *athletic sickness* and is due to the fact that sugar is withdrawn from the blood into the muscle tissue so rapidly that it cannot be replenished at once from the glycogen stores of the liver, and hypoglycemia results. This condition soon disappears with rest and has no unfavorable prognostic significance. Occasionally there is slight bleeding from the oral, nasal, and pharyngeal mucous membranes.[30]

In more prolonged events such as a marathon run an exhausted athlete may display symptoms similar to those of insulin shock. Some of these runners show muscular twitching, extreme pallor, cold moist skin, nervous irritability, cyanosis, incoordination of muscular movements, extreme exhaustion, collapse, and unconsciousness.[31] It is impossible to say which part of the athlete fails first since the whole organization breaks down together.

Final physical exhaustion is reached when the cerebral distress from peripheral stimuli becomes so great that the athlete is unable to initiate any voluntary effort.[32] Frequently the onset of fatigue may be indicated by a clouding of the consciousness. The runner may continue to run but to do so reflexly, with complete amnesia concerning the events that transpire. A case has been recorded in which a tennis player was informed by his friends after the game that he had continually done foolish things, such as trying to give or throw his racket away. He had no recollection of this. This episode was also attributable to hypoglycemia, which may lead to confusion, epileptiform attacks, abdominal distress, migrainous headaches, vertigo, or precordial distress.[33]

After vigorous exercise the muscles may go into contraction more readily than do rested muscles or it may not even be possible to relax them completely, and the presence of tremor may reveal a residue of activity. In some cases muscular spasm within a muscle may render an area ischemic or press on intramuscular pain fibers, resulting in myalgia. Hypersensitive muscles often develop myalgia, and once it appears the sensitivity of the muscle and its disposition to contract without apparent cause are increased.[34]

Examination of the urine of athletes after severe exercise reveals the appearance of formed elements (protein, epithelial, and red and white blood cell casts) that might under other circumstances be indicative of kidney disease. Albumin may be present in quantities varying from traces to a heavy cloud.[45, 36] The urine may be coffee colored or bloody after severe exercise because of the presence of hemoglobin.

During exercise accompanied by high velocity, intravascular friction of the blood flow results in some destruction of the blood cells. The more serious the disturbance of the general circulatory system, the more marked are the evidences of blood destruction found in the urine.[37] In body-contact sports the factor of actual trauma to the kidneys is superimposed upon the effects resulting from exercise alone.[38]

It is interesting that fatigue and exhaustion of the kind just described virtually never seem to result in lasting injury to a trained athlete. This is not true in the case of untrained men or convalescents. A "generalized neuromuscular exhaustion syndrome" has been noted when victims of poliomyelitis and certain other patients have been exercised at or near their maximal capacity, resulting in a long-lasting decrement of performance.[39]

## Fatigue prevention and recuperation

Measures effective in delaying the onset of fatigue and methods of recuperation from fatigue are discussed in detail in this textbook and elsewhere.[40] Some of these are briefly discussed for the purpose of planning programs of work and sport of any type in order to avoid, as far as possible, the debilitating effects of fatigue.

1. Selection of the man for the job should include considerations of the man's physical and mental competence and his interest in the work.

2. Heavy muscular work tires the nervous system more quickly than the muscles, and therefore a combination of heavy muscular work and mental work performed simultaneously should not be required. All planning and processing should be done by those who are not engaged in heavy work. Signs, signals, and colors should be used to simplify heavy jobs.

3. Work of great intensity should be of short duration.

4. Work that must be carried on for long periods should be of low intensity.

5. Hoists and conveyors should be used when the weight of the material is a factor. A workman who must move a heavy weight every 10 minutes is very tired at the end of the day.

6. Work of great intensity should be preceded by a warming up period of work progressive in intensity from low to great or should be commenced at a reduced rate, load, or range of movement and then gradually increased.

7. Work should be simplified so as to be adapted to the structure (physical dimensions and space requirements) and functions (strength, speed, and accuracy) of the human body.

8. Principles of motion economy utilizing momentum—easy and natural rhythm, arrangement of work, place, chair, materials and controls, and positioning of levers to achieve greatest mechanical advantage—should be employed.

9. Positions at work and movements such as carrying, pulling and pushing, and lifting should avoid muscular and ligamentous stresses and strains and should be performed with the glottis open to avoid sudden alterations in blood circulation.

10. Rhythm (the regular repetition of a group of motions) regularizes work labor, makes it easier, lightens it, and enlivens it. Rhythm smooths out semiautomatic activities that would otherwise be jerky and intermittent.

11. When a worker can set his own rhythm, there is less fluctuation in his rate of work, there is a greater interest and satisfaction in the work, and he feels less tired than when working with an imposed rhythm.

12. The speed of the worker's machine should be synchronized with the worker's customary rhythm.

13. When a group of machines is operated by a single prime mover, the speed of the machines should be adjusted to the ability of the workers to keep pace with it.

14. Workers who are not adept at high speed or cannot keep up with the average pace should be transferred to jobs requiring a slower pace.

15. In nonmachine operations placement of a worker among others who have superior strength, skill, and speed encourages him to attempt to keep up with the swift pace and may lead to injury. He should work alongside those with a similar or only slightly faster pace.

16. Advantages and limitations due to different structures and functions in different ages, sexes, races, and body builds should be considered in a job assignment.

17. Waste movement should be reduced.

18. A change of activity should be provided, especially during periods when work output falls off.

19. A midafternoon snack should be eaten when work has been continuous throughout the day.

20. Rest periods from 5 minutes' duration at hourly intervals in moderate work to 45 minutes in strenuous work, such as between running races in track, should be provided.

21. A greater work output can be achieved by working steadily for short periods and then resting than by working steadily without rest periods.

22. Workers voluntarily take rest periods ranging from 3 minutes an hour in light work to 12 minutes an hour in heavier work. When such rest periods are authorized, the worker is able to relax without tension.

23. Accuracy of mental work requiring close concentration is improved if a rest period of 5 minutes at the beginning of each hour is provided.

24. Rest in a horizontal position, preferably with the legs elevated, should be allowed between bouts of strenuous work. Relaxation techniques should be taught if the worker is incapable of voluntary, complete relaxation. Massage will provide additional recovery. If it is not feasible to recline, mild exercise that promotes blood flow through working muscles is preferable to inactivity in a standing or seated position.

25. Broadcasts of music and entertainment through a public address system should be provided during periods when work output ordinarily falls off except in work requiring intense concentration in which the broadcasts would be distracting.

26. Rest is generally much more effective if taken in a quiet rest room instead of in the workshop since noise is inseparable from most industrial work.

27. The performer should get 8 hours of sleep nightly, preferably in a comfortable bed in a dark, quiet, cool room.

28. The work area should have ample space for free movement and vision; it should be air-conditioned if necessary to achieve comfort in temperature, humidity, ventilation and clean air free from dust, fumes, and undesirable odors. The light source should illuminate the work surface, providing about 100 foot-candles of illumination without glare, and noise and vibration should be reduced.

29. Machine design should provide for normal postures and positions. The dimensions of the machine should not require undue stretching, reaching, or stooping.

30. The height of the work bench and chair should be determined by the kind of work to be performed. The chair seat should be broad, front edge rounded, not too deep (so circulation will not be cut off), and flat. The seat back should be designed so as not to interfere with arm movement. Standing or sitting positions are tiresome if either is constantly maintained throughout the day without change. An operation that requires alter-

nate standing and sitting is the ideal combination of work to keep fatigue at a minimum level.

31. Diet should provide essential elements of nutrition and should be in sufficient quantity to maintain normal body weight.

32. Food intake at mealtimes, especially at breakfast, should be adequate to support subsequent activity.

33. Midmorning and midafternon snacks (glass of milk and piece of cake) increase work output.

34. Work at high altitudes should be progressive in intensity to allow for acclimatization. Supplementary oxygen during work is useful at altitudes above 8,000 feet.

35. The use of drugs to allay sensations of fatigue should be restricted to very severe emergency situations.

36. Exposure to extreme fatigue, very high altitudes, or great depths should be followed by ample periods of rest to promote full recovery and prevent progressive deterioration resulting in excessive aging.

## Advanced study topics

1. Why can trained athletes work to exhaustion nearly every day without injury?
2. Review the recent literature on fatigue and recovery in current issues of the *Journal of Applied Physiology*.
3. Develop a procedure for predicting the onset of exhaustion.
4. Work to exhaustion and describe the events that occur, especially the nature of the end point at which work is terminated.
5. How is general fatigue differentiated from muscular fatigue?

## References

1. Kirkpatrick, F.: Music in industry, J. Appl. Psychol. 27:268, 1943.
2. Dill, D. B.: The nature of fatigue, Geriatrics 10:474, 1955.
3. Schwab, R. S., and DeLorme, T.: Psychiatric findings in fatigue, Am. J. Psychiat. 109:621, 1953.
4. Wharton, G. K.: The fatigue syndrome, Canad. M.A.J. 38:339, 1938.
5. Clarke, H. H., Shay, C. T., and Mathews, D. K.: Strength decrement index: a new test of muscle fatigue, Arch. Phys. Med. 25:377, 1955.
6. Clarke, H. H.: Strength decrements from carrying various Army packs on military marches, Res. Quart. 26:253, 1955.
7. Burkardt, E. A.: Fatigue—diagnosis and treatment, New York J. Med. 56:62, 1956.
8. Merton, P. A.: Problems of muscular fatigue, Brit. M. Bull. 12:219, 1956.
9. Sherrington, C. S.: The integrative action of the nervous system, New Haven, 1906, Yale University Press.
10. Torda, C., and Wolff, H. G.: Depression of acetylcholine synthesis by serum from working muscles, Proc. Soc. Exper. Biol. & Med. 59:13, 1945.
11. Miller, H., and Darrow, D.: Relation of serum and muscle electrolytes, particularly potassium, to voluntary exercise, Am. J. Physiol. 132:801, 1941.
12. Simonson, E.: Effect of amphetamine (Benzedrine) sulfate on state of motor centers, J. Exper. Psychol. 29:517, 1941.
13. Simonson, E., and Enzer, N.: State of motor centers in circulatory insufficiency, Arch. Int. Med. 68:498, 1941.
14. Fritze, C., and Simonson, E.: A new electronic apparatus for the measurement of the fusion frequency of flicker, Science 113:547, 1951.
15. Burge, W. E.: Muscular exercise, fatigue and exhaustion in relation to brain potentials, Fed. Proc. 2:5, 1943.
16. Quo, S.: A new method of measuring fatigue by the threshold stimulus of the Achilles tendon reflex, J. Appl. Physiol. 2:148, 1949.

17. Simonson, E., Enzer, N., and Benton, R.: The influence of muscular work and fatigue on the state of the central nervous system, J. Lab. & Clin. Med. 28:1555, 1943.

18. Tyler. D. B., Goodman, J., and Rothman, T.: The effect of experimental insomnia on the rate of potential changes in the brain, Am. J. Physiol. 149:185, 1947.

19. Edwards, A. S.: Effects of the loss of one hundred hours of sleep, Am. J. Psychol. 54:80, 1941.

20. Foltz, E. E., Jung, F. T., and Cisler, L. E.: Effect of some internal factors on human work output and recovery, Am. J. Physiol. 141:641, 1944.

21. Simonson, E., and Enzer, N.: Measure of fusion frequency of flicker as a test for fatigue of the central nervous system, J. Indust. Hyg. & Toxicol. 23:83, 1941.

22. Tussing, L.: Perceptual fluctuations of illusions as possible physical fatigue index, J. Exper. Psychol. 29:85, 1941.

23. Brozek, J.: Quantitative criteria of oculomotor performance and fatigue, J. Appl. Physiol. 2:247, 1949.

24. Chamberlain, D.: Occupational deafness: audiometric observations on aural fatigue and recovery; preliminary report, Arch. Otolaryng. 35:595, 1942.

25. Laird, D.: Psychology and profits, New York, 1929, B. C. Forbes Publishing Co.

26. Laird, D. A.: The influence of noise on production and fatigue as related to pitch, sensation level, and steadiness of noise, J. Appl. Psychol. 17:320, 1933.

27. Behnke, A., and Stephenson, C.: Applied physiology, Ann. Rev. Physiol. 4:575, 1942.

28. Locke, A.: Non-specific factors in resistance; problem of common cold, J. Immunol. 36:365, 1939.

29. Hinrichs, M. A.: Further studies on some effects of physical fatigue on the peripheral circulation of athletes, Res. Quart. 21:175, 1950.

30. Jokl, E.: Medical research on physical education. Some physiological limitations of athletic performance, Acta Med. Orient. 5:71, 1946.

31. Best, C. H., and Partidge, R. C.: Observations on olympic athletes, Proc. Roy. Soc., London, sB 105:323, 1929.

32. Owen, T.: Fatigue, rest and exercise, Canad. M.A.J. 47:41, 1942.

33. Sippe, C., and Bostock, J.: Hypoglycaemia: a survey and an account of twenty-five cases, M. J. Australia 1:207, 1933.

34. Darcus, H. D.: Some effects of prolonged muscular exertion. In Floyd, W. F., and Welford, A. T., editors: Symposium on fatigue, London, 1953, H. K. Lewis & Co., Ltd.

35. Gardner, K. D., Jr.: "Athletic pseudonephritis"—alteration of urine sediment by athletic competition, J.A.M.A. 161:1613, 1956.

36. Rasch, P. J., Faires, L. B., and Hunt, M. B.: The effects of combative sport (amateur wrestling) on the kidneys, Res. Quart. 29:54, 1958.

37. Stahl, W. C.: March hemoglobinuria, J.A.M.A. 164:1458, 1957.

38. Alyea, E. P., and Boone, A. W.: Urinary findings resulting from nontraumatic exercise, South. M. J. 50:905, 1957.

39. Knowlton, G. C., and Bennett, R. L.: Overwork, Arch. Phys. Med. 38:18, 1957.

40. National Safety Council, Inc.: Practical methods for reducing fatigue, Safe Practices, Pamphlet No. 50, 20 North Wacker Drive, Chicago, 1940.

# 26

# *Training*

## *Summary of the effects of training on the physiological systems*

The effects of frequent and regular exercise on the physiological systems of the body have been observed repeatedly during standard work experiments. Among the changes that have been reported are the following:

1. Slight increase in body weight
2. Longer duration of effort before exhaustion
3. Slight decline in the rate and depth of breathing at rest
4. Decreased pulmonary ventilation during moderate work
5. Ability to attain a greater minute volume of ventilation in exhausting work
6. Ability to attain a greater oxygen consumption during exhausting work
7. Greater mechanical efficiency as indicated by a lower oxygen consumption for a given amount of work
8. Greater utilization of anaerobic energy reserves
9. Increase in glycogen and creatine content of the muscles
10. Lower resting heart rate
11. Smaller increase in heart rate during moderate work
12. Larger stroke volume
13. More rapid return of heart rate and blood pressure to normal following activity
14. Lower blood lactate concentration for the performance of a given amount of work
15. Ability to achieve a higher blood lactate concentration before exhaustion occurs
16. Reduction in the number of movements required for a task
17. Reduction in concentration on task required by higher centers of the nervous system

## Performance

**Work output.** Training diminishes the individual differences among performers in endurance events. Runners who are in good condition at the start of a training period show a small improvement, whereas those in poor condition in the beginning improve rapidly during the training season.

An increase in work output as a result of training has been observed in track and treadmill runners and in bicycle riders. In one study[1] college students unselected for athletic ability trained for a period of 6 months. Track and treadmill running was supplemented with gymnastics and other activities. An average reduction of 1 minute in the time required to run a mile occurred between the second and sixth months. The maximal grade of treadmill running was increased 50%. In another experiment subjects who trained on a bicycle ergometer for 3 months were capable of about 3 times the work output of untrained subjects.[2] Such large increases in work output as the result of training cannot be explained in terms of improved mechanical efficiency alone. In two careful work experiments in which training resulted in comparable increases in work output, the mechanical efficiency remained unchanged in one[3] and increased only 5 to 10% in the other.[4] In both of these experiments it was noted that in the trained subjects the R.Q. during work was lower, the volume of oxygen removed from each liter of inspired air was greater, the oxygen consumption was greater, and the oxygen debt was smaller.

Work during fatigued states on a bicycle ergometer was carried on at a 31% higher rate in trained persons (women physical education majors) than in untrained (student nurses). The trained persons also had an 11% greater capacity for maximum work.[5]

**Muscular form.** Muscular form is changed if the training is begun at an early age. The skeleton of the youth is also affected by training so that running may actually produce a "runner type." Active muscles of animals are often redder than less active muscles due, perhaps, to an increased myoglobin content.

**Oxygen consumption.** The ability of the muscles to absorb and utilize oxygen during rest and exercise is increased by training. A trained athlete can consume considerably larger volumes of oxygen during exhausting work than he could before training started. While in training he is not only able to consume more oxygen, but he can also contract a much larger oxygen debt. Training also decreases the length of time that is necessary to attain a steady state of oxygen consumption during moderate activity. If the work is long-continued, the oxygen consumption of a trained subject remains constant throughout, whereas in untrained subjects the oxygen consumption is increased as exhaustion is approached (Chapter 18). The increased oxygen consumption at the onset of exhaustion is attributed in part to the inefficiency of movement as coordination begins to be impaired by fatigue.

**Basal metabolic rate.** The average basal metabolic rate of 20 Springfield College athletes was 3 to 4% below the average normal standards.[6] This difference may have been due to the greater ability of the athletes to relax under test conditions and thus to achieve a more nearly basal state. Or perhaps athletes actually exist on a more economical level of energy consumption. The basal metabolic rate of athletes often increases slightly (about 2%) during training and falls to the pretraining level after the season of competition is over. This is probably related to the increase in mass and tone of the skeletal muscles during the period of training.

Seasonal changes in the basal metabolic rate in the Springfield College athletes were greater than the change due to training. The lowest rates were recorded in late December and the highest rates in early March. The drop in December was probably the result of a general reduction in physical activity because of examinations and holidays. The rise in the metabolic rate in March was perhaps caused by a general increase in physical activity since most of the athletic competition took place at that time.

*Capillary growth.* An interesting experiment[7] demonstrates the importance of circulatory changes in the improvement in muscular performance due to training. Prior to training the performance of muscles was measured under ischemic conditions (blood supply cut off) and with free circulation. These measurements were repeated after training, and it was observed that the performance of the muscles under ischemic conditions was increased less than 30%, whereas under conditions of free circulation the increase amounted to 100%. The slow rate of the improvement in work performance indicated an actual growth of new capillaries rather than a simple dilatation of existing vessels.

The fact that the improved circulation in training is due in part to an increase in the number of capillaries in the active muscles is shown by the results of several careful experiments. Training guinea pigs to run increased the proportion of capillaries in heart muscle and in the gastrocnemius muscle by 40 to 45%. There was no change in the number of capillaries in skeletal muscles not used in the training exercise.[8] In the normal, growing heart the number of capillaries increases along with the increase in size of the muscle fibers. In young subjects the increase in vascularity caused by training is added to the increase caused by growth. Growth and training seem to be specific factors in the increase in capillarity of heart muscles. The increase in the size of the heart muscle fibers (hypertrophy) that occurs in certain types of heart disease is not accompanied by a proportional increase in the number of capillaries.[9]

The smaller increase in heart rate during exercise and the increased work output in trained individuals are both to be attributed to improved vascularization of the skeletal muscles. The fact that the decreased heart rate in exercise is caused by peripheral changes and not by changes in the heart itself is indicated by an experiment that showed that training the arm muscles did not lower the heart rate during exercise involving untrained leg muscles.[10] This experiment furnishes objective evidence that training is specific; that is, training in one type of activity does not necessarily improve performance in a different type of activity.

Paralleling the increased vascularization of the heart and skeletal muscles in training is an increase in the capillary supply of the motor area of the cerebral cortex. In growing guinea pigs the vascularity of the motor cortex increases progressively with the development of motor activity.[11] A period of training is accompanied by a marked increase in vascularity of the motor cortex and the ventral horn of the spinal cord at the level of the fifth cervical segment. The sensory areas of the cerebral cortex share in the increased vascularization.[12]

*Heart size.* Very severe training results in enlargement of the heart beyond the limits commonly accepted as normal for a person. Participation in college athletics apparently does not increase the size of the normal heart, but the heart shadows of older champion athletes are longer than the norms. Endurance sports enlarge the right side of the heart, whereas short, intense exertion produces greater change in the left side of the heart. Hypertrophy of the right heart is attributed to elevated pulmonary circulatory resistance and increased venous return to the right heart during prolonged and repeated exercise. Hypertrophy of the left heart following repeated short bouts of violent exertion may be due to the increased work of the rapidly contracting heart against the elevated blood pressure in the systemic circulation.

Heart size is related to constitutional type and thoracic circumference. If a larger than average heart is associated with a high vital capacity, the average heart rate and blood pressure are usually lower and there is a greater than normal capacity for the performance of work and sports. The increase in the heart size of racing greyhounds may proceed so rapidly that the activity of the heart is impaired by lack of space.[13]

Serial electrocardiographic studies were made on 48 athletes during one entire training season. In 43 there were no changes. In 5 persons there were minor changes of obscure significance; they were not considered pathological in view of the excellent performance of their hearts.[14]

*Heart rate.** With training there is a small but consistent reduction in the resting heart rate. Although the heart beats more slowly, each contraction is more powerful, and the increased stroke volume more than compensates for the slower heart rate so that the minute volume (cardiac output) is not reduced and may actually be greater than average. Training does not increase the rapidity with which the heart rate accelerates at the beginning of exercise, but the heart rate returns to normal more quickly at the cessation of exercise in a trained subject.

There was little difference between the circulatory measurements of 14 college athletes and 11 nonathletes when they were studied under basal conditions.[15] Increased diastolic pressure after exertion is an outstanding characteristic of the trained subject.

*Nervous system.* Changes in the central nervous system as a result of training are evidenced by improvements in motor skills. Improved mechanical efficiency follows as a consequence of greater skill that eliminates unnecessary muscle contractions. Practice guides soldiers in selecting the most

---

*Review Chapter 11.

metabolically economical step length for every change in road grade, it conditions athletes to inhale at the physiologically and mechanically most opportune moment during a rowing stroke, and it improves the stride and the arm-leg coordination in runners.[16] In industrial work training usually levels individual differences in rather simple tasks, whereas in more complicated operations training increases individual differences.[17]

Psychological factors and specific skills are so important in determining individual performances in exhausting exercise that improved performance can be acquired with almost no improvement in fundamental physiological capacities. It is practically impossible, therefore, to assess physiological effects of athletic conditioning unless some direct physiological determination such as measurement of oxygen debt is made.[18]

**Cross education.** When work is practiced with one hand, not only is the mechanical ability of that hand improved but also there is significant improvement in the other hand that remained idle. This suggests that the nature of the motor nervous system is such that the whole body is responding even when only a part of the body appears to be performing the work.[19] It also suggests that both sides of the body should be exercised in order to secure the most rapid return of normal neuromuscular function following injury or disease.[20]

## Specialization as opposed to all-around training

All-around training, giving equally extensive exercises to develop strength, endurance, and speed, gives the best all-around development. For example, basketball players score well on tests of strength, endurance, and speed. But they do not excel in any of them.

Specialized training directed toward the development of either strength, endurance, or speed naturally results in unilateral adaptation, but the degree of adaptation is higher than that resulting from all-around training. Thus athletes trained for strength do better in weight lifting than athletes with all-around training or than those who trained for endurance or speed. Training for strength improves speed, but endurance is not affected. Weight lifters, although the strongest of all athletes, are even worse than novice athletes in endurance tests. Running endurance is not improved during the course of training for weight lifting.

Training for speed gives the best all-around adaptation. Sprinters score moderately well on strength and endurance tests. Endurance training, however, improves endurance alone; strength or speed is not significantly affected. Cross-country skiers score best in endurance tests but are the poorest in strength and speed.[21] Distance swimmers possessing outstanding endurance are the weakest and slowest of all athletes. During their training swimmers must lift weights in order not to lose strength.

## Physicochemical changes

Training produces physicochemical changes in the tissues that enable the athlete to maintain an almost unchanged internal environment in spite of very strenuous exertion.

*Blood.* Training diminishes the rate of lactic acid formation in moderate exercise so that the blood lactate concentration is lower than in untrained subjects. During exhausting exercise trained subjects can withstand considerably higher concentrations of blood lactate. The interaction of these two factors considerably elevates the work tolerance of a trained subject.

Extensive training lowers the osmotic resistance of red blood corpuscles, apparently as a result of the repeated rises in body temperature associated with exercise. Decreased red cell resistance is observed after hot baths but not after swimming.[22]

The number and diameter of the erythrocytes are increased by training, perhaps as an adjustment to their increased fragility, but the increase in hemoglobin concentration is somewhat less, indicating a smaller amount of hemoglobin in each red cell.

*Respiration.* Frequently repeated episodes of deep, labored breathing that accompany training exercises may produce extensive changes in the respiratory system. The increased stretching of the lung tissues results in a thickening of the alveolar septa, an increase in elastic fibers, and perhaps the actual production of new alveoli. This excessive multiplication of alveolar tissue represents a true hyperplasia (formation of new elements, not simple enlargement of already existing elements), and is called "sport lung." Training also causes a marked hypertrophy of the diaphragm. The improved respiratory efficiency resulting from training is manifested by a greater absorption of oxygen per liter of ventilation.

### Advanced study topics

1. Differentiate skill training from strength training and endurance training.
2. Review the recent literature on training in current issues of the *American Journal of Physiology.*
3. Describe a protocol for the measurement of maximal oxygen consumption.
4. Plot a training curve from practice session scores while learning a new skill.
5. Construct a specific training schedule designed to stimulate each element of physiological adaptation to exercise.

### References

1. Robinson, S., and Harmon, P. M.: Effects of training and of gelatin upon certain factors which limit muscular work, Am. J. Physiol. **133**:161, 1941.
2. Foltz, E., Ivy, A. C., and Barborka, E.: Use of double work periods in the study of fatigue and influence of caffeine on recovery, Am. J. Physiol. **136**: 79, 1942.
3. McNelly, W. C.: Some effects of training on the respiratory response to exercise, Am. J. Physiol. **116**:100, 1936.
4. Knehr, C., Dill, D. B., and Neufeld, W.: Training and its effect on man at rest and at work, Am. J. Physiol. **136**: 148, 1942.
5. Tuttle, W. W.: Effect of physical training on capacity to do work as measured by the bicycle ergometer, J. Appl. Physiol. **2**:393, 1950.
6. Morehouse, L. E.: Unpublished data, 1937.
7. Maison, G. L., and Broeker, A. G.: Training in human muscles working with and without blood supply, Am. J. Physiol. **132**:390, 1941.
8. Petrén, T., Sjöstrand, T., and Sylvén, B.: Der Einfluss des Trainings auf die Häufigkeit der Capillaren in Herz- und Skeletmuskulatur, Arbeitsphysiol. **9**: 376, 1936.
9. Roberts, J. T., Wearn, J. T., and Badal, J. J.: Capillary-muscle ratio in normal and hypertrophied human hearts, Proc. Soc. Exper. Biol. & Med. 38:322, 1938.
10. Müller, E. A.: Die Pulszahl als Kennzeichen für Stoffaustausch und Ermud-

barkeit des arbeitenden Muskels, Arbeitsphysiol. **12**:92, 1942.

11. Petrén, T.: Die Kapillarisierung der motorischen Hirnrinde bei Cavia Coboyo, Morphol. Jahrb. **82**:537, 1938.

12. Petrén, T.: Quantitative Studien an den Kapillaren des zentralen Nervensystems bei Cavia Coboyo, Morphol. Jahrb. **82**:554, 1938.

13. McDowall, R. J. S.: The control of the circulation of the blood, London, 1938, Longmans, Green & Co.

14. Tuttle, W. W., and Korns, H. M.: Electrocardiographic observations on athletes before and after a season of physical training, Am. Heart J. **21**:104, 1941.

15. Stewart, H. J., and Watson, R. F.: Circulation in athletics, J. Clin. Invest. **19**:35, 1940.

16. Hubbard, A. W.: An experimental analysis of running and of certain fundamental differences between trained and untrained runners, Res. Quart. Am. A. Health, Phys. Ed. & Rec. **10**:28, 1939.

17. Tiffen, J.: Industrial psychology, New York, 1942, Prentice-Hall, Inc.

18. Henry, F. M., and Berg, W. E.: Physiological and performance changes in athletic conditioning, J. Appl. Physiol. **3**:103, 1950.

19. Hellebrandt, F. A.: Cross education: ipsilateral and contralateral effects of unimanual training, J. Appl. Physiol. **4**:136, 1951.

20. Hellebrandt, F. A., and Houtz, S. A.: Influence of bimanual exercise on unilateral work capacity, J. Appl. Physiol. **2**:446, 1950.

21. Iakovlev, N. N., Yeremenko, N. P., Leshkevich, A. G., Makarova, A. F., and Popova, N. K.: The development of strength, rapidity of movement and endurance in the course of training in various forms of athletic activity, Sechenov. Physiol. J. USSR **14**:11, 1959.

22. Davis, J. E.: Changes in erythrocyte fragility due to physical exercise and variation of body temperature, J. Lab. & Clin. Med. **23**:786, 1939.

# Part five

# Fitness and health

# 27

# *Fitness*

The term "fitness" implies a relation between the task to be performed and the individual's capability to perform it. If the task is a specific one, such as lifting a heavy weight, a person's fitness for it can be easily demonstrated by an attempt to lift it. If he is successful, it can be said that his fitness for that task is adequate. If he fails to lift it, he can be judged unfit. A simple test such as this, however, does not reflect the individual's *degree* of fitness; perhaps the weight was just barely too heavy for him. Neither does it tell his *capacity;* perhaps a few weeks of training would enable him to lift it. Further, it is not known why he failed; perhaps it was because of a fear of injuring himself.

If the task is nonspecific, such as the carrying out of normal daily life activities, fitness implies that the individual accomplishes these with a reasonable degree of efficiency, without undue fatigue, and with complete recovery before the next day's activities are begun. He is unfit if any of the activities are performed unsatisfactorily, if he is overly fatigued by them, or if his recovery is too slow. In this circumstance one can always become more "fit" by reducing the intensity of his daily life activities or by improving his efficiency, increasing his resistance to fatigue, and adopting more effective recovery procedures.

Fitness relates to a task; it does not describe a state of health. Diabetic persons have become tennis champions. Individuals with heart disease have become successful distance runners. Victims of cancer continue to perform well in the early stages of the disease. In such instances the pathological condition had not become a limiting factor in the performance of work. It is not until the disease becomes debilitating that it affects fitness.

## Aspects of fitness

An individual's state of fitness for exercise is dependent upon the suitability of his body structure for the work to be performed, the effectiveness with which his organs and systems support the effort, and the view that the individual takes of the task as he approaches it and carries it through to completion.

*Anatomical fitness.* In order to be fit, the individual must possess all of the body parts essential to the performance of the task and must possess the appropriate body size and shape for the task. Genetic imperfections in organs and tissues are responsible for weakness in structure and function. These limit the individual's capacity for strength, endurance, and skill.

Slight individual differences in the points of attachment of tendons to bones and differences in lengths of bones result in different mechanical leverage advantages or disadvantages for various events. Thus one person is fit for weight lifting, another for sprint running, and another for jumping. If a person enters a competition for which he is anatomically unfit, he does so with a distinct disadvantage to his opponents who possess anatomical features more fit to the event.

*Physiological fitness.* For the physiological systems of the body to be fit they must function well enough to support the particular activity that the individual is performing. Since different activities make different demands upon the organism with respect to neurological, respiratory, circulatory, metabolic, and temperature-regulating functions, physiological fitness is specific to the activity. Physiological systems are highly adaptable to exercise, as has been shown in preceding chapters. The response of each system is discrete; hard work in the heat is necessary to improve the fitness of the temperature-regulation mechanism. Each task has its major physiological components, and fitness for the task requires effective functioning of the appropriate systems.

*Psychological fitness.* If the individual possesses the necessary perceptions, emotional stability, motivation, intelligence, and educability to accomplish the task, he is psychologically fit for it. Anxiety can become a barrier to performance by contributing tension, elevated heart rate and blood pressure, and endocrine disturbances that add to the stress of the task and therefore contribute to the individual's unfitness for it. No one is without anxieties, but some are better able to adapt to the stress of anxiety in their lives, and these persons are more psychologically fit for arduous work.

## Assessment of general fitness

General fitness implies more than one task and is usually meant to include not only the activities of everyday life but also emergencies in which a person is unexpectedly called upon to perform activities demanding unusual expenditures of strength, energy, and adaptive ability under extremely unfavorable environments. Examples of these are motor vehicle accidents, home fires, floods and mudslides, shipwreck, falls, and physical attacks.

It would be unrealistic to expect that the person in a sedentary occupation would prepare himself by regular exercise to meet all of these emergencies. The demands of this spectrum of emergencies are so widespread that the person trained to meet them adequately would have spent several hours every day in preparation. Only an exercise addict would do this.

A more rational goal that would keep the individual prepared to cope to some extent with emergencies and also to enjoy physical recreations would be at that level represented by an hour of vigorous tennis or an afternoon of moderately heavy yard work. This gross level of fitness implies that the individual possesses appropriate anatomical, physiological, and psychological capabilities that permit the organism to function adequately under the stress of lengthy periods of strenuous activity.

## Physiological factors in fitness

**Homeokinetics.** Physiological fitness for exertion is dependent for the most part upon nervous system coordination of metabolism, respiration, circulation, and temperature regulation. This coordination, which ultimately regulates behavior, is crucially dependent upon effective functioning of homeostatic mechanisms that have been established for survival in and adaptation to situations involving stress. It is the function of these homeostatic mechanisms to maintain the internal environment of the organism within the range of limitations necessary for the normal activity of the cells.[1]

When an individual exerts himself, the internal environment is upset, and the stress, which occurs as a result of the upset, stimulates the mechanisms that reestablish homeostasis. If the activity is sustained and a steady state is established in the internal environment, a new level of metabolic, respiratory, circulatory, and temperature-regulatory balance may be achieved. In a sense the internal environment is "at rest" during activity; the processes are in balance at an elevated level. The process of establishing a steady state at elevated levels of physical activity may be termed *homeokinetic*. The ability to establish and maintain a steady state at elevated levels of physical activity is a measure of a person's *homeokinetic fitness*. The highest level of activity at which a person can maintain a steady state represents his *homeokinetic capacity*.

Limiting factors in homeokinetic capacity are the maintenance of adequate blood sugar levels, the preservation of optimal hydrogen ion concentration, and the provision of adequate oxygen supply. On each of these depends the proper function of the nervous system. The first sign of failure of any of them is a lightheaded or dazed sensation followed by fatigue and dizziness and, in extreme failure, collapse and coma. In the fit person coordination, strength, and other characteristics of performance are affected less in early stages of homeokinetic breakdown. In advanced stages both fit and unfit behave alike; they reel, stumble, and fall.

**Maintenance of blood sugar level.** Heavy physical activity causes fluctuations in the blood sugar level above and below the 60 to 90 mg. per 100 ml. normal level. Blood sugar levels above the 90 mg. upper limit (*hyperglycemia*) are reached in heavy physical exercise in which exhaustion occurs after 10 to 40 minutes.[2] Activity that results in exhaustion in less than 10 minutes usually raises blood sugar somewhat but not beyond the normal range. If exhaustion occurs in less than 3 minutes, there is usually only a small elevation in the blood sugar level. Although fit individuals tend to experience less hyperglycemia than those less fit for exertion, the elevated blood sugar during this temporary period seems to have neither beneficial nor detrimental effects.

If hard work is continued for over an hour, as in marathon running, and no food is taken, the blood sugar level falls below 60 mg. per 100 ml. and *hypoglycemia* occurs. In the fit individual regulatory mechanisms that cause the liver to maintain normal blood sugar levels operate more effectively, so that activity can proceed longer before hypoglycemia occurs. In the unfit person the fall in blood sugar concentration after an hour of hard work is more rapid and reaches lower levels than in the person fit for exertion.[3] The lessened fluctuations in blood sugar levels in the fit individuals in both brief and prolonged exhausting exercise are a measure of the superiority of their homeokinetic mechanisms.

***Preservation of hydrogen ion concentration.*** The pH of the blood is usually about 7.4, with a normal range of 7.4 to 7.6 and an extreme range of from 6.8 to 7.8.[1] The acid residues of heavy work almost never change the blood from slightly alkaline (above 7) to acid (below 7). The catabolic acids are reduced by the buffers in the blood, acid excretion from the kidneys, and elimination of carbon dioxide through the lungs. As a result, 30 minutes of moderately heavy work followed by a sprint to exhaustion reduces the pH only to 7.25.[4] Fit individuals are only slightly better able to maintain normal pH than those unfit for exertion.

***Provision of oxygen.*** Continuous muscular work depends upon an adequate supply of oxygen. Although fuels for energy may be present and some of them can be used without oxygen, without sufficient oxygen energy production soon fails to support physical activity. The relation between oxygen consumption and the production of work is linear, and this linearity has been widely used as a basis for determining fitness for exertion.

Maximum oxygen consumption is an index of aerobic capacity and is also the best measure of fitness for continuous exercise. The estimation of oxygen consumption requires special apparatus and is time consuming; therefore classifying the fitness of individuals using this method is impractical if many subjects are to be tested.

Fortunately, however, pulse rate, which is easy to measure, correlates significantly with oxygen consumption during exercise. This correlation has been employed successfully in a number of fitness tests. The Harvard step test,[5] in which the individual steps on and off a 20-inch platform 30 times a minute until exhaustion or until 5 minutes has elapsed, yields a score that represents an indication of fitness which is representative of that determined by maximum oxygen intake.

Master's step test[6] is less strenuous than the Harvard step test and therefore is less accurate in matching the maximum oxygen intake as an index of fitness. Its use of the electrocardiograph makes its application more restricted, but the electrocardiogram presents useful information concerning the compensatory ability of the heart to support exercise.

The Balke treadmill test of fitness[7] establishes through stepwise increases in work a pulse curve that is extrapolated to estimate the work required to elevate the pulse rate to 180, the hypothetical end point of homeostasis. This test is more difficult to administer than the Harvard step test and is no better as a predictor of fitness for maximal effort.

Åstrand and Rhyming's nomogram,[8] which also extrapolates pulse rate data to predict maximal oxygen intake, is simpler than determining oxygen consumption directly and gives a highly significant correlation.

The ability to accumulate a large oxygen debt is an index of the individual's capacity for certain types of prolonged work,[9] but exertions of brief duration do not produce oxygen debts of sufficient magnitude to attach any significance to them. Also in work of extremely prolonged nature, that is, the marathon race, the work is carried out in a homeokinetic state, so the oxygen debt is only slight. Estimations of blood lactic acid as anaerobic indices of fitness are limited for the same reason. Both oxygen debt and lactic acid determinations do, however, differentiate the fit from the unfit in bouts of work of moderate duration.

Although positive differentiation between the fit and the unfit can be made only under conditions of hard physical work, there are some differences that are usually seen during work of *moderate* intensity (Table 12).

The easier the work, the smaller and less regular will be the difference between the fit and the unfit. Thus it is seen that fitness for exertion is essentially an expression of the organism's ability to maintain an internal environment that permits normal function of the cells during manyfold increases in metabolic rate.

## The step test

A rapid form of the *Harvard Fatigue Laboratory test of physical fitness,* abridged for use on large numbers of men, will be described. The test is useful for selecting men for hard work, for evaluating the progress of physical training, and for determining the adequacy of diets.

In this shortened form of the test, speed and simplicity have been increased by sacrificing some of the accuracy of the longer form. The 20-inch

*Table 12.* Differences in fit and unfit subjects during moderate work*

| Measurement | Fit | Unfit |
|---|---|---|
| Oxygen consumption | Lower | Higher |
| Pulse rate during work | Lower | Higher |
| Stroke volume during work | Larger | Smaller |
| Blood pressure during work (systolic) | Lower | Higher |
| Blood lactate during work | Lower | Higher |
| Return of blood pressure to normal after work | Faster | Slower |

*Data from Johnson, Brouha, and Darling: Rev. Canad. Biol. 1:491, 1942.

step is so high that it tends to penalize short men and also to involve to some extent the factor of agility as well as general fitness. Consequently gross errors may sometimes be made in judging very short or clumsy men. However, if a lower step is used, the work is too easy for men in good condition, which increases the number of errors and impairs the value of the test.

If it is desired to apply the test to groups of women, to age groups below 17 years of age, to ill persons, to convalescents, or to others for whom the work on the 20-inch stool is too difficult, the height of the stool may be lowered until approximately all but one third of the group can complete the full 5 minutes of exercise.

*Equipment necessary to conduct the step test:*

1. One watch, preferably a stopwatch, is needed for each observer.

2. A stepping platform 20 inches high (plus or minus not more than ¼ inch) is required. This should be sturdily constructed so as not to "give" when stepped on. It should be at least 14 inches from front to back. When many men are to use the same step simultaneously, it should be long enough to allow at least 30 inches for each man. These 30-inch spaces should be marked off. Standard gymnasium stools, if adjusted to 20 inches in height, are satisfactory.

*Conducting the step test:*

1. As many subjects as there are observers line up in front of the stepping platform. Subjects should be stripped to the underwear and should wear rubber-soled shoes or no shoes at all.

2. One observer calls the rhythm. (A simple pendulum consisting of a weight on a string 39 inches long helps in keeping time.) At the signal "Start!" each subject places one foot on the platform, steps up placing both feet on the platform, straightens the legs and back, and immediately steps down again, bringing down first the same foot he placed up first. At exactly 2-second intervals the signal "Up" is given, and rhythm is maintained by giving the following count: UP! - 2 - 3 - 4 UP! - 2 - 3 - 4 UP! - 2 - 3 - 4, etc., the command "UP" coming every 2 seconds. The subject should "lead off" with the same foot each time, and not try to alternate feet. However, one or two changes of "lead off" during the test are immaterial. He must not touch anything with his hands but may move his arms freely.

3. Begin counting the time when the subject starts exercising and exercise him at the rate of 30 times a minute for 5 minutes, continuously unless he stops before then from exhaustion. If he falls behind, stop him after he has been unable to keep up the pace for 20 seconds. Note the duration of his effort to the nearest second. All men are stopped at 5 minutes if they can go that long.

4. When the subject stops, start counting the time and have him sit quietly on a chair.

5. Beginning exactly 1 minute after he stops, count the number of heartbeats for exactly 30 seconds. The base of the neck (carotid artery) is an easy place to find the pulse after exercise.

*Table 13.* General physical fitness (the step test)*

| Duration of effort | Heartbeats from 1 to 1½ minutes in recovery | | | | | | | | | | |
|---|---|---|---|---|---|---|---|---|---|---|---|
| | 40-44 | 45-49 | 50-54 | 55-59 | 60-64 | 65-69 | 70-74 | 75-79 | 80-84 | 85-89 | 90-over |
| 0 - 29" | 5 | 5 | 5 | 5 | 5 | 5 | 5 | 5 | 5 | 5 | 5 |
| 0'30"-0'59" | 20 | 15 | 15 | 15 | 15 | 10 | 10 | 10 | 10 | 10 | 10 |
| 1' 0"-1'29" | 30 | 30 | 25 | 25 | 20 | 20 | 20 | 20 | 15 | 15 | 15 |
| 1'30"-1'59" | 45 | 40 | 40 | 35 | 30 | 30 | 25 | 25 | 25 | 20 | 20 |
| 2' 0"-2'29" | 60 | 50 | 45 | 45 | 40 | 35 | 35 | 30 | 30 | 30 | 25 |
| 2'30"-2'59" | 70 | 65 | 60 | 55 | 50 | 45 | 40 | 40 | 35 | 35 | 35 |
| 3' 0"-3'29" | 85 | 75 | 70 | 60 | 55 | 55 | 50 | 45 | 45 | 40 | 40 |
| 3'30"-3'59" | 100 | 85 | 80 | 70 | 65 | 60 | 55 | 55 | 50 | 45 | 45 |
| 4' 0"-4'29" | 110 | 100 | 90 | 80 | 75 | 70 | 65 | 60 | 55 | 55 | 50 |
| 4'30"-4'59" | 125 | 110 | 100 | 90 | 85 | 75 | 70 | 65 | 60 | 60 | 55 |
| 5' | 130 | 115 | 105 | 95 | 90 | 80 | 75 | 70 | 65 | 65 | 60 |

*Instructions: (1) Find the appropriate line for duration of effort. (2) Then find the appropriate column for the pulse count. (3) Read off the score where the line and column intersect. (4) Interpret according to the following scale (the score is an indication of general fitness on the day of measurement): *below 50,* poor general physical fitness; *50-80,* average general physical fitness; *above 80,* good general physical fitness.

6. Record the duration of effort and the number of heartbeats in the 30-second period, beginning 1 minute after he stops. No other observations are necessary.

7. Read the score from Table 13. The scores for normal, healthy young men are interpreted as follows: *poor,* below 50; *average,* 50 through 80; *good,* above 80.

**Precautions:**

1. *The platform must be 20 inches high.*

2. The rhythm should be maintained as closely as possible. It is easy to distinguish between those unable to keep pace from exhaustion and those who merely have a poor sense of rhythm. Only exhausted men should be stopped before 5 minutes. Those with a poor sense of rhythm can be kept to the pace by a tap on the elbow every 2 seconds.

3. *Times must be followed strictly.*

4. *The subjects must straighten legs and back at each step.*

5. Observers unaccustomed to counting rapid pulse rates must practice before they can be expected to obtain accurate results.

**Sample step test:** A sample step test is shown in the accompanying form.

---

**Name:** John Doe
**Date:** January 7, 1963
**Duration:** 3 minutes, 35 seconds
**Pulses from 1 minute to 1½ minutes in recovery:** 79
**Score (from Table 12):** 55
**Fitness for hard work:** *Low average*

---

## Advanced study topics

1. Is it possible to describe a person's fitness without observing his performance in the task for which he is being evaluated?
2. Review the recent literature on fitness in current issues of the *Research Quarterly*.
3. Compare the scores of a group of individuals on various physical fitness tests.
4. Tabulate the incidence of colds and similar infections in individuals who are highly fit, and in others who are less fit.
5. Select a task and construct a fitness test for performers of that task. Validate the test on the basis of task performance scores or ratings.

## References

1. Bard, P., editor: Medical physiology, St. Louis, 1961, The C. V. Mosby Co.
2. Dill, D. B., Edwards, H. T., and Mead, S.: Blood sugar regulation in exercise, Am. J. Physiol. 111:21, 1935.
3. Steinhaus, A. H.: Chronic effects of exercise, Physiol. Rev. 13:103, 1933.
4. DeLaune, R., Barnes, J. R., Brouha, L., and Massart, F.: Changes in acid-base balance and blood gasses during muscular activity and recovery, J. Appl. Physiol. 14:328, 1959.
5. Brouha, L., Fradd, N. W., and Savage, B. M.: Studies in physical efficiency of college students, Res. Quart. 15:211, 1944.
6. Master, A. M., Nuzie, S., Brown, R. C., and Parker, R. C.: The electrocardiogram and the "two-step" exercise; a test of cardiac function and coronary insufficiency, Am. J. Med. Sc. 207:435, 1944.
7. Balke, B., Grillo, G. P., Konecci, E. B., and Luft, U. C.: Work capacity after blood donation, J. Appl. Physiol. 7:231, 1954.
8. Åstrand, P. O., and Rhyming, I.: A nomogram for calculation of aerobic capacity (physical fitness) from pulse rate during sub-maximal work, J. Appl. Physiol. 7:218, 1954.
9. Robinson, S., and Harrison, P. M.: The effects of training and of gelatin upon certain factors which limit muscular work, Am. J. Physiol. 133:161, 1941.
10. Johnson, R. E., Brouha, L., and Darling, R. C.: A test of physical fitness for strenuous exertion, Rev. Canad. Biol. 1:491, 1942.

# 28

# Age, sex, body type, and race

Limits of physical ability among persons are determined in part by body structure. Variations due to structure are exhibited when well-trained athletes perform in competition. In the competitive situation the athletes have received sufficient motivation and training to enable them to approach the physiological limits of function of the critical organs. The difference in performance is then affected by differences in structure. Variations in structure that affect performance are found among different age groups, between the two sexes, among different body types, and among different racial groups.

Persons with wide differences in structure may all be able to execute the same *kind* of movement, but the difference in the *quality* of execution of the movement shown by each person results largely from variations in the amount of strength, speed, skill, and endurance that is possessed by each. Furthermore a piece of work that requires only a low grade of organic function does not differentiate individuals in a population. It is not until the work is increased in intensity or complexity, requiring coordinate increases in strength, speed, skill, or endurance, that differences among persons become apparent.

## Age

***Responses of young children to exercise.*** The physiological systems of younger children are apparently not as well developed to meet the demands of strenuous exercise as they become when puberty is reached.[1, 2] Children under 12 years of age possess a highly active sympathetic nervous system that predisposes to a high heart rate and an easily depleted capacity for endurance activities such as running. They do not have the capacity to

*Table 14.* Heart rates in males during grade walking on a treadmill*

| Age (years) | Heart rate |
|:-----------:|:----------:|
| 6  | 170 |
| 10 | 164 |
| 14 | 160 |
| 18 | 150 |
| 22 | 146 |
| 26 | 143 |
| 30 | 140 |
| 34 | 137 |
| 38 | 134 |
| 42 | 134 |

*Data from Dill and Consolazio: J. Appl. Physiol. 17:645, 1962.

utilize oxygen that older boys do because of a relatively smaller stroke volume of the heart and a consequent smaller capacity for increased circulation of blood through the lungs.[3] The younger boys also possess a lesser supply of carbohydrate fuel.[4]

A comparison of heart rates of boys and men of different ages during grade walking on a treadmill is given in Table 14.

The net mechanical efficiency (work done divided by excess oxygen used above the basal level) in cycling was observed to be greatest in boys between 9 and 11 years of age, as shown in Table 15. Similar previous studies[3, 4] are not in agreement with this observation, and their prepuberal boys required more oxygen than 13-year-old boys for a given output of energy of the muscles and also had a lower mechanical efficiency in grade walking.

The physiological processes involving the brain, nerves, heart, lungs, and kidneys, which are coordinated to maintain normal constancy of the internal environment of the body (homeostasis), are weak during infancy and early childhood, become maximum by puberty, and then decline. This strengthening at puberty may be a result of the hormonal factors associated with puberty.[3, 7]

Before puberty maximum physical output is directly proportional to age, circumference of the chest and thigh, and vital capacity.[2] From puberty upward to 19 years of age physical fitness for maximal exercise is related more to body size than to age.[8-10]

The ability of the body to respond and recover from exercise and other stresses of the homeostatic mechanisms reaches a peak at about 14 years of age. This vitality declines in boys with the onset of adolescence, showing a significant decrease at the age of 17 years, then rises slightly between the ages of 21 to 25 years, and thereafter declines gradually. In girls there is a temporary increase in fitness for strenuous exercise at 17 years of age and possibly again at 20 years of age.[11]

The ability of boys to perform athletic activities requiring strength, speed,[11] endurance,[12] and skill[13] increases steadily between 5 and 20 years of age, adolescence retarding but not interrupting the progress. Athletic abil-

*Table 15.* Mechanical efficiency of males during cycling

| Ages | Efficiency |
|---|---|
| 7 to 9 | 18.4° |
| 9 to 11 | 22.8° |
| 12 to 15 | 17.9° |
| Young men | 17.2† |

°Data from Taylor, Bal, Lamb, and MacLeod: J. Appl. Physiol. 2:563, 1950.
†Data from Lamb: A comparison of the energy expenditure and mechanical efficiency of boys and young men and some observations upon the influence of age and work done on the mechanical efficiency of boys, unpublished dissertation, Columbia University, 1942.

ity in girls reaches a maximum at the age of 13 or 14 years and then tends to decline so that a 6-year-old girl usually has a better performance than a girl 18 years of age.[10]

*Physical capacity of adults.* After 25 years of age the ability of men to perform maximal work declines about 1% each year. It decreases slightly more in women. A decrease in aerobic capacity is accompanied by similar declines in functional capacity of the skeletomuscular, the respiratory, and the cardiovascular systems. The ability to perform moderate work in extreme heat, at least for brief exposures, does not appear to decline with age.[4]

When working within the limit of their ability, many men well advanced in years can carry on long-continued work with a lower heart rate and less evidence of fatigue than that exhibited by young men. The capacity for anaerobic work appears to be maximal in the early twenties and to be small in young boys and old men. The highest lactate levels are reached in the twenties, and there is only a slight lactate increase in the hardest work attempted by young boys or old men. Work or sport activities with the emphasis on speed and strength are best suited to young men. Older men are best fitted for jobs or sports requiring skill, coordination, and endurance.[4]

*Sickness absenteeism in industry.* Absenteeism increases with age so that the total rate is about twice as high in the 50-year to 59-year age group as in the 20-year to 40-year age group.[14] Age increases the average number of days lost per absence (severity rate) more than the average number of absences per 1,000 workers (frequency rate). The increase of absenteeism with age is most pronounced in work performed under conditions of high humidity. It appears that an age over 35 years is a definite handicap for work in high humidity.[15]

## Sex

*Sickness absenteeism in industry.* The rate of sickness absenteeism of women workers exceeds that of men workers by 50 to 300%, due mainly to the large number of short-time (1 to 3 days) absences. The excess can be explained only partially by menstrual irregularities.[16] The increase of absenteeism with age is more pronounced with men than with women, so that the discrepancy between men and women is greatest in the younger age groups.[17] The difference in the sickness rate between unemployed men and women is even higher than that between employed men and women. The greater rate of absenteeism among women is an inherent characteristic, and accumulated fatigue from a greater amount of extra work is a secondary factor.[18]

*Response to exercise.* The physiological responses of young women to moderate exercise do not differ sufficiently from those of men to necessitate wide differentiation of physical performance standards. The only difference in the response to moderate exercise is a more rapid and greater increase in the pulse rate in women. When the work is strenuous, more significant differences in response appear. The endurance of women in running is only one half that of men. The maximal pulmonary ventilation, oxygen intake, and respiratory quotient are higher in men. In general the sex differences are similar to those found between men of low and high fitness for exercise. There is considerable overlapping between the groups, and the performance of the best women is comparable to that of the poorest men.[19] In one other study,[11] Ceylonese girls gave consistently lower mean fitness indices at all ages in both moderate and severe exercise.

The difference in performance ability between the two sexes is not apparent until after puberty. At puberty development of performance ability stops or even declines in females, whereas it continues to advance at a slightly retarded rate in males. At puberty boys begin to excel in strength and endurance. Maximal endurance declines rapidly in girls after 14 years of age.[20]

Untrained women are about two thirds as strong as men. Women are less responsive to training and require more work and time to increase their strength. Their maximal strength capacity is about one half that of men.[21]

Male and female are equally efficient at all ages in skilled work of mild intensity. No significant sex differences in work decrement are found when women and men work together at routine tasks. Women in general tend to drop in the level of production sooner, and men have a slightly higher level of performance except in small manipulative operations such as handwriting. Out of 1,900 different operations in 21 industries, only 331 are unfit for women.[22]

*Effect of exercise on reproductive system.* Transitory modifications of menstrual function among athletic women disappear with the cessation of programs of heavy exercise. Muscular work has a favorable influence on some. There should be no prohibition of moderate physical activity during the menses. Exercise has no detrimental effect upon fertility, and the supposed increase in the strength of the musculature of the pelvic floor resulting from participation in competitive athletics appears to have no pathological influence on childbirth.

## Body type

*Structure and work.* There exists a mutual interrelation between body structure and heavy physical work. First, activity modifies structure. The result of many years of using a shovel or performing on a particular piece of gymnastic apparatus is a change in physique that characterizes the worker or the athlete. Second, structure modifies activity. The differences in inherent structure affect the performance of work and sport. A linear person is at a disadvantage in performing work and sport that require the carrying of heavy loads or the receiving of body blows. Persons with a lateral body build yield to those with a linear body build in the performance of activities requiring a wide range of movement (Fig. 47).

A demonstration that activity modifies structure is provided in the asymmetry of strongly right-handed or left-handed individuals. There is a marked difference in size between the right and left upper extremities. Measurements repeated from time to time show that the superiority of the right upper extremity over the left increases with age, demonstrating the effects of development through use.[23] Asymmetry in somatic development is induced by certain types of sports and gymnastics. Swimming gives the most symmetrical development.

*Feminine body build.* The fear among young women that vigorous physical activity may result in masculinity of build is unfounded. Hard physical labor during youth does not tend toward the development of a significant degree of masculinity in the build of young American Negro women.[24] Young women who already have masculine builds have some advantage in athletic ability, but muscular strength and power are of much greater importance to athletic performance than is body build.[25] Adolescent girls with broad, lateral builds possess a physical capacity superior to girls with a linear type of body build.[26]

*Structural differences affecting performance.* Variations in the position of the muscular attachments, the structure of the joints, and the lengths of the bony levers all affect the performance of physical activity. Usually when the anatomical structure is particularly advantageous for strength, it is disadvantageous for speed. Large joints are strong, but they also may limit motion. Long-distance runners are observed to have very flat longitudinal arches, and sprinters have smaller feet and higher arches.

Although physique plays an important part in the performance of severe exercise, it plays only a minor role in determining a person's response to moderate exercise. Severe exercise is best performed by those with a slim body build. In general persons with thin legs have better endurance. Persons with a normal or stocky build have, on the average, the greatest speed, the greatest strength, and the greatest ability to sustain prolonged moderate muscular effort. Good muscular development is required for success in activities requiring speed and strength.[11, 27]

*Size and energy exchange during work.* Differences in body size affect the energy exchange during physical activity. Even at rest a large man may consume as much as 58% more oxygen than a small man. During light work (simulating operation of an airplane) a large man may require 42% more oxygen than a small man. Among 27 men the correlation coefficient between the oxygen consumption and body surface was plus 0.76 at rest

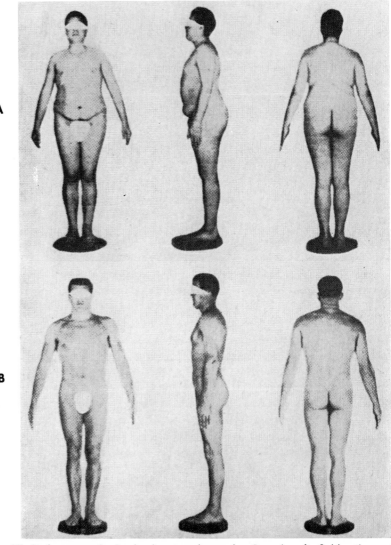

**Fig. 47.** Body types. **A,** Predominant endomorphy. Round, soft, flabby tissue, floats in water. Physically weak. **B,** Predominant mesomorphy. Muscular, square, hard, strong. Professional athlete. Predilection for muscular exercise. (From Sheldon, W. H.: Varieties of temperament, New York, 1942, Harper & Brothers.)

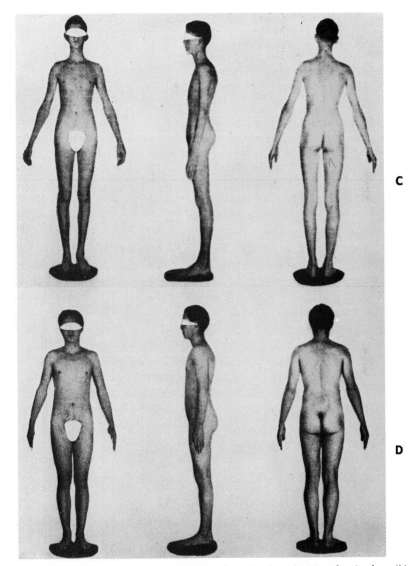

**Fig. 47 (cont'd). C,** Predominant ectomorphy. Slender, fragile, fond of walking, adept at games not requiring weight and sheer strength (basketball center, baseball pitcher, tennis player). **D,** An average person. Sleek, smooth, supple, strong, but vulnerable. (From Sheldon, W. H.: Varieties of temperament, New York, 1942, Harper & Brothers.)

and plus 0.82 at work.[28] Because of the larger energy requirement during work, a large man accumulates heat under conditions in which a smaller man attains a heat balance. The ratio of heat production to surface area in a 218-pound man was observed to be 20% greater than in a 97-pound man.[29]

*Heart size.* Heart size is related to constitutional type and thoracic circumference. Measurements of heart size by the orthodiagraph in 233 athletes indicated moderate hypertrophy as compared with Hodges-Eyster standards. Such hypertrophy is judged to be normal for athletes.[30] If a larger than average heart is associated with a high vital capacity, an athlete usually also has a slower than average pulse rate and low blood pressure and possesses a large capacity for performance of work.

## Race

*Negro compared with white.* Negroes show a higher rate of sickness absenteeism in industry, but as the occupations and socioeconomic status of the Negro and white males become more nearly alike, the excess of the frequency rate of disabilities among Negroes tends to decrease, if not to disappear entirely. Negroes can stand humid heat better than white workers. The rate of sickness absenteeism in very humid climates is lower among Negroes than among whites.[31]

The superior ability of Negroes to work in the heat is due in part to greater efficiency, a higher ratio of body surface to weight, the secretion of a more dilute sweat, and a greater water intake. Negro and white sharecroppers and a group of northern white men (from the Harvard Fatigue Laboratory) were tested during a summer in Mississippi. Subjects walked for 2 hours on a motor-driven treadmill at a rate that elevated the metabolism to 7 times basal. Room temperature averaged 88° F. and humidity 79%. This work raised the body temperature of the partially acclimatized northern white men to intolerable levels, increased their heart rates to nearly maximal values, and forced most of the men to discontinue the walk before the end of the 2 hours. Negro sharecroppers who were acclimatized by field work performed the walk without marked elevation of body temperature or heart rate. They perspired less but drank more water than did the northern whites. White sharecroppers, also accustomed to field work, were intermediate between the other groups in adaptability to the conditions of the experiment. The superiority of the Negro sharecroppers was related to lower energy requirements for performing the walk. Negro servants were no more successful than northern whites in regulating body temperature but were able to sweat at much higher rates. Most of the Negroes reached an equilibrium with a rectal temperature of about 101° F. and a pulse rate of 150 as compared with a temperature of about 102° F. and a pulse rate of 170 in the white workers. Sweating was of the order of 1 to 2 liters an hour. The major item was superior cardiovascular condition. Final mechanical efficiencies were 25.6% in Negroes and 27.5% in whites. Of 23 Negroes two were below the white average, and of 7 white men one was better than the average Negro.[32]

In maximal work Negroes reach a greater blood lactate concentration, have a slightly lower maximum oxygen consumption, and breathe more rapidly, thus using a smaller fraction of the vital capacity as tidal air. The higher blood lactate indicates greater motivation.[33] Psychological explanation on a similar basis is advanced for the frequent supremacy of the Negro in athletic competition.[34]

## Advanced study topics

1. From a physiological point of view, what is the youngest age at which children should compete in various athletic events?
2. Review the recent literature on age, sex, body type, and race in current issues of the *Journal of Applied Physiology*.
3. Why does fitness for strenuous work decline in young women after puberty?
4. Which body types are particularly well suited to various athletic events?
5. Which physical characteristics account for Negro supremacy in certain sports?

## References

1. Metheny, E.: Breathing capacity and grip strength of pre-school children, Iowa City, 1940, University of Iowa Press.
2. Seham, M., and Egerer-Seham, G.: Physiology of exercise in childhood. I. A study of normal children of school age, Am. J. Dis. Child. **25**:1, 1923; II. A study of collapse in normal children, Am. J. Dis. Child. **26**:254, 1923.
3. Morse, M., Schultz, F. W., and Cassels, D. E.: Relation of age to physiological responses of the older boy (10-17 years) to exercise, J. Appl. Physiol. **1**: 683, 1949.
4. Dill, D. B., and Consolazio, F. C.: Responses to exercise as related to age and environmental temperature, J. Appl. Physiol. **17**:645, 1962.
5. Taylor, C. M., Bal, M. E. R., Lamb, M. W., and MacLeod, G.: Mechanical efficiency in cycling of boys seven to fifteen years of age, J. Appl. Physiol. **2**:563, 1950.
6. Lamb, M. W.: A comparison of the energy expenditure and mechanical efficiency of boys and young men and some observations upon the influence of age and work done on the mechanical efficiency of boys, Unpublished dissertation, Columbia University, 1942.

7. Brody, S.: Bioenergetics and growth with special reference to the efficiency complex in domestic animals, New York, 1945, Reinhold Publishing Corp.
8. Gallagher, J. R., and Brouha, L.: A simple method of testing the physical fitness of boys, Res. Quart. **14**:31, 1943.
9. Gallagher, J. R., Brouha, L., Gallagher, C. D., and Johnson, T. J.: Studies in physical fitness in adolescence, Yale J. Biol. & Med. **15**:657, 679, 1943.
10. Johnson, R. E., Brouha, L., and Gallagher, J. R.: Evaluation of physical fitness by the step test, Yale J. Biol. & Med. **15**:781, 1943.
11. Collumbine, H., Bibile, S. W., Wikramanayake, T. W., and Watson, R. S.: Influence of age, sex, physique and muscular development on physical fitness, J. Appl. Physiol. **2**:488, 1950.
12. Jokl, E.: Physical fitness, J.A.M.A. **116**: 2388, 1941.
13. Morehouse, L. E., and Cooper, J. M.: Kinesiology, St. Louis, 1950, The C. V. Mosby Co.
14. Court, A. T.: Sickness absenteeism, Indust. Med. **11**:271, 1942.
15. Brinton, P. H., Seifert, H. E., and Frasier, E. S.: Disabling morbidity among employees in the slaughter and meat packing industry, U. S. Pub. Health Rep. **54**:2196, 1939.
16. Simonson, E.: Industrial physiology, Ann. Rev. Physiol. **6**:543, 1944.
17. Lynch, D. L.: Industrial health and the war, New England J. Med. **227**: 209, 1942.
18. Emerson, H.: Administrative medicine, New York, 1941, Thomas Nelson & Sons.
19. Metheny, E. L., Brouha, L., Johnson, R. E., and Forbes, W. H.: Some physiologic responses of women and men to moderate and strenuous exercise: a comparative study, Am. J. Physiol. **137**: 318, 1942.

20. Jokl, E., and De Jongh, T. W.: Physical efficiency as a secondary sex characteristic, Manpower (South Africa) **1**:17, 1943.

21. Hettinger, T.: Physiology of strength, Springfield, Ill., 1961, Charles C Thomas, Publisher.

22. Burnell, M. R.: Placement and health maintenance, Indust. Med. **11**:521, 1942.

23. Van Dusen, C. R.: Anthropometric study of upper extremities of children, Human Biol. **11**:277, 1939.

24. Adams, E. H.: A comparative anthropometric study of hard labor during youth as a stimulator of physical growth of young colored women, Res. Quart. Am. A. Health Phys. Ed. & Rec. **9**:102, 1938.

25. Carpenter, A.: Strength, power and "femininity" as factors influencing the athletic performance of college women, Res. Quart. Am. A. Health Phys. Ed. & Rec. **9**:120, 1938.

26. Pryor, H. B., and Smith, R. T.: Physical strength of adolescent girls, J. Pediat. **14**:610, 1939.

27. Collumbine, H.: Relationship between body build and capacity for exercise, J. Appl. Physiol. **2**:155, 1949.

28. Karpovich, P. V., and Ronkin, R. R.: Oxygen consumption for men of various sizes in the simulated piloting of a plane, Am. J. Physiol. **146**:394, 1946.

29. Robinson, S.: Effect of body size upon energy exchange in work, Am. J. Physiol. **136**:363, 1942.

30. Wilce, J.: Range of normal heart in athletes, Am. Heart J. **25**:613, 1943.

31. Gafafer, W. M.: Manual of industrial hygiene, Philadelphia, 1943, W. B. Saunders Co.

32. Robinson, S., Dill, D. B., Wilson, J. W., and Nielsen, M.: Adaptation of white men and Negroes to prolonged work in humid heat, Am. J. Trop. Med. **21**:261, 1941.

33. Robinson, S., Dill, D. B., Harmon, P. M., Hall, F. G., and Wilson, J. W.: Adaptation to exercise of Negro and white sharecroppers in comparison with northern whites, Human Biol. **13**:139, 1941.

34. Holloman, L. L.: On supremacy of Negro athletes in white athletic competition, Psychoanal. Rev. **30**:157, 1943.

# 29

# Stress

## Mechanism

Stress as defined by Selye is "the state manifested by the specific syndrome which consists of all the nonspecifically induced changes within a biologic system."[1] More simply, it consists of the bodily changes produced by physiological or psychological conditions that tend to upset the homeostatic balance. Our understanding of how this comes about and whether exercise may elicit some features of the alarm reaction is by no means complete. In Selye's theory a stressor produces a generalized stress reaction in the body through either neural or hormonal pathways. Acting through the nerves, it stimulates the secretion of epinephrine and acetylcholine. Acting through the pituitary gland, the stressor produces an increased secretion of ACTH (adrenocorticotropic hormone). This in turn stimulates the adrenal cortex to produce glucocorticoids that increase gluconeogenesis, raising the concentration of liver glycogen and blood sugar. The pituitary gland secretes STH (somatotropic hormone), which Selye believes may act upon the adrenal cortex to stimulate production of mineralocorticoids that cause the retention of sodium and the loss of potassium. Under stress the pituitary secretions also intensify the production of TSH (thyroid-stimulating hormone), which stimulates the metabolism as a whole.

## Effects

Stressful situations may affect persons differently, depending upon their inherited and acquired characteristics. As stress develops, the corticoid activity rises sharply. The body attempts to limit the stress to the smallest area possible. If it is successful, corticoid activity falls to a normal level. If the stress continues so long that the affected cells break down, the reaction spreads to adjacent areas, and corticoid production again rises. If it overwhelms the resistances of the body, exhaustion appears and death follows. However, if the body is able to maintain its defenses, a general adaptation to this form of stress develops. A gradual diminution in ability to adapt occurs during aging.

## Measurement

Certain bodily changes are characteristic of increased corticoid activity —the disappearance of certain white blood cells termed eosinophils, involution of the lymphatic tissue, and a generalized loss of body weight. The inverse relationship between the adrenal cortical activity and the number of circulating eosinophils in the blood has been utilized by a number of investigators as a convenient method of measuring the effects of stressors on the homeostatic balance. Eosinophil counts by Wake and co-workers[2] on men who exercised were lower than on those who rested, signifying that exercise caused an activation of the adrenal cortex. After counting eosinophils in the blood of university oarsmen, Renold and associates concluded that if eosinophils are a valid index of an increase in circulating adrenal oxysteroids, stimulation of the adrenal cortex occurs during competitive strenuous physical exercise.[3] The fact that on race days the coxswains and the coach showed an eosinophil response comparable to that of the oarsmen led to the conclusion that emotional stress, not physical stress alone, seems to be a maximal stimulus for the stress mechanism. These findings concerning the importance of the emotional aspect have been confirmed in subsequent studies by Persky,[4] Hill and associates,[5] and Ulrich,[6] but it is not clear whether the specific stresses result from a disturbance of the sympathetic system, as postulated by Cannon[7] or of the parasympathetic system, as suggested by Richter.[8]

## Role of exercise

Since exposure of the body to a given stress may result in the development of an adaptation that enables it to withstand that stress, it has been suggested that exercise may act to stabilize the homeostatic balance by providing a means of offsetting the physiological consequences of emotional stress. Although evidence is lacking, it has been suggested by Michael[9] that a possible mechanism for this is that exercise may increase the size and lower the threshold of the adrenal glands, thereby resulting in a greater reserve of antistress steroids and a shorter time of response to stress. Bannister,[10] however, contends that men voluntarily expose themselves to the strain of sport in order to resolve inner tensions, and in his opinion it is unwise to attempt to draw too close a parallel between the stress that occurs during athletics and the type of stress studied by Selye. Selye's type of stress, he suggests, may simply be a common feature in several different diseases.

## Prestart phenomenon

An explanation of physiological processes that underlie the stress response of athletes in competition has been offered by Russian students of physiology of exercise.[11] This explanation does not rely on hormonal mechanisms but turns toward Pavlov's doctrine of higher nervous activity. It is from the standpoint of conditioned reflex regulation of body functions in exercise that the attempt to elucidate the stressful effect of competitive conditions in athletic activities is made.

The competitive setting is regarded as a conditioned stimulus that causes body activities to increase even before the event starts. These elevations in body functions prior to activity are known as *prestart* increases. They can be made to disappear simply by discontinuing preliminary exercises—in other words, stopping the "warming up" activities before the contests. By doing this, functional depression is sometimes seen instead of the former prestart elevations in function when preliminary exercises had been the athlete's habit before competition.

These Russian studies suggest that "not only does the competitive setting influence the state of the organism before the start, but it also affects its activity during the period of the effort and in the restorative period after its termination."[11]

This theory has been used to explain various peculiarities of function regulation in athletes, such as individual differences in cardiovascular response. Greater increase in pulse rate and blood pressure are found among individuals of the "weak" or "quiet" type because of their higher nervous activity according to Pavlov's classification. The "active" or "unrestrained" athletes do not overreact this way and perform better than the former group in important competitions such as the olympic games. Training does not reduce the prestart responses; in fact the "weak" type tends to get worse.

Age is a factor, adolescents showing higher prestart reactions than adults. The explanation is given that overreaction may be caused by the increased excitability of the growing individual, particularly in the period of sexual maturation. During adolescence functional efficiency is less than in adulthood.

Reduction of blood eosinophils during the prestart state and during competitive effort is explained on the basis of a linkage between conditioned reflex reactions and the increased activity of endocrine glands.

## Stress syndrome in training and overtraining

Zimkin,[12] another Russian student of exercise physiology, has observed that well-spaced periods of regular light exercise are of benefit to the individual by increasing his nonspecific resistance to such unfavorable stresses as overheating, cooling, hypoxia, irradiation, and infections. On the other hand, athletes in competition in the presence of great emotional tensions often work too hard to obtain this benefit. As a result their nonspecific resistance to stress is lowered, certain vegetative functions, that is, sleep and appetite, are disrupted, and motor skills that are not fixed or automatized are coordinated with difficulty.

In forced training under high emotional tensions the nonspecific resistance to stress is lost first, the vegetative functions deteriorate second, and finally the motor coordinations are affected—eventually resulting in a decrement in performance. This is seen as the mechanism of *overtraining,* and it may be the cause of increased morbidity observed in a number of top athletes.

Since in severe athletic competition physical work or emotional tensions cannot be removed, means of meeting these stresses are sought such as diet, pharmacological and physiotherapeutic media, and improved routines of training, work, and relaxation.

## Advanced study topics

1. Does exercise training increase resistance to stress?
2. Review the recent literature on stress in current issues of *Psychosomatic Medicine.*
3. Describe the method of eosinophil count as a means of measuring stress response.
4. Observe the responses of various personality types to the stress of highly organized competition.
5. How should rest and relaxation be spaced to avoid overtraining?

## References

1. Selye, H.: The stress of life, New York, 1956, McGraw-Hill Book Company.
2. Wake, R. F., Graham, B. F., and Mc-Grath, S. D.: A study of the eosinophil response to exercise in man, J. Aviat. Med. **24:**127, 1953.
3. Renold, A. E., Quigley, T. B., Kennard, H. E., and Thorn, G. W.: Reaction of the adrenal cortex to physical and emotional stress in college oarsmen, New England J. Med. **244:**754, 1951.
4. Persky, H.: Response to stress: evaluation of some biochemical indices, J. Appl. Physiol. **6:**369, 1953.
5. Hill, S. R., and others: Studies on adrenocortical and psychological response to stress in man, Arch. Int. Med. **67:**269, 1956.
6. Ulrich, C.: Measurement of stress evidenced by college women in situations involving competition, Res. Quart. **22·**160, 1957.
7. Cannon, W. B.: The wisdom of the body, New York, 1939, W. W. Norton & Company, Inc.
8. Richter, C. P.: On the phenomenon of sudden death in animals and men, Psychosomat. Med. **19:**191, 1957.
9. Michael, E. D.: Stress adaptation through exercise, Res. Quart. **28:**50, 1957.
10. Bannister, R.: Stress and sport, Practitioner **172:**63, 1954.
11. Smirnov, K. M., Bakulin, S. A., Golovina, L. L., Zak, E. Ia., and Kogan, S. D.: Effect of competitive conditions on respiratory exchange, pulse rate, arterial pressure and efficiency in athletes, Sechenov. Physiol. J. USSR **45:** 289, 1959.
12. Zimkin, N. V.: The importance of size of load, in rate of performance and duration of exercises, and of the intervals between sessions in relation to effective muscular training, Sechenov. Physiol. J. USSR **46:**860, 1960.

# 30

# *Medical aspects of exercise*

Many of the physiological effects of exercise are of vital interest to the physician as well as to the physical educator. Both are concerned with the answers to such questions as these: What are the beneficial effects of moderate exercise, and what ill effects result from the lack of exercise? Is strenuous exertion ever harmful to a healthy subject? Under what medical conditions should exercise be forbidden? Unfortunately the difficulty of obtaining the necessary data under controlled laboratory conditions makes a complete answer to these questions impossible at present. A resort to statistical analysis is no more satisfactory because of the difficulty in evaluating the part played by inherent physical traits and contributing factors other than exercise. However, a partial answer is better than none, and something may be gained by a summary of the present status of our knowledge.

## *Influence of exercise on longevity*

The older literature contains many references to the early death of famous athletes. The impression was common at the turn of the century that strenuous exertion, such as varsity sports, frequently strains the heart and leaves a subject in a weakened condition that makes him ready prey to heart disease, pneumonia, tuberculosis, and similar afflictions later in life. The first thorough statistical study of the influence of athletics on life expectancy was made by Dublin,[1] who collected the life histories of 4,976 college athletes of 10 American colleges. The men finished college in the year 1905 or earlier, and the sports in which they participated included football, basketball, rowing, track and field events, hockey, and lacrosse. In 1925 there had occurred 1,202 deaths among the 4,976 athletes. The number of expected deaths according to the American men table[1] was

1,314 or a difference in favor of the athletes of 8.5%. As Dublin emphasized, however, the athletes were inherently a picked physical group, so that it is difficult to say whether or not the statistical difference in life expectancy is significant. Of perhaps greater significance is the fact that of the deaths from known causes occurring after 45 years of age 32% were ascribed to heart disease as compared with 20% of deaths caused by heart disease among selected insured persons in similar age groups. Dublin's conclusion is that, on the whole, the data indicate that participation in college sports has no significant influence on life expectancy.

## Athletics and the heart

Much of the controversy over the possible dangers of athletics has centered around the effects on the heart. The term "athletic heart" or "athlete's heart" has been applied to a heart presumed to have been injured by strenuous exertion. The available evidence indicates that this is a misconception and that there is no such entity as "athletic heart." The evidence is as follows.

In heart disease one of the compensatory adjustments is an enlargement of the heart called dilatation. The ventricular cavities enlarge by a stretching and thinning of the muscular walls of the ventricles. The beneficial effect of this adjustment is an increase in the force of contraction of the ventricle through the operation of Starling's law of the heart so that the diseased heart may more nearly meet its requirements, at least during rest. A dilated heart is mechanically less efficient, however, and requires a greater expenditure of energy for the same cardiac output than does a smaller, healthy heart. A chronically dilated heart has come to be recognized as one of the surest indications of heart disease.

It was pointed out in an earlier chapter that a normal heart increases its output during exercise not by greater filling (which would require dilatation) but rather by more complete systolic emptying. How then may we explain the reports that the heart of an athlete, as seen on x-ray films, sometimes appears to be relatively larger than that of a nonathlete?

The most reliable evidence at present is derived from experiments on animals because of the greater ease with which other variables can be controlled. The data from experiments on animals are on the whole consistent. Many studies (see Steinhaus[2] for references) have shown that the heart size of an animal reflects the amount of activity characteristic of its mode of life. Thus domesticated animals have smaller ratios of heart to body weight than do their undomesticated relatives. In experimentally controlled studies Külbs[3] showed that the ratio of heart weight to body weight in dogs exercised by running was considerably greater than that of their unexercised litter mates. Secher[4] trained rats by daily running in a drum for about 2 months. Then all were retired to inactivity, and small groups were killed at intervals for 75 days. In those killed immediately the heart weight constituted 5 to 6% of the body weight. This percentage decreased until the forty-eighth day, when it had receded to the normal value of 3.3 to 3.6%. This is the first demonstration of the regression of cardiac hypertrophy after the cessation of training and has important implications for the study of the effects of exercise on the human heart.

Experiments on rats[5] indicate that moderate exercise with regular rest periods may benefit the heart more than heavy, frequent exercise. The difference seems to be that periodic moderate exercise increases the relative size of the coronary vascular tree, while regular heavy exercise does not. Cardiac hypertrophy that is not accompanied by a corresponding increase in the blood supply to the heart muscle is an undesirable change.

The evidence for hypertrophy of the heart in human subjects as a result of exercise is not so consistent. Some observers have reported that the heart sizes of athletes and heavy workers fall within the range for normal persons of the same size and age. Others believe that the heart shadow (x-ray) in trained athletes averages larger than that of nontrained subjects but attribute this to a dilatation in which the psychic strain and excitement of certain sports play an important role. A third group supports the claim that true hypertrophy occurs. This view has been most forcefully championed by Herxheimer,[6] who presented the theory that exercises of speed, strength, or intense effort induce hypertrophy of skeletal muscle and only to a small extent of the heart muscle, whereas exercises of endurance lead to hypertrophy of the heart but have little effect on the size of the skeletal muscles. This is a logical extension of the principle that the muscle that is taxed beyond its capacity is the one that responds with hypertrophy.

It has been postulated from time to time that extremely violent exercise may subject the heart to acute strain with immediate ill effects such as rupture of the wall of one of the heart chambers. There is no evidence that a normal healthy adult heart is ever incapable of handling the largest volume of blood that the venous return can provide. Occasional cases of rupture of the heart have been reported but only in subjects whose heart muscle had been weakened by disease. It is, however, possible that strenuous exertion may produce acute heart damage in children and adolescents in whom the full development of the heart has not been reached; the available evidence does not justify a definite opinion at present. (See discussion of age in relation to tolerance for exercise in Chapter 28.)

The following conclusions seem to be justified by the bulk of the experimental and clinical data:

1. In adult subjects with healthy hearts the most exhausting exercise of which the subject is capable does not strain the heart.
2. Repeated exercise of the endurance type may result in gradual hypertrophy of the heart, but this is probably a beneficial adjustment not a pathological change, and it usually regresses if the exercise is discontinued.
3. Exercises of speed or strength produce little or no change in the size or weight of the heart.

## Beneficial effects of exercise

A detailed account of the physiological adjustments resulting from training or from a regular program of physical exercise is presented elsewhere

(Chapter 26). The present discussion is concerned with the general improvement in physical and mental efficiency and sense of well-being that results from properly planned and executed programs of exercise. It must be emphasized at the outset that our present physiological knowledge is inadequate for a complete explanation of many of the benefits whose existence is a matter of common observation.

The pertinent clinical observations and research studies reviewed by Hein and Ryan[7] indicated that regular physical exercise makes significant contributions to physical health in the following ways:

1. Aids in prevention of obesity and thereby helps to delay associated degenerative diseases and increases the life-span
2. Acts to prevent conditions leading to coronary heart disease
3. Assists in preventing premature aging and preserves physical characteristics of youth
4. Improves the effectiveness of the individual in meeting emergencies, thereby preserving health and avoiding disabilities and possibly death

One of the most fundamental of physiological laws is that the functional efficiency of an organ or system improves with use and regresses with disuse. Everyone is familiar with the increased power and efficiency of the skeletal muscles that result from usage and with the atrophy of muscles whose activity is prevented by paralysis. It is generally believed that heart muscle reacts in a similar manner. When these changes are considered in conjunction with the increased efficiency of lung ventilation, it is clear that both the power and the endurance of the skeletal muscles are improved by regular exercise. From the standpoint of general health great muscular power is of minor importance. Of greater significance is the fact that the usual types of activity can be carried out with a lesser degree of fatigue and hence with greater enjoyment.

Physicians and physical educators alike are becoming increasingly aware of the fact that improvement in the *postural tone* of the skeletal muscles is one of the most important benefits of regular exercise. The faulty posture commonly seen in sedentary persons is said to be responsible for many of the "minor ills" that from time to time afflict a large portion of the population. The basic anatomical and physiological factors in the relation between posture and general health are too complex to permit even a brief summarization. They constitute the science of body mechanics, a field of increasing interest to physicians, physiotherapists, and physical educators. For a systematic presentation of this science, the reader is referred to monographs on this subject.[8]

One of the most important objectives of a program of physical education is the development of motor skills. The coordinated activity of the skeletal muscles that is the basis of grace, agility, and proficiency in sports and games is dependent on training of the nervous system. Although there is some uncertainty as to the extent to which the acquisition of one motor skill influences performance in another activity ("carry-over of motor skill"), there is no doubt that almost any type of training improves general neuromuscular coordination. The functional efficiency of the nervous system is also benefited by the general improvement in other systems of the body. This is reflected particularly in an increased mental alertness and zest for meeting and solving the problems that arise in the course of daily life. As Bock and Dill[9] point out, one of the major benefits of exercise is that it serves to divert the mind into fresh channels and gives an emotional outlet for the cares and worries of daily life, especially in later life. The relief of emotional tension in turn reacts favorably upon the physical state of a person, so that the improvement in general well-being may be out of proportion to the actual amount of muscular exercise involved.

It must be emphasized that the beneficial effects of exercise just discussed are not permanent; they are achieved slowly in the course of training and disappear slowly if training is discontinued. For this reason, preservation of these benefits requires that a certain amount of exercise be continued in the form of a regular program. It is probable that spasmodic bouts of exercise interspersed in an otherwise sedentary life may actually do more harm than good. Finally, the age of a person has an important bearing on the type of exercise that is most beneficial. In this regard no hard and fast rules can be laid down; a great deal depends on the extent to which training has been continued after the school years. However, in spite of occasional exceptions it appears to be a valid generalization that the intensity and duration of exercise should be gradually diminished with advancing age. This question is analyzed in greater detail later.

## Possible dangers of exercise

Although the bulk of the evidence indicates that a healthy young adult subject in good training is unharmed by the most strenuous exertion, this is not necessarily true of persons who do not meet these specifications. On the one hand, there is evidence that the intensity of exercise should be limited in the case of children and adolescents, of women, and of men past the age of 40 years; on the other hand, there are certain diseases, especially those involving the heart and blood vessels, in which exercise must be forbidden entirely or adjusted in intensity. Although this is ordinarily a matter of concern for the physician rather than the physical educator, the latter can contribute much to the planning of suitably adjusted regimes of exercise.

There is a common misconception that all forms of exercise must be forbidden in subjects with heart disease. Although this is true in some persons, carefully adjusted exercise is not only permissible but also actually beneficial in other persons.[10] A thorough physical examination should be a prerequisite for participation in any type of strenuous activity, and the intensity of exercise should be limited, when necessary, on the advice of the examining physician. One additional point is deserving of emphasis. After certain acute infections, in particular diphtheria and focal infections such as diseased tonsils and teeth, the heart is sometimes left in a temporarily weakened condition. For this reason, exercise should be resumed gradually following acute infections, and a medical examination of the heart is strongly recommended. Fortunately the formerly prevalent belief that nearly all types of acute infections involve the heart to some extent is now regarded as overly pessimistic,[10] and the weakened condition that so often follows acute infections is ascribed to a generalized functional exhaustion of a temporary nature, not to damage of the heart itself.

## Age and sex in relation to tolerance for exercise*

Most of the studies of maximal capacity for exertion have concerned themselves with healthy, adult male subjects or with subjects suffering from cardiac or pulmonary disease. There has been comparatively little quantitative analysis of the limits of exertion in children, in older adults, and in women.

**Children.** The first accurate study of the physical capacity of children was made by Seham and Egerer-Seham,[11] with 110 Minneapolis school children between the ages of 6 and 15 years as subjects. Normal cardiovascular standards (changes in heart rate and blood pressure) were established for the following procedures: changes in posture, moderate exercise on a bicycle ergometer, weight lifting, and stair climbing. Finally, maximal capacity for exertion was determined in terms of the total work performed when the subjects rode to the point of exhaustion on the ergometer. Heart rate and blood pressure were recorded at intervals during and after the exercise period. Some of their most significant conclusions may be summarized as follows:

1. The maximum physical output is directly proportional to the age, circumference of the chest and thigh, and the vital capacity. It is apparently not influenced by height or weight.
2. During moderate exercise the increase in heart rate and blood pressure and the time required for blood pressure to return to normal following exercise are usually in direct proportion to the speed and the amount of work performed. The relationship is less exact in exhausting work.

The magnitude of the *increase* in heart rate in exhausting exercise ranged from 48 to 116 beats per minute. The highest heart rate recorded was 193, and contrary to previous opinions, heart rates above 160 were not associated with nausea, fainting, and other signs of physical exhaustion and therefore are not indicative of abnormal heart function. The *increase* in systolic blood pressure ranged from 16 to 57 mm. Hg and was not closely correlated with the total amount of work performed. The highest systolic pressure recorded was 172 mm. Hg.

In the course of the study of exhausting exercise there were 16 cases of collapse. These are analyzed in the second paper of the series.[11] Most of

---

*This section is concerned primarily with the medical aspects of the influence of age and sex on exercise tolerance. A more detailed account of the general relation of age and sex to performance capacity is found in Chapter 28.

the collapses occurred in older children, which the authors attribute to their greater competitive spirit. (Later workers have also commented on the fact that lack of competitive spirit usually makes it unlikely for exercise to be pushed to the point of exhaustion in young children.) The subjective signs of collapse never occurred during exercise, but they became apparent after cessation of exercise when practically all the boys were dyspneic and covered with sweat. In every subject there was nausea and in one subject vomiting. Two children complained of chills, and two others had a tremor of the entire body. In all cases the heart sounds became so faint that they could scarcely be heard. There was a marked drop in heart rate and systolic blood pressure after exercise, suggesting that the collapse was caused by a condition resembling primary shock. There was no evidence of acute dilatation of the heart in any of the cases, and recovery was complete in a few hours in every child.

In the third paper of this series[11] the cardiovascular response to exercise was compared in normal children and in children with heart disease and tuberculosis. The results with the Schneider, Barringer, and Crampton tests and the response to maximal exercise (lifting dumbbells) were practically identical in all three groups of children, which led the authors to conclude that all of these tests are of doubtful value in evaluating physical fitness or cardiovascular function in children.

From the standpoint of physical education and athletic programs in the public schools, more information is needed on the tolerance for exercise in each age group involved. This would permit scientific answers to such problems as the advisability of including such strenuous events as the cross-country run in high school track events. An approach to this important problem was made in a study[12] on boys in the 10-year to 17-year age group. It was found that exhaustion in treadmill running was reached at the lowest levels of oxygen consumption at the age of 13 years and that the ability to increase the oxygen consumption rose to a maximum at the age of 17 years. This would indicate a progressive increase in the ability to sustain exhausting exercise with increasing age. On the other hand, in the age group 12 to 14 years, the acceleration of the heart rate in response to standard exercise was greatest and the postexercise deceleration of the heart rate was most rapid. It is not clear whether this is merely an example of the lability of the cardiovascular system in younger children or if it indicates a lesser cardiac reserve.

The relation of age to motor achievement has also been studied.[13] There was some indication that motor proficiency is hindered by the process of maturation in the pubescent group, a factor that should be considered in the planning of athletic programs.

*Older adults.* The last two decades have witnessed a growth of interest in the nature of the aging process. As a result much more is known of the structural changes that take place in the body with increasing age. Less is known of the changes in functional capacity of the body, especially of the capacity for maximal exertion. The most systematic studies of physical fitness in relation to age have been carried out by workers at the Harvard Fatigue Laboratory, notably by Robinson.[14] They found that the cardiovascular response to moderate exercise (walking on a treadmill at 3.5 miles per hour up a grade of 8.6%) depends to a significant extent on age. It may be seen from Table 16 that the increase in heart rate declines progressively with advancing age.

Apparently the greater increase in heart rate in young subjects is due to a more pronounced influence of the sympathetic nervous system.[15] In commenting on these results, Dill[16] states: "These facts suggest that the high heart rates among boys reflect the prodigality of youth as contrasted with the conservatism of age; it is well established that youth excels in bursts of intense activity, but that the older man may be superior in sustained activity of more modest intensity."

Oxygen consumption during moderate activity shows no significant variation with age, but the maximal oxygen intake during strenuous exertion declines slowly with advancing age. A subject who is able to use 4 liters of oxygen per minute at the age of 20 years will probably be able to use not more than 3 liters per minute at the age of 50 years. At the same time, the maximal heart rate he can attain during exercise falls off; it is likely to be between 160 and 170 at the age of 50 years and may not exceed 150 at the age of 70 years. These measurements indicate that man's best performance during intense activity is attained between the ages of 18 and 25 years. His maximal heart rate then lies between 190 and 210, and he can reach higher levels of oxygen consumption during this time than at any period either earlier or later.

On the whole, the evidence, although far from complete, indicates that after the age of 25 to 30 years, the capacity for intense effort slowly decreases, while the capacity for exercise of endurance may suffer little impairment *provided some degree of training is maintained.* The greatest danger in participation in athletics or sports in middle age (assuming that a subject is otherwise in good health) is the interspersing of spasmodic bouts of strenuous exercise in a sedentary life. This usually results in more

*Table 16.* Heart rates during grade walking*

| Age (years) | Heart rate |
|:---:|:---:|
| 6 | 170 |
| 10 | 164 |
| 14 | 160 |
| 18 | 150 |
| 22 | 146 |
| 26 | 143 |
| 30 | 140 |
| 34 | 137 |
| 38 | 134 |
| 42 | 134 |

*From Robinson: Arbeitsphysiol. **10:**18, 1938.

harm than good, even though the heart and blood vessels are sound, and it may have serious effects if disease or degenerative changes of the cardiovascular system are present. The following principles should be observed:

1. If possible, a regular though necessarily curtailed program of exercise should be maintained after the school years.
2. If exercise is to be commenced again after a long period of sedentary life, it should be begun in moderation and gradually increased to the desired level of intensity.
3. There should be a thorough physical examination at regular intervals, preferably once each year.

*Women.* The physiological responses of young women to moderate exercise do not differ sufficiently from those of men to require special consideration. There is a somewhat greater increase in heart rate in women than in men, but this merely limits the maximal severity of exercise that can be tolerated. The endurance of women is also usually less than that of men in comparable health, but there is considerable overlap between the more fit women and the less fit men.

Strenuous exercise occasionally induces transitory menstrual irregularities that disappear when the severity of exercise is reduced. There is no indication for prohibition of moderate exercise during the menstrual period, nor is there any evidence that athletics diminishes fertility and causes complications in childbirth.

## Advanced study topics

1. What is the rationale for the prescription of exercise during recovery from a heart attack?
2. Review the recent literature on the medical aspects of exercise in current issues of the *Journal of the American Medical Association.*
3. How is relief of emotional tension measured?
4. What is the relation of posture to health?
5. What is the daily exercise load necessary to prevent hypokinetic deterioration of body structure and function?

## References

1. Dublin, L. I.: Longevity of college athletes, Intercollegiate Association, Amateur Athletics of America, Bull. No. 13, 1929.
2. Steinhaus, A. H.: Chronic effects of exercise, Physiol. Rev. **19:**103, 1933.
3. Külbs, F.: Experimentelles über Herzmuskel und Arbeit, Arch. f. exper. Path. u. Phar. **55:**288, 1906.
4. Secher, K.: Experimentelle Untersuchungen über den Einfluss der Anstrengungen auf die Grösse des Herzens, Ztschr. f. ges. exper. Med. **14:**113, 1921.
5. Stevenson, J. A. F., Feleki, V., Rechnitzer, P., and Beaton, J. R.: Effect of exercise on coronary tree size in the rat, Circulat. Res. **15:**265, 1964.
6. Herxheimer, H.: Die Herzgrösse bei Sportsleuten und ihre Beurteilung, Klin. Wchnschr. **3:**2225, 1924.
7. Hein, F. V., and Ryan, A. J.: The contributions of physical activity to physical health, Res. Quart. **31:**263, 1960.
8. Metheny, E.: Body dynamics, New York, 1952, McGraw-Hill Book Company.
9. Bainbridge, F. A.: The physiology of muscular exercise, ed. 3, rewritten by Bock, A. V., and Dill, D. B., London, 1931, Longmans, Green & Co.
10. White, P. D.: Heart disease, ed. 3, New York, 1944, The Macmillan Company.
11. Seham, M., and Egerer-Seham, G.: Physiology of exercise in childhood. I. A study of normal children of school

age, Am. J. Dis. Child. **25**:1, 1923; II. A study of collapse in normal children, Am. J. Dis. Child. **26**:254, 1923; III. An investigation of cardiovascular tests in normal children and in children with tuberculosis and valvular heart disease, Am. J. Dis. Child. **26**:554, 1923.

12. Morse, M., Schultz, F. W., and Cassels, D. E.: Relation of age to physiologic responses of the older boy (10-17 years) to exercise, J. Appl. Physiol. **1**: 683, 1949.

13. Nevers, J. E.: The effects of physio-logical age on motor achievement, Res. Quart. Am. A. Health, Phys. Ed. & Rec. **19**:103, 1948.

14. Robinson, S.: Experimental studies of physical fitness in relation to age. Arbeitsphysiol. **10**:18, 1938.

15. Brouha, L., Cannon, W. B., and Dill, D. B.: Heart rate of the sympathecto-mized dog in rest and exercise, J. Physiol. **87**:345, 1936.

16. Dill, D. B.: Effects of physical strain and high altitudes on the heart and cir-culation, Am. Heart J. **23**:441, 1942.

# Glossary

*acapnia* A decreased arterial carbon dioxide tension (hypocapnia).

*acid-base balance* The factors involved in the maintenance of a slightly alkaline state of the blood and tissues.

*acidosis* A shift of the acid-base balance toward the acid side. In uncompensated acidosis, both the pH and the buffer capacity are lowered; in compensated acidosis, the pH has been restored to normal but the buffer capacity remains lowered.

*action current* The voltage change across a cell membrane that results in excitation of the cell in response to a stimulus. A better term is action potential.

*acute* Of brief duration; disappearing on removal or cessation of the immediate stimulus, for example, the increase in heart rate during exercise.

*adrenal glands* Two small endocrine glands, one located just above each kidney. Each gland has two parts, an outer cortex that secretes the adrenal cortical hormones and an inner medulla that secretes adrenaline (epinephrine).

*adrenaline (epinephrine)* A hormone secreted by the medulla of the adrenal glands, especially under conditions of emotional stress. The physiological effects of adrenaline include increase in heart rate and arterial blood pressure, dilatation of muscle blood vessels, and increase in the blood sugar concentration.

*aerobic* Requiring the presence of oxygen.

*alkali reserve* The amount of alkali in the blood that is available for buffering acids other than carbonic. Bicarbonate accounts for most of the alkali reserve.

*alkalosis* A shift of the acid-base balance toward the alkaline side.

*alveolar air* Literally, the air present in the pulmonary alveoli that participates in gas exchange with the blood in the pulmonary capillaries. This air cannot be obtained for analysis, so that for practical purposes the last portion of air expelled in a deep expiration, which probably comes from the respiratory bronchioles and alveolar ducts, is assumed to be approximately equivalent in composition.

*alveoli* The terminal air sacs of the lungs in which most of the gas exchange occurs.

*anaerobic* Occurring in the absence of oxygen.

*anoxia* A deficiency of oxygen in the blood or tissues (hypoxia).

*antigravity muscles* The muscles (predominantly extensors) that maintain the body in an upright posture against the force of gravity.

*aortic body* A small mass of tissue located between the aorta and the pulmonary artery and having a function similar to that of the carotid body.

*aortic sinus* A dilatation of the aortic arch having a function similar to that of the carotid sinus.

*arterioles* The small terminal arteries that regulate the flow of blood into the capillaries.

*athlete's heart* A dilated heart resulting

from overstrenuous exertion; it is no longer believed to exist.

*atrophy* A wasting of tissues. Muscular atrophy is usually the result of disuse, as in poliomyelitis.

*autonomic nervous system* The division of the nervous system that controls the activity of smooth muscle, heart muscle, and glands.

*Bainbridge reflex* An increase in heart rate resulting from stimulation of stretch receptors in the walls of the right atrium and its great veins by the rise in venous pressure associated with increased venous return of blood to the heart. (The existence of this reflex is doubtful.)

*basal metabolism* The energy expenditure of the body under conditions of complete rest.

*blood pressure* The force with which the blood distends the walls of the blood vessels.

*bronchiole* Small terminal branch of a bronchus.

*bronchus* One of the larger air passages in the lung resulting from the branching of the trachea.

*buffer* A compound that minimizes the change in pH of a fluid when acids or alkalies are added.

*Calorie* The amount of heat required to raise the temperature of 1 kilogram of water 1° C.

*capillaries* The tiny, thin-walled blood vessels interposed between the arteries and the veins in which occurs the exchange of materials between blood and tissues or in the lung between blood and alveolar air.

*cardiac* Pertaining to the heart.

*cardiac cycle* The sequence of events in the heart—volume and pressure changes and valve actions—during one complete period of contraction and relaxation.

*cardiac impulse* The impulse that originates in the pacemaker of the heart and stimulates the heart muscle, producing systolic contraction.

*cardiac output* The volume of blood pumped by each ventricle of the heart in 1 minute.

*cardiac reserve* The ability of the heart to increase its output of blood by increasing the heart rate, the stroke volume, or both.

*cardiotachometer* An instrument that makes a continuous record of the heart rate.

*carotid body* A small mass of tissue located near the bifurcation of the carotid artery at the angle of the jaw.

*carotid body reflex* Reflex increase in the minute volume of breathing due to stimulation of receptors in the carotid body by chemical changes in the blood (decreased oxygen tension, increased carbon dioxide, or increased acidity).

*carotid sinus* A small dilatation of the internal carotid artery at the bifurcation of the artery near the angle of the jaw.

*carotid sinus reflex* A reflex decrease in heart rate and blood pressure resulting from stimulation of stretch receptors in the wall of the carotid sinus by a rise in arterial blood pressure.

*cerebellum* A portion of the brain concerned with the adjustment of the strength, range, and smoothness of muscle contractions.

*chronic* Continuing for a long time; persisting after cessation of the immediate stimulus, for example, the increase in muscle size resulting from training.

*coronary blood vessels* The blood vessels that supply blood to the heart muscle.

*crest load* The largest work load for which the oxygen intake of the body is adequate to meet the oxygen requirement.

*cyanosis* A bluish discoloration of the skin and mucous membranes caused by deficient oxygenation of the blood.

*dead space* The combined volume of all the air passages in which no gas exchange occurs. It includes the trachea, bronchi, and bronchioles down to, but not including, the respiratory bronchioles.

*diaphragm* The domelike sheet of skeletal muscle that separates the thoracic and abdominal cavities and whose contraction during inspiration increases the size of the thoracic cavity.

*diastasis* The latter portion of the period of diastole after filling of the ventricle is virtually complete—the "rest period" of the heart.

*diastole* The period during which the heart is relaxing after a previous contraction (including the pause or diastasis during which the whole heart is completely relaxed).

*diastolic pressure* The lowest level to which the arterial blood pressure falls in the interval between successive heartbeats.

*dissociation curve* The oxygen dissociation

curve expresses the relation between the percentage saturation of hemoglobin and the oxygen tension of the blood.

*distensibility* The capacity of a body for being stretched.

*dry-bulb temperature* The temperature recorded by a thermometer exposed to the air in the usual manner. This value is unaffected by humidity.

*dynamic contractions* Contractions alternating with relaxations, as in alternate flexion and extension of an extremity in running.

*dynamometer* An apparatus for testing muscular strength.

*dyspnea* Labored breathing associated with unpleasant sensations of breathlessness.

*elasticity* The capacity of a body for recovering its original shape after having been distended or otherwise deformed.

*electrocardiogram* A graphic record of the spread of the cardiac impulse through the heart.

*electrocardiograph* An instrument that amplifies and records the electrical changes resulting from the spread of the cardiac impulse in the heart.

*endocrine gland* A gland that pours its secretion directly into the bloodstream. The secretions of the various endocrine glands contain specific hormones that influence growth, metabolism, reproduction, and similar processes in the body.

*enzyme* An organic catalyst, that is, a substance produced by living cells that speeds the velocity of chemical reactions in the body. Each enzyme is ordinarily highly specific for a single type of chemical reaction and is without influence on other types of reactions.

*ergograph* An instrument for recording the work done by contracting muscles. In the instrument designed by Mosso a record is made of the contractions of the finger lifting a weight.

*ergometer* An apparatus for measuring the amount of work performed by a subject. The bicycle ergometer is a stationary bicycle in which the rear wheel is replaced by a heavy flywheel against which the subject performs work.

*erythrocyte* A red blood cell or corpuscle. It contains the pigment hemoglobin, which is responsible for the transport of oxygen in the blood.

*expiratory reserve volume* The volume of air that can be expelled by the strongest possible expiratory effort after the tidal air has been allowed to escape naturally.

*extension* The straightening out of two parts of the body bent upon one another by a previous flexion.

*fatigue* A diminished capacity for work caused by previous work. The term is also frequently applied to accompanying subjective sensations.

*flexion* The bending of one part of the body upon another part.

*functional residual capacity* The volume of air left in the lungs at the end of a natural, unforced expiration.

*glucose* A simple sugar having the formula $C_6H_{12}O_6$; the form in which carbohydrate is transported in the blood and metabolized in the tissues.

*glycogen* The form in which carbohydrate is stored in the body; a complex animal starch molecule built up of large numbers of glucose molecules.

*glycogenesis* The formation of glycogen from simple sugar or lactic acid.

*glycolysis* The breakdown of glucose to lactic acid.

*great veins* The superior and inferior venae cavae; the large veins that empty blood into the right auricle.

*heart sounds* Sounds produced by the closure and vibration of the valves of the heart.

*hematocrit* The percentage of the volume of a sample of blood that is occupied by the blood cells.

*hemoglobin* A pigment present in the red blood cells that combines reversibly with oxygen.

*homeokinesis* Maintenance of steady state in the organism at elevated levels of metabolism.

*homeostasis* The normal constancy of the internal environment of the body.

*hormone* A chemical agent produced in one of the endocrine glands and transported in the blood to other tissues or organs where it produces a specific alteration of function.

*hydrogen ion* The positively charged ion (proton) that results from the dissociation of acids; the concentration (or "activity") of hydrogen ions determines the acidity of a solution.

*hyperglycemia* An increased concentration of glucose in the blood.

*hyperpnea* Increased minute volume of breathing.

*hypertension* A pathological increase in the resting arterial blood pressure.

*hypertrophy* An increase in the size of a tissue or organ independent of the general growth of the body. There is no increase in the number of cells, but each cell becomes larger.

*hyperventilation* Pulmonary ventilation increased out of proportion to metabolic requirements.

*hypocapnia* A decreased arterial carbon dioxide tension.

*hypoglycemia* A below normal blood sugar concentration.

*hypoxia* A deficiency of oxygen in the blood or tissues.

*inspiratory reserve volume* The volume of air that can be taken in by a maximal inspiratory effort over and above the tidal volume.

*internal environment* The tissue fluid that bathes the cells of the body and through which occurs the exchange of materials between the blood and tissue cells.

*intraperitoneal* Within the abdominal (peritoneal) cavity.

*intrapleural* Within the pleural cavity (the potential space between the outer surface of the lungs and the inner surface of the chest wall).

*intrapulmonary* Within the lungs.

*intrathoracic* Within the chest (thoracic) cavity.

*in vitro* Occurring outside the body, for example, in a test tube.

*in vivo* Occurring in the body.

*isometric contraction* A contraction in which a muscle is unable to shorten, the total tension developed eventually being dissipated as heat. No movement is produced and no work is performed.

*isotonic contraction* A contraction in which a muscle shortens against a load, resulting in movement and the performance of work.

*lactic acid* An organic acid having the formula $C_3H_6O_3$; the end product of the anaerobic metabolism of glucose or glycogen.

*left heart* A term applied to the left atrium and ventricle.

*leukocyte* A white blood cell.

*leukocytosis* An increase in the number of leukocytes per unit volume of blood.

*lung volume* The volume of air in the lungs after a maximal inspiration; the sum of the vital capacity and the residual volume.

*mechanical advantage* The ratio of the length of the weight arm to that of the power arm in a lever. This determines the amount of load that can be moved by the application of a given amount of force.

*mechanical efficiency* The proportion of the energy requirement of an act that is converted into mechanical work. The mechanical efficiency of the human body ranges from 15 to 30%, according to the type of activity.

*metabolism* The chemical reactions that occur in living tissues; the term is often confined to the oxidations that are the ultimate source of biological energy.

*metabolite* One of the intermediate or final products in the metabolic breakdown of foodstuffs in the body.

*motor area* The area of the cerebral cortex that controls the contractions of individual skeletal muscles in voluntary movements.

*motor nerve* A nerve that transmits excitation to a muscle.

*motor pool* The group of motor nerve cells (ventral horn cells) in the spinal cord that give rise to the nerve fibers that comprise the motor nerve to a muscle.

*motor unit* The unit of neuromuscular function, including a ventral horn cell, its motor nerve fiber, and the group of muscle fibers supplied by branches of the nerve fiber.

*muscle spindle* A type of receptor, located among the fibers of a skeletal muscle, that is stimulated by changes in tension (stretching or contraction) in the muscle.

*muscle tone* See *tonus.*

*myofibrils* The longitudinally arranged contractile elements embedded in the sarcoplasm of a skeletal muscle fiber.

*myogram* A graphic record of muscle contractions.

*myograph* An instrument for recording muscle contractions.

*nerve impulse* The electrochemical wave that travels along nerve fibers and stimulates muscles, glands, or other nerve cells.

*neurasthenia* A condition of nervous instability characterized by irritability, ready fatigability, and circulatory and digestive disturbances. A common example is the so-called "soldiers' heart" or "effort syndrome" in which mild exertion results in rapid heart rate, fatigue, and physical exhaustion.

*neuromuscular* Pertaining to the relation between nerve and muscle.

*neuromuscular coordination* The nervous control of muscle contractions in the performance of motor acts.

*normal load* A light or moderate load of work in which the oxygen intake is adequate to supply the needs of the body.

*optimum* The most favorable condition (as of temperature) for a particular function or process.

*overload* A heavy work load in which the oxygen intake is inadequate to meet the requirement.

*oxidation* The removal of hydrogen or electrons from a compound. Oxygen does not directly combine with the substance being "oxidized," but it must ultimately combine with the hydrogen to form water.

*oxygen debt* The amount of oxygen required in the postexercise recovery period to reverse the anaerobic reactions of the exercise period. Quantitatively, the difference between the oxygen requirement of a task and the oxygen intake during performance of the task.

*oxygenation* The loose, reversible combination of oxygen with hemoglobin; not a true chemical oxidation.

*oxyhemoglobin* Hemoglobin loosely combined with oxygen.

*pericardium* The fibrous sac that encloses the heart.

*pH* A convenient notation for expressing the degree of acidity or alkalinity of a solution. At neutrality, pH = 7; values above 7 indicate alkalinity; those below 7, acidity.

*phasic contraction* A contraction of a muscle or group of muscles that results in movement.

*plasma* The liquid part of the blood in which the blood cells are suspended.

*platelet* One of the three major types of blood cells; concerned in the clotting of blood.

*plethysmograph* An instrument that measures volume changes in an organ or other part of the body.

*postural contraction* A contraction of a muscle or group of muscles that results in no movement but serves to maintain a posture or attitude.

*postural tone* The slight sustained contraction of muscles engaged in maintaining a posture or attitude; especially pronounced in the extensor muscles, which maintain the body in an upright posture against the force of gravity.

*posture* A position or attitude of the body as a whole or of parts of the body with respect to one another.

*prestart* Conditioned response to exercise resulting in elevation of body processes prior to activity.

*proprioceptor* A receptor located within the body and stimulated by mechanical deformation (pressure, stretching, tension, etc.), for example, muscle spindles, stretch receptors in the carotid sinus.

*psychic* Pertaining to or originating in the higher centers of the brain (cerebral cortex).

*pulmonary ventilation* The periodic renewal of the air in the lung alveoli.

*pulse* The distention of the arterial walls (by the systolic ejection of blood) which travels down the arteries as a wave.

*pulse pressure* The difference between the systolic and the diastolic blood pressures.

*receptor* A specialized sensory organ in which the sensory nerve fibers terminate peripherally and which is stimulated by some specific type of environmental disturbance (heat, cold, light, sound, etc.).

*reflex* An involuntary motor response resulting from stimulation of sensory receptors.

*reflex arc* The nervous pathway that forms the anatomical basis of a reflex, consisting of a receptor, a sensory nerve fiber, a synapse, a motor nerve fiber, and an effector (muscle, gland, etc.).

*relative humidity* The ratio of the amount of moisture in the air to the amount that would be present if the air were completely saturated with moisture at a certain temperature—usually expressed in percent of complete saturation.

*renal* Pertaining to the kidney.

*residual volume* The volume of air (about 1,500 ml.) that remains in the lungs after the deepest possible expiration.

*respiration* The sum total of the processes involved in the exchange of gases between an organism and its environment.

*respiratory center* A group of nerve cells in the medulla that controls contraction of the respiratory muscles and thus regulates the rate and depth of breathing.

*respiratory quotient (R.Q.)* The ratio of the volume of carbon dioxide expired to the volume of oxygen absorbed during a given period of time.

*right heart* A term applied to the right atrium and ventricle.

*sarcolemma* The cell membrane of a striated muscle fiber.

*sarcoplasm* The protoplasm of a skeletal muscle fiber in which the myofibrils are embedded.

*sarcostyle* See *myofibrils.*

*smooth muscle* Involuntary muscle occurring in the walls of the hollow viscera (blood vessels, gastrointestinal tract, etc.).

*sphygmomanometer* An instrument that is used to measure arterial blood pressure in man.

*spirometer* An apparatus for the collection, measurement, or storage of gases. It consists of a movable bell inverted in a cylinder filled with water; the bell rises when gas enters and falls when gas leaves, so that a record of the rate and depth of breathing may be made with a suitable recording device.

*splanchnic* Pertaining to the abdominal organs.

*Starling's law* The stroke volume of the heart is proportional to its diastolic volume. This results from the fact that the force of muscle contraction is increased by stretching of the muscle fibers.

*static contractions* Contractions in which muscle tension is sustained throughout the period of activity, as in weight lifting.

*stretch reflex* A reflex contraction of a muscle resulting from stretching of the muscle.

*striated muscle* Skeletal muscle; voluntary muscle whose contraction produces movement of parts of the skeleton with reference to other parts.

*stroke volume* The volume of blood ejected by each ventricle of the heart during a single systole.

*synapse* The points of contact between the terminal branches of a nerve fiber and the cell body and dendrites of the next neuron in the chain.

*systole* The contraction phase of heart muscle.

*systolic pressure* The highest level to which the arterial blood pressure rises following the systolic ejection of blood from the left ventricle.

*tendon* A tough cord or band of dense, fibrous connective tissue that unites a muscle to a bone.

*tendon organ* A receptor located in muscle tendon that is stimulated by stretching, with a resulting reflex contraction of the muscle.

*tension (gas)* The pressure exerted by a gas dissolved in a liquid.

*tension (muscular)* The force exerted by a contracting muscle.

*tetanus* A smooth sustained contraction of skeletal muscle caused by fusion of individual muscle twitches.

*tidal volume* The volume of air exchanged in each normal inspiration and expiration.

*tonus* A slight, sustained contraction of muscle; in skeletal muscle, tonus is the result of incomplete tetanus in a small fraction of the fibers.

*treadmill* An apparatus with a continuous moving belt that can be made to run at various speeds and inclinations.

*treppe* A progressive increase in the tension developed by a muscle in the first few contractions following a period of inactivity.

*vasoconstriction* Decrease in the caliber of arterioles produced by contraction of the circular rings of smooth muscle in the vessel walls.

*vasoconstrictor center* A group of nerve cells in the medulla that discharges impulses over the vasoconstrictor nerves and that regulates the amount and distribution of constriction of the arterioles in various parts of the body.

*vasoconstrictor nerve* A nerve that stimulates the smooth muscle in the arterioles, causing narrowing of the lumen of the vessels.

*vasodilatation* An increase in the caliber of a blood vessel.

*vasodilator nerve* A nerve that produces an increase in the caliber of a blood vessel (usually an arteriole) by inhibiting the tone of the smooth muscle in the wall of the vessel.

*ventilation* See *pulmonary ventilation.*

*viscosity* Resistance to flow (in fluids) or to change in shape (in solids).

*vital capacity* The greatest volume of air that can be forcibly exhaled after a maximal inspiration.

*wet-bulb temperature* The temperature recorded by a thermometer whose bulb is kept moist (usually by wrapping it with moist cotton) and is moved rapidly through the air to be tested by a sling device. The lower the humidity, the greater is the evaporation of moisture from the bulb wrapping, and hence the greater the cooling of the bulb and the lower will be the wet-bulb temperature. If both the wet-bulb and dry-bulb temperatures are known, the relative humidity may be read from a table.

*work* The product of a force and the distance through which the force is applied; for example, if a 1-pound weight is lifted a distance of 1 foot, the work performed is 1 foot-pound.

*work load* The intensity of work, usually expressed in terms of foot-pounds or kilogram-meters of work per minute; sometimes the work load is expressed in terms of the oxygen requirement per minute.

# Weights and measures

## Conversion factors

| To change | to | Multiply by |
|---|---|---|
| millimeters | inches | 0.03937 |
| meters | inches | 39.37 |
| meters | feet | 3.2808 |
| meters | yards | 1.0936 |
| kilometers | miles | 0.62137 |
| cubic meters | cubic yards | 1.3079 |
| liters | cubic inches | 61.02 |
| liters | liquid quarts | 1.0567 |
| liters | gallons ( U. S. ) | 0.2642 |
| liters | ounces of water | 35.275 |
| liters | pounds of water | 2.205 |
| liters | kilograms of water | 1.0 |
| kilograms | pounds avdp. | 2.2046 |
| kilograms | ounces | 35.274 |
| inches | millimeters | 25.4 |
| feet | meters | 0.3048 |
| yards | meters | 0.9144 |
| cubic yards | cubic meters | 0.7646 |
| pounds avdp. | ounces | 16.0 |
| pounds avdp. | grams | 453.6 |
| pounds avdp. | kilograms | 0.4536 |
| ounces | grams | 28.35 |
| liquid quarts | liters | 0.9463 |
| centimeters | inches | 0.3937 |
| square centimeters | square inches | 0.155 |
| cubic centimeters | milliliters | 1.0 |
| cubic centimeters | cubic inches | 0.061 |
| cubic centimeters | grams of water | 1.0 |
| cubic centimeters | ounces of water | 0.0353 |
| cubic centimeters | grains of water | 15.432 |
| cubic centimeters | drops | 12.0 |
| feet | centimeters | 30.48 |

| To change | to | Multiply by |
|---|---|---|
| square feet | square inches | 144.0 |
| square feet | square centimeters | 929.0 |
| cubic feet | gallons | 7.4805 |
| cubic feet | quarts | 29.922 |
| cubic feet | kilogram of water | 28.32 |
| cubic feet | liters of water | 28.32 |
| cubic feet | pounds of water | 62.43 |
| cubic feet | ounces of water | 999.0 |
| gallons | quarts | 4.0 |
| gallons | liters | 3.785 |
| gallons | pounds of water | 8.345 |
| gallons | kilograms of water | 3.785 |
| grams | ounces | 0.035274 |
| grams | pounds | 0.002205 |
| grams | grains | 15.432 |
| inches | centimeters | 2.54 |
| square inches | square centimeters | 6.4516 |
| cubic inches | cubic centimeters | 16.387 |
| cubic inches | pints | 0.0346 |
| cubic inches | liters | 0.0164 |
| cubic inches | grams of water | 16.39 |
| cubic inches | ounces of water | 0.578 |
| cubic inches | pounds of water | 0.0361 |
| cubic inches | grains of water | 252.89 |
| square meters | square yards | 1.2 |
| square meters | square feet | 10.764 |
| square meters | square inches | 1,550.0 |
| square meters | square centimeters | 10,000.0 |
| cubic meters | liters | 1,000.0 |
| cubic meters | quarts | 1,056.7 |
| cubic meters | cubic feet | 35.31 |
| cubic meters | metric tons water | 1.0 |
| cubic meters | pounds of water | 2,204.6 |
| miles | feet | 5,280.0 |
| miles | meters | 1,609.4 |
| miles | kilometers | 1.6094 |
| square miles | acres | 640.0 |
| square miles | square kilometers | 2.59 |
| ounces | grams | 28.3495 |
| ounces | pounds | 0.0625 |
| ounces | grains | 437.5 |
| pints | quarts | 0.5 |
| pints | cubic centimeters | 473.18 |
| pints | ounces of water | 16.69 |
| pints | pounds of water | 1.043 |
| pints | kilograms of water | 0.47318 |
| pints | cups | 2.0 |
| pints | tablespoons | 32.0 |
| pints | teaspoons | 96.0 |
| quarts | pints | 2.0 |
| quarts | cups | 4.0 |
| quarts | cubic centimeters | 946.4 |
| quarts | tablespoons | 64.0 |

*Continued*

| To change | to | Multiply by |
|---|---|---|
| quarts | teaspoons | 192.0 |
| quarts | ounces of water | 33.38 |
| quarts | pounds of water | 2.086 |
| quarts | kilograms of water | 0.946 |
| tablespoons | cups | 0.0625 |
| tablespoons | cubic centimeters | 15.0 |
| tablespoons | dessert spoons | 1.5 |
| tablespoons | teaspoons | 3.0 |
| tablespoons | drops | 180.0 |
| teaspoons | cubic centimeters | 5.0 |
| teaspoons | cups | 0.02 |
| teaspoons | drops | 60.0 |

1 foot-pound = 0.1382 kilogram meter = 0.000324 Calorie
= 0.001286 B.T.U. = 0.0005 foot-ton
1 foot-pound per minute = 0.02261 watt
1 kilogram-meter = 7.233 foot-pounds = 0.002344 Calorie
= 0.009298 B.T.U.
1 horsepower-hour = 1,980,000 foot-pounds = 641.3 Calories
1 joule = 0.2423 Calorie = 10,000,000 ergs = 10,198 gram centimeters
= 0.00987 liter centimeter
1 horsepower = 33,000 foot-pounds per minute = 550 foot-pounds
per second = 1,980,000 foot-pounds per hour
= 4562.4 kilogram meters per minute = 746 watts
= 0.746 kilowatt = 2.1 liters of oxygen/minute
= 10.7 Calories/minute = 642 Calories/hour
1 B.T.U. = 0.252 Calorie at 15° C. = 778 foot-pounds
Watt = work at the rate of about ¼ Calorie per second
= 0.012 kilogram meter per second
1 watt-minute = 6.12 kilogram meters per second
= 0.01435 Calorie
1 atmosphere of pressure = 760 mm. Hg
= 29.92 in. Hg
= 10.33 meters water
= 33.9 ft. water
= 1033.3 Gm./sq. in.
= 14.7 lb./sq. in.
= 2116.3 lb./sq. ft.
Temperature conversion:

$$°C. = \frac{°F. - 32}{1.8}$$

$$°F. = (°C. \times 1.8) + 32$$

Heat equivalent of 1 liter of oxygen:
5.14 Calories for glycogen
4.4  Calories for oils
4.6  Calories for fat
4.6  Calories for protein
5.06 Calories for starch
5.08 Calories for sucrose
22.4 liters of oxygen = 30 grams of glycogen
1 liter of oxygen = approximately 5 Calories = approximately 15,000 foot-pounds
= 2,134 kilogram meters
1 gram of oxygen = approximately 3.5 Calories

At 0° C., 760 mm. pressure, 1 liter $CO_2$
 = 1.9652 grams; 1 liter $O_2$ = 1.4292 grams; 1 liter air
 = 1.2928 grams; 1 liter water vapor = 0.8038 gram;
 1 gram water vapor = 1.2440 liters

1 Calorie = 1 kilogram calorie = 1,000 gram calories
   = 3.968 B.T.U. at 60° F. = 4,185 joules
   = 3,086 foot-pounds = 426.7 kilogram meters
   = 69.7 watt-minutes

Kilowatt = 101.9 kilogram meters per second = 737.56 foot-pounds
   per second = 1,000 joules per second = 10 billion
   ergs per second = 1.34 horsepower

1 kilogram meter per second = 9.81 watts
    1 watt hour = 0.85968 Calorie

1 kilowatt hour = 3,412 B.T.U.

# Index